Lectures on
Rings and Modules

A BLAISDELL BOOK
IN PURE AND APPLIED MATHEMATICS

CONSULTING EDITOR
George Springer, *Indiana University*

Lectures on Rings and Modules

JOACHIM LAMBEK

McGill University

BLAISDELL PUBLISHING COMPANY

A DIVISION OF GINN AND COMPANY

Waltham, Massachusetts · Toronto · London

Preface

THIS BOOK is designed primarily for graduate students and conceivably for advanced undergraduates who wish to know something about associative rings and their modules. (All rings are assumed to have unity elements, as the generality gained by dropping this condition would have to be paid for.) The book touches on various topics, without assuming to pronounce the last word on any of them; but some topics, in which the author feels personally involved, are treated at greater length than others. Compared to earlier books on the subject, particular prominence is given to the concept "ring of quotients" as it appears in the work of Johnson, Utumi, Goldie, and others.

The introductory Chapter One attempts to cover enough of the fundamental concepts of algebra to make these notes self-contained. Chapter Two contains selected results in the case of Boolean and other commutative rings, even if some of these results are treated in greater generality later. Chapter Three deals with the classical structure theory of associative rings, anything that can be done conveniently without the concept of "injectivity." In Chapter Four, injective modules and rings of quotients are studied in some detail. Chapter Five offers an introduction to homological algebra, culminating in a new technique for chasing squares.

My ideas developed in the process of writing, and I should probably organize the material differently now. Yet I have refrained from excessive revisions, for fear of destroying the spontaneity of presentation. I also regret that many important topics were not included, among them division rings, the Brauer group, quasi-Frobenius rings, polynomial identities, ultraproducts, direct and inverse limits, homological dimension.

The reader is advised not to follow the order of presentation too rigidly, but to skip forward and backward, as prompted by his interest and success in understanding. Some preliminary material may be left out by the more advanced reader, to be consulted only when needed, for instance, Chapter 1 and Sections 2.1 and 2.2. Some topics, although of special interest to the writer, may be omitted at first reading; for example, Sections 2.3 to 2.5, Sections 4.3 to 4.7, and Appendix 1.

Having attended courses in Ring Theory given by Hans J. Zassenhaus and Donald G. Higman many years ago, I am indebted to them and absolve them from any blame for the shortcomings of this text. This essentially describes the contents of a graduate course in Ring Theory given at McGill University in 1962–63 and part of a course on Homological Algebra. One part was written up at the Summer Research Institute of the Canadian Mathematical Congress. Some of the material is the result of an old collaboration with George D. Findlay. Appendix 3 was kindly contributed by Ian G. Connell.

I wish to thank my students and colleagues for their stimulating interest and encouragement. I am particularly grateful to the following for checking portions of the manuscript: Kenneth W. Armstrong, Mira Bhargava, Rosemary G. Bonyun, Marta Bunge, Walter D. Burgess, George C. Bush, Ian G. Connell, Carl C. Faith, Israel Kleiner, Dana I. Schlomiuk, Hans H. Storrer, Yuzo Utumi, and Diana Y. Wei.

Montreal, Canada   *Joachim Lambek*

Contents

CHAPTER ONE

Fundamental Concepts of Algebra

1.1 Rings and related algebraic systems

We begin with a series of definitions, more to assure completeness and to fix our notation than to present new concepts.

A *semigroup* is a system $(S,\cdot)$, where S is a set and $\cdot$ is a binary operation on S which satisfies the associative law:

$$(a \cdot b) \cdot c = a \cdot (b \cdot c).$$

(It is understood that an identity such as this holds for all a, b, c in S.) Henceforth we shall usually omit the $\cdot$ and write simply ab instead of $a \cdot b$. A semigroup with 1 (often called "monoid") is a system $(S,1,\cdot)$, where $(S,\cdot)$ is a semigroup and 1 is a designated element of S (we may regard it as a 0-ary operation) satisfying the identity:

$$a1 = a = 1a.$$

A *group* is a system $(S,1,^{-1},\cdot)$, where $(S,1,\cdot)$ is a semigroup with 1 and $^{-1}$ is a unary operation such that

$$aa^{-1} = 1 = a^{-1}a.$$

Following tradition, we place the operation symbol $^{-1}$ after its argument. An *Abelian* group is a group satisfying the commutative law:

$$ab = ba.$$

An Abelian group is frequently written additively as $(S,0,-,+)$. However, the symbol $+$ is never omitted, and $-$ is placed before its argument.

A *ring* (associative with 1) is a system $(S,0,1,-,+,\cdot)$, where $(S,0,-,+)$ is an Abelian group and $(S,1,\cdot)$ is a semigroup with 1, satisfying the distributive laws:

$$a(b + c) = ab + ac, \qquad (a + b)c = ac + bc.$$

A *commutative* ring is a ring which satisfies the law $ab = ba$. The element 1 in a ring is often called the "unity" element. The reader should be warned that many authors do not insist on the existence of unity elements in rings.

All of the algebraic systems introduced so far have been presented as sets with certain operations (0-ary, unary, binary, . . .) satisfying certain identities. We shall call the class of all systems sharing a given set of operations and satisfying a given set of identities an *equationally defined* class. Such equationally defined classes are the class of groups and the class of rings.

A *division ring* is a ring which satisfies the following law:

$$0 \neq 1 \quad \& \quad \forall_{a \neq 0} \exists_b (ab = 1 \quad \& \quad ba = 1).$$

A commutative division ring is called a *field*.

The class of division rings has not been presented equationally; moreover it cannot be presented equationally, as we shall see later.

It has been suggested that the law $0 \neq 1$ should also be included in the definition of a ring. If we added this postulate we should lose only one ring (the zero ring), but we should also destroy the useful property that the class of rings is equationally defined.

An *ordered* set (sometimes called "partially" ordered) is a system $(S, \leq)$, where S is a set and $\leq$ is a binary relation on S satisfying the reflexive, transitive, and antisymmetric laws:

$$a \leq a, \quad (a \leq b \quad \& \quad b \leq c) \Rightarrow a \leq c, \quad (a \leq b \quad \& \quad b \leq a) \Rightarrow a = b.$$

(Universal quantifiers are assumed.) Note that $\leq$ is not an operation but a relation, and that the postulates for an ordered set are not equations but implications. An ordered set is called *simply ordered* if for any two elements $a \leq b$ or $b \leq a$. A *semilattice* is an ordered set in which any two elements a and b have a greatest lower bound or inf (for "infimum") $a \wedge b$. Thus a semilattice is a system $(S, \leq, \wedge)$, where $(S, \leq)$ is an ordered set and $\wedge$ is a binary operation satisfying the law:

$$c \leq a \wedge b \Leftrightarrow (c \leq a \quad \& \quad c \leq b). \tag{1}$$

Clearly, a simply ordered set is a semilattice.

We hasten to consider some examples of ordered sets.

Example 1.   The positive integers, with the relation "less than or equal to."

Example 2.   The positive integers, with the relation "divides."

Example 3.   The set of all subsets of a set N (say $N =$ the set of positive integers), with the inclusion relation "is contained in."

Only the first of these is simply ordered. However, all three are semi-lattices, the infimum of two elements being their (1) minimum, (2) greatest common divisor, and (3) intersection.

PROPOSITION 1.   *The class of semilattices can be equationally defined as the class of all semigroups* $(S,\wedge)$ *satisfying the commutative and idempotent laws:*

$$a \wedge b = b \wedge a, \qquad a \wedge a = a.$$

Proof (sketched).   If $\wedge$ is introduced by (1), the associative, commutative, and idempotent laws for $\wedge$ are easily deduced, and so is the rule

$$a \leq b \Leftrightarrow a \wedge b = a. \tag{2}$$

Conversely, given the semigroup $(S,\wedge)$, one uses (2) to define $\leq$ and readily deduces the reflexive, transitive, and antisymmetric laws as well as (1).

A *lattice* is a system $(S,\leq,\wedge,\vee)$ in which any two elements a and b have an inf $a \wedge b$ and a least upper bound or sup (for "supremum") $a \vee b$. Clearly, a simply ordered set is a lattice in which $a \wedge b = a$ (or b) and $a \vee b = b$ (or a). A lattice with 0 and 1 is a lattice with elements so designated, such that always

$$0 \leq a, \qquad a \leq 1.$$

An element a' is called a *complement* of a if

$$a \wedge a' = 0, \qquad a \vee a' = 1.$$

If every element has a complement, the lattice is called *complemented*. A lattice is called *distributive* if identically

$$a \wedge (b \vee c) = (a \wedge b) \vee (a \wedge c).$$

We remark that in a distributive lattice complements (if they exist) are unique. Thus suppose a' and a^* are both complements of a, then

$$a^* = a^* \wedge 1 = a^* \wedge (a \vee a') = (a^* \wedge a) \vee (a^* \wedge a')$$
$$= 0 \vee (a^* \wedge a') = a^* \wedge a' = \cdots = a'.$$

It is not difficult to see that in a distributive lattice also the dual distributive law holds:

$$a \vee (b \wedge c) = (a \vee b) \wedge (a \vee c).$$

We pause again to look at our three examples. Actually all three are lattices, the supremum of two elements being defined as their (1) maximum, (2) least common multiple, and (3) union. All three examples are distributive lattices, but only the third is complemented. Lest the reader conclude from our illustrations that all ordered sets are distributive lattices, he is invited to inspect the following examples: All finite subsets of N with the relation "is contained in;" all infinite subsets of N with the relation "contains;" all subsets of N with at least two elements, with the relation "is contained in;" and so on.

Here are some further examples of complemented distributive lattices.

Example 4. All "square-free" positive integers (that is, not divisible by the square of an integer greater than 1), with the relation "divides."

Example 5. All finite subsets and complements of finite subsets of N, with the relation "is contained in."

Example 6. All subsets of N "modulo" the finite subsets (that is we identify two subsets of N if they differ only by a finite set).

A *Boolean ring* is a ring which satisfies the idempotent law

$$aa = a.$$

A *Boolean algebra* is a system $(S,0,',\wedge)$ where $(S,\wedge)$ is a semilattice, 0 is an element of S, and $'$ is a unary operation such that

$$a \wedge b' = 0 \Leftrightarrow a \wedge b = a \qquad \text{(i.e., } a \leq b\text{).}$$

The following two propositions show that complemented distributive lattices, Boolean algebras and Boolean rings are all the same objects. First we require a lemma.

LEMMA. *In any Boolean algebra* $a'' = (a')' = a$.

Proof. From $a' \leq a'$ we deduce $a' \wedge a'' = 0$ hence $a'' \leq a$. From this follows on the one hand that $a''' \leq a'$ (on replacing a by a') and on the other hand (on replacing a by a'') that $a'''' \leq a'' \leq a$, whence $a'''' \wedge a' = 0$ and so $a' \leq a'''$. Thus $a''' = a'$. Finally, from $a \leq a$ we deduce $a \wedge a''' = a \wedge a' = 0$ and so $a \leq a''$.

PROPOSITION 2. *A Boolean algebra becomes a complemented distributive lattice by defining*

$$a \vee b = (a' \wedge b')', \qquad 1 = 0'.$$

Conversely, any complemented distributive lattice is a Boolean algebra in which these equations are provable identities.

Proof. Let $(S,0,',\wedge)$ be a Boolean algebra. Then

$$\begin{aligned}
a \vee b \leq c &\Leftrightarrow (a' \wedge b')' \wedge c' = 0 \\
&\Leftrightarrow c' \leq a' \wedge b' \\
&\Leftrightarrow c' \leq a' \quad \& \quad c' \leq b' \\
&\Leftrightarrow c' \wedge a = 0 \quad \& \quad c' \wedge b = 0 \\
&\Leftrightarrow a \leq c \quad \& \quad b \leq c.
\end{aligned}$$

Thus $a \vee b$ is the sup of a and b, and so we have a lattice. Moreover

$$a \wedge (b \vee c) \leq x \Leftrightarrow a \wedge (b \vee c) \wedge x' = 0$$
$$\Leftrightarrow a \wedge x' \leq b' \wedge c'$$
$$\Leftrightarrow a \wedge x' \leq b' \quad \& \quad a \wedge x' \leq c'$$
$$\Leftrightarrow a \wedge x' \wedge b = 0 \quad \& \quad a \wedge x' \wedge c = 0$$
$$\Leftrightarrow a \wedge b \leq x \quad \& \quad a \wedge c \leq x$$
$$\Leftrightarrow (a \wedge b) \vee (a \wedge c) \leq x,$$

and so the distributive law holds. Finally a' is a complement of a, since

$$a \wedge a' = 0 \qquad \text{(which follows from } a \leq a)$$

and

$$a \vee a' = (a' \wedge a'')' = (a' \wedge a)' = 0' = 1.$$

(The reader should verify that $0 \leq a$ and $a \leq 1$.)

Conversely, assume that $(S,0,1,',\wedge,\vee)$ is a complemented distributive lattice. Then $a \wedge b' = 0$ implies

$$a = a \wedge 1 = a \wedge (b \vee b') = (a \wedge b) \vee (a \wedge b') = a \wedge b,$$

and $a \wedge b = a$ implies

$$a \wedge b' = a \wedge b \wedge b' = a \wedge 0 = 0.$$

Moreover

$$(a \vee b) \wedge (a' \wedge b') = (a \wedge a' \wedge b') \vee (b \wedge a' \wedge b') = 0 \vee 0 = 0$$

and

$$(a \vee b) \vee (a' \wedge b') = (a \vee b \vee a') \wedge (a \vee b \vee b') = 1 \vee 1 = 1,$$

and therefore $a' \wedge b'$ is a complement of $a \vee b$. But complements are unique, hence $a' \wedge b' = (a \vee b)'$. Similarly $1 = 0'$ follows from $0 \wedge 1 = 0$ and $0 \vee 1 = 1$.

COROLLARY. *If $(S,0,',\wedge)$ is a Boolean algebra, then so is $(S,1,',\vee)$.*

Each of these is called the *dual* of the other.

PROPOSITION 3. *A Boolean algebra $(S,0,',\cdot)$ can be turned into a Boolean ring $(S,0,1,-,+,\cdot)$ by defining*

$$1 = 0', \qquad -a = a, \qquad a + b = ab' \vee ba',$$

where $a \vee b = (a'b')'$ as usual. Conversely, any Boolean ring can be regarded as a Boolean algebra with $a' = 1 - a$, and the above definitions of 1, $-$, and $+$ then become provable identities.

To facilitate the statement of this proposition we have written *ab* in place of *a* ∧ *b*. The proof is straightforward and will be omitted.

Consider an ordered set $(S, \leq)$. The element *s* of *S* is called an *upper bound* of the subset *T* of *S* if $t \leq s$ for all $t \in T$; it is called a *sup* or least upper bound of *T* if $s \leq s'$ for every upper bound s' of *T*. If both *s* and s' are least upper bounds of *T*, we have $s \leq s'$ and $s' \leq s$, hence $s = s'$. The sup of a subset *T* of *S* is therefore uniquely determined, if it exists at all, and we may denote it by "sup *T*." Clearly, every element of *S* is an upper bound of the empty set; if *S* has a least element 0, this is the sup of the empty set. If *t* and t' are elements of *S*, the sup of $\{t, t'\}$ coincides with the element $t \vee t'$, where ∨ is the lattice operation considered earlier. "Lower bound" and "inf" are defined dually.

An ordered set $(S, \leq)$ is called a *complete lattice* if every subset of *S* has both an inf and a sup. It suffices to postulate an inf for each subset of *S*; for the sup of any subset *T* may then be defined as the inf of all its upper bounds,

$$\sup T = \inf \{ s \in S \mid \forall_{t \in T} t \leq s \}.$$

In particular, the sup of the empty set is inf *S*. It follows that every pair of elements has both an inf and a sup, hence a complete lattice is in fact a lattice.

An ordered set $(S, \leq)$ is called *well-ordered* if every nonempty subset has a least element. A well-ordered set with a greatest element is evidently a complete lattice.

A Boolean algebra is called *complete* if it is a complete lattice.

The lattices of Examples 1 and 2 are not complete. However, Example 1 becomes complete if we throw in the extra element infinity. The Boolean algebra of Example 3 is complete. The Boolean algebras of examples 4, 5, and 6 are not complete. In Example 6, this is a nontrivial fact [see Halmos (1963), § 25]. The positive integers with the relation "less than or equal to" are well-ordered. However, with the relation "greater than or equal to" they are no longer well-ordered, though still simply ordered.

By a *closure* operation on a complete lattice $(S, \leq)$ is understood a mapping $a \to a^c$ of *S* into *S* such that

$$a \leq a^c, \qquad (a^c)^c \leq a^c, \qquad a \leq b \Rightarrow a^c \leq b^c.$$

An element *a* of *S* is called *closed* if $a^c \leq a$, hence $a^c = a$. Obviously $1^c = 1$, if 1 is the greatest element of *S*.

Here is an example of a closure operation: If *A* is a subset of the group *G*, let A^c be the smallest subset of *G* which contains *A* and is closed under the group operations.

PROPOSITION 4.   *Given a closure operation on a complete lattice, the inf of any set of closed elements is again closed, hence the closed elements form another complete lattice. Conversely, any subset of a complete lattice which is closed under the "operation" inf can be obtained in this way.*

Proof.   Let X be a set of closed elements and $a = \inf X$. Then for any $x \in X$, $a \leq x$, hence $a^c \leq x^c \leq x$. Thus $a^c \leq a$ as required.

Conversely, let T be any subset of the complete lattice S which is closed under the "operation" inf. If $a \in S$, define $a^c = \inf \{t \in T \mid a \leq t\}$. It is easily seen that ^{c} is a closure operation and that T consists precisely of the closed elements.

EXERCISES

1. Show that in defining a group it suffices to postulate the associative law and the identities $a1 = a$ and $aa^{-1} = 1$. Show that there are systems other than groups which satisfy the associative law and the identities $a1 = a$ and $a^{-1}a = 1$.

2. Show that a group may equivalently be defined as a system $(S,1,/)$, where $/$ is a binary operation satisfying the identities

$$a/1 = a, \qquad a/a = 1, \qquad (a/c)/(b/c) = a/b.$$

[*Hint:* Let $a/b = ab^{-1}$, and conversely define $a^{-1} = 1/a$, $ab = a/(1/b)$.]

3. Show that in defining a ring the commutative law for addition is redundant. Show that in any ring the following identities hold:

$$a0 = 0 = 0a, \qquad (-a)(-b) = ab.$$

4. Show that in any Boolean ring we have the identities $a + a = 0$, $ab = ba$.

5. Fill in the gaps in the proof of Proposition 1.

6. Show that a lattice may be defined equationally as a system $(S,\wedge,\vee)$, where $(S,\wedge)$ and $(S,\vee)$ are semilattices and furthermore

$$a \wedge (a \vee b) = a, \qquad a \vee (a \wedge b) = a.$$

7. Show that in any distributive lattice we also have the dual distributive law

$$a \vee (b \wedge c) = (a \vee b) \wedge (a \vee c).$$

8. Prove Proposition 3.

9. Prove that $\sup T = \inf T^{\vee}$, where

$$T^{\vee} = \{s \in S \mid \forall_{t \in T} t \leq s\}.$$

1.2 Subrings, homomorphisms, ideals

A subset S of a ring $(R,0,1,-,+,\cdot)$ is called a *subring* if it is closed under all the operations of R, that is to say if it contains 0 and 1 and if with a, b in S one also has $-a$, $a + b$, and ab in S. Surely then $(S,0,1,-,+,\cdot)$ is also a ring.

One easily verifies that the intersection of any family of subrings of R is again a subring of R. This is not true for the union of a family of subrings except in special cases, for example when the family is simply ordered under inclusion—that is, if for S and T in the family either $S \subset T$ or $T \subset S$. We thus have:

PROPOSITION 1. *The subrings of a ring form a complete lattice under inclusion. The inf of any family of subrings is their intersection. The sup of a simply ordered family of subrings is their union.*

This result has nothing to do with rings; it remains valid in any equationally defined class of algebraic systems, if subrings are replaced by the appropriate subsystems, e.g., subgroups, sublattices, etc.

Let R and S be given rings. A mapping $\phi : R \to S$ is called a *homomorphism* if it preserves all operations; that is,

$$\phi 0 = 0, \qquad \phi 1 = 1, \qquad \phi(-a) = -\phi a, \qquad \phi(a + b) = \phi a + \phi b,$$

$$\phi(ab) = \phi a \phi b.$$

These conditions are not all independent. The same definition with appropriate operations applies to any equationally defined class of algebraic systems. Examples of homomorphisms are the identity mapping of R into itself and the inclusion mapping of a subring of R into R. A homomorphism is called *monomorphism* if it is one-one, *epimorphism* if it is onto, *isomorphism* if it is both one-one and onto. A homomorphism of R into itself is called *endomorphism*, if it is also an isomorphism it is called *automorphism*.

If $\phi : R \to S$ and $\psi : S \to T$ are homomorphisms, so is their composition or product

$$\psi \circ \phi : R \to T$$

which is defined by

$$(\psi \circ \phi)r = \psi(\phi r).$$

In some countries people drive on the left side of the road, in other countries they drive on the right side. We have written homomorphisms on the left side of their arguments, but we could equally well have written them on the right. If this is done (and we shall occasionally find it convenient to do so) the natural definition of the product of $\phi : R \to S$ and $\psi : S \to T$ is

$$\phi * \psi : R \to T$$

where

$$r(\phi * \psi) = (r\phi)\psi.$$

Note that $\phi * \psi = \psi \circ \phi$. The reader should be warned that switching from left to right may force a change in the statement of many theorems.

For future reference, we assemble here without proof some statements about homomorphisms which are valid in any equationally defined class of algebraic systems:

PROPOSITION 2.

If ϕ and ψ are mono, so is $\psi \circ \phi$. (1)

If ϕ and ψ are epi, so is $\psi \circ \phi$. (2)

If $\psi \circ \phi$ is mono, so is ϕ. (3)

If $\psi \circ \phi$ is epi, so is ψ. (4)

COROLLARY. *The homomorphism $\phi : R \to S$ is an isomorphism if and only if there exists a homomorphism $\psi : S \to R$ such that $\phi \circ \psi$ is an automorphism of S and $\psi \circ \phi$ is an automorphism of R.*

Proof. Assume the condition, then ϕ is mono by (3) and epi by (4), hence iso. Conversely, if ϕ is iso, let $\psi = \phi^{-1}$ be its inverse mapping and verify that this is a homomorphism.

More general than homomorphism is the concept of homomorphic relation. Thus let θ be a binary relation between the rings R and S, that is essentially a subset of the Cartesian product $R \times S$, then θ is called *homomorphic* if $0 \theta 0$, $1 \theta 1$, and $r_1 \theta s_1$, $r_2 \theta s_2$ imply $(-r_1) \theta (-s_1)$, $(r_1 + r_2) \theta (s_1 + s_2)$, $(r_1 r_2) \theta (s_1 s_2)$. Of course a similar definition can be made for any equationally defined class of algebraic systems. θ may be regarded as a many-valued mapping of part of R into S. When it is single-valued and everywhere defined it is an ordinary homomorphism and $r \theta s$ then means the same as $r\theta = s$.

A homomorphic relation on R (that is, between R and itself) is called a *congruence* relation if it is an equivalence relation, that is reflexive, symmetric, and transitive. Many students mistakenly believe that a transitive and symmetric relation is always reflexive. Actually, it is not difficult to see that a symmetric and transitive homomorphic relation on R is a congruence relation on a subring of R. It is however surprising that the converse of the above statement holds:

PROPOSITION 3 (Findlay). *If θ is a reflexive homomorphic relation on a ring, then θ is symmetric and transitive, hence a congruence relation.*
   Proof.   Assume $a \, \theta \, b$.   Since $a \, \theta \, a$ and $b \, \theta \, b$, we have

$$b = a - a + b \ \theta \ a - b + b = a.$$

Thus θ is symmetric.
   Assume $a \, \theta \, b$ and $b \, \theta \, c$.   Since $b \, \theta \, b$, we have

$$a = a - b + b \ \theta \ b - b + c = c.$$

Thus θ is transitive.
   It is clear from the proof that this result remains valid in any equationally defined class of algebraic systems in which it is possible to define a ternary operation $f(x,y,z)$ such that $f(x,y,y) = x$ and $f(y,y,z) = z$. This can be done for example in groups and complemented lattices.
   If θ is a congruence relation on a ring R, it partitions R into a set R/θ of disjoint equivalence classes or *cosets*. Let θr be the coset to which r belongs, that is

$$\theta r = \{r' \in R \mid r' \, \theta \, r\}.$$

R/θ may itself be given the structure of a ring by defining

$$0 = \theta 0, \quad 1 = \theta 1, \quad -(\theta a) = \theta(-a),$$

$$\theta a + \theta b = \theta(a + b), \quad \theta a \theta b = \theta(ab).$$

Of course, before making these definitions we must verify that $-(\theta a)$, for instance, depends only on the coset θa and not on its representative element a. But $\theta a = \theta a'$ means $a \, \theta \, a'$, which implies $(-a) \, \theta \, (-a')$, hence $\theta(-a) = \theta(-a')$ as required. Finally one verifies that R/θ is a ring by realizing that any equation valid in R remains valid in R/θ. Thus for example the commutative law in R gives rise to

$$\theta a + \theta b = \theta(a + b) = \theta(b + a) = \theta b + \theta a.$$

If we introduce the mapping $\pi : R \rightarrow R/\theta$ by defining $\pi r = \theta r$, it is immediate that π is an epimorphism, we call it the canonical epimorphism of R onto R/θ.

PROPOSITION 4.   *If $\phi : R \rightarrow S$ is a homomorphism then there exists a congruence relation θ on R, an epimorphism $\pi : R \rightarrow R/\theta$ and a monomorphism $\kappa : R/\theta \rightarrow S$ such that $\phi = \kappa \circ \pi$.*
   Proof.   Define $r \, \theta \, r'$ to mean $\phi r = \phi r'$. It is readily seen that θ is a congruence relation. Let π be the canonical epimorphism of R onto R/θ. Define $\kappa(\theta r) = \phi r$; this makes sense since $\theta r = \theta r'$ implies $r \, \theta \, r'$ hence $\phi r = \phi r'$. It is readily seen that κ is a homomorphism of R/θ into

S. It is mono, because $\phi r = \phi r'$ implies $r \,\theta\, r'$ hence $\theta r = \theta r'$. Finally, $\phi r = \kappa(\theta r) = \kappa(\pi r) = (\kappa \circ \pi)r$.

Needless to say, this result has nothing to do with rings; it remains valid for any equationally defined class of algebraic systems. So does the following result, which is quite analogous to Proposition 1.

PROPOSITION 5. *The congruence relations on a ring form a complete lattice under inclusion. The inf of any family of congruence relations is their intersection. The sup of a simply ordered family of congruence relations is their union.*

When we speak of inclusion, intersection, and union for congruence relations, we regard these as subsets of $R \times R$. Actually any homomorphic relation θ between R and S may be regarded as a subring of $R \times S$, if the latter is given the structure of a ring in the usual fashion. (See Section 1.3.)

The notion of "congruence relation" on rings is usually eclipsed by that of "ideal." An *ideal* of the ring R is an additive subgroup K of R such that $kr \in K$ and $rk \in K$ for all $k \in K$ and $r \in R$. Clearly, any intersection of ideals is an ideal.

PROPOSITION 6. *There is a one-to-one correspondence between the ideals K and the congruence relations θ of a ring R such that*

$$r - r' \in K \Leftrightarrow r \,\theta\, r'.$$

This is an isomorphism between the lattice of ideals and the lattice of congruence relations.

Proof. Given a congruence relation θ, a routine verification shows that $K = \theta 0 = \{r \in R \mid r \,\theta\, 0\}$ is an ideal. Conversely, given an ideal K one defines $r \,\theta\, r'$ to mean $r - r' \in K$ and verifies that θ is a congruence relation. Obviously intersections of ideals correspond to intersections of congruence relations.

If K is the ideal corresponding to the congruence relation θ, we write R/K in place of R/θ. We write $R \cong S$ to mean that R and S are isomorphic.

PROPOSITION 7. *If ϕ is a homomorphism of a ring R into another ring, then $\phi R \cong R/\phi^{-1}0$. ϕR is called the* image, $\phi^{-1}0 = \{r \in R \mid \phi r = 0\}$ *the* kernel *of ϕ.*

Proof. By Proposition 4, and in the notation of that proposition, $\phi R = \kappa(\pi R) \cong \pi R = R/\theta$. By Proposition 6, $R/\theta = R/K$, where $K = \{r \in R \mid r \,\theta\, 0\} = \{r \in R \mid \phi r = \phi 0\} = \{r \in R \mid \phi r = 0\} = \phi^{-1}0$.

If A is any additive Abelian group and B and C are subgroups, we define their *sum* $B + C$ as the set of all $b + c$, where $b \in B$ and $c \in C$. More generally, let $\{B_i \mid i \in I\}$ be any family of subgroups of A, we define their sum $B = \sum_{i \in I} B_i$ as the set of all sums $\sum_{i \in I} b_i$, where $b_i \in B_i$ and all but a finite number of the b_i are 0. B is also a subgroup of A, in fact the smallest subgroup containing all the B_i.

We observe that the subgroups of A satisfy the *modular law:*

$$\text{If } C \subset B \text{ then } B \cap (C + D) = C + (B \cap D).$$

For clearly the right side is contained in the left. Now let $b = c + d$ be any element of the left side, $b \in B$, $c \in C$, $d \in D$, then $d = b - c \in B \cap D$, and so $b \in C + (B \cap D)$ as required.

More generally, we define a *modular lattice* as any lattice in which $c \le b \Rightarrow b \wedge (c \vee d) = c \vee (b \wedge d)$. We can now sharpen Proposition 5 a little:

PROPOSITION 8.   *The ideals in a ring form a complete modular lattice under inclusion. The inf of any family of ideals is their intersection. The sup of any family of ideals is their sum.*

Proof.   This follows immediately from Propositions 5 and 6 and the above remarks together with the observation that a sum of ideals is an ideal.

In addition to the lattice operations there are other operations on the set of ideals, more generally on the set of additive subgroups of a ring.

If A and B are additive subgroups of the ring R we define subgroups AB, $A \cdot B$, and $A \cdot\, B$ as follows:

AB consists of all finite sums $\sum_{i=1}^{n} a_i b_i$, where $a_i \in A$ and $b_i \in B$.   (1)

$A \cdot B = \{r \in R \mid rB \subset A\}$.   (Read "$A$ over B.")   (2)

$B \cdot\, A = \{r \in R \mid Br \subset A\}$.   (Read "$B$ under A.")   (3)

Here of course $rB = \{rb \mid b \in B\}$. $A \cdot B$ and $B \cdot\, A$ are often called *residual quotients.*

PROPOSITION 9.   *If A, B, and C are additive subgroups of R then $(AB)C = A(BC)$. Moreover*

$$AB \subset C \Leftrightarrow A \subset C \cdot B$$

$$\Leftrightarrow B \subset A \cdot.\, C.$$

Proof.   The associative law for subgroups is an obvious consequence of the associative law for elements. Now $AB \subset C$ implies $aB \subset C$ for all $a \in A$, that is $a \in C \cdot B$ for all $a \in A$, that is $A \subset C \cdot B$. Conversely, we deduce from this that $ab \in C$ for all $a \in A$ and $b \in B$, hence $AB \subset C$. The equivalence with $B \subset A \cdot.\, C$ follows by symmetry.

A number of other identities are easy consequences of Proposition 9.

COROLLARY.   *If A, B, C, A_i, and B_i $(i \in I)$ are subgroups of R then*

$$(A \cdot B) \cdot C = A \cdot (CB), \qquad (A \cdot B) \cdot C = A \cdot (B \cdot C),$$

$$A \cdot (B \cdot C) = (BA) \cdot C, \qquad (\textstyle\sum A_i)B = \sum (A_i B),$$

$$(\textstyle\bigcap A_i) \cdot B = \bigcap (A_i \cdot B), \qquad A \cdot \sum B_i = \bigcap (A \cdot B_i).$$

Here for example is a proof of the last identity:

$$C \subset A \cdot \textstyle\sum B_i \Leftrightarrow \sum B_i \subset C \cdot A$$

$$\Leftrightarrow \forall_i (B_i \subset C \cdot A)$$

$$\Leftrightarrow \forall_i (C \subset A \cdot B_i)$$

$$\Leftrightarrow C \subset \textstyle\bigcap (A \cdot B_i).$$

When applied to ideals the above operations yield other ideals. We shall omit the proof of the following:

PROPOSITION 10.   *If A and B are ideals of R so are AB, $A \cdot B$, and $A \cdot B$. Moreover*

$$AR = A = RA, \qquad A \cdot R = A = R \cdot A,$$

$$A \cdot A = R = A \cdot A, \qquad AB \subset A \cap B.$$

EXERCISES

1. Prove that the union of a simply ordered family of subrings is a subring.

2. Prove the assertions of Proposition 2.

3. Prove that the endomorphisms of an algebraic system form a semigroup with 1 and that the automorphisms form a group. (In particular, the set of all mappings of a set into itself is a semigroup with 1.)

4. Prove that the endomorphisms of an Abelian group form a ring if addition is defined in a natural way.

5. If θ is a homomorphic relation between R and S and T is a subring of S, show that $\theta T = \{r \in R \mid \exists_{t \in T} r \; \theta \; t\}$ is a subring of R.

6. If θ and θ' are homomorphic relations between R and S and S and T, respectively, show that $\theta\theta'$ defined by $r \; \theta\theta' \; t \Leftrightarrow \exists_{s \in S}(r \; \theta \; s \; \& \; s \; \theta' \; t)$ is a homomorphic relation between R and T. Show that this "relative product" specializes to the composition of homomorphisms. (If θ is regarded as a many-valued mapping of part of R into S, this will be the composition of homomorphisms written on the right.)

7. Consider an equationally defined class of algebraic systems with a ternary operation $f(x,y,z)$ such that $f(x,y,y) = x$ and $f(y,y,z) = z$ identically.

(a) If θ_1 and θ_2 are congruence relations on one system of this class, show that $\theta_1\theta_2 = \theta_2\theta_1$.

(b) Show that the congruence relations on such a system form a modular lattice.

(c) If θ is a homomorphic relation between R and S and θ^{-1} is its "converse," defined by $s\theta^{-1}r \Leftrightarrow r\,\theta\,s$, show that $\theta\theta^{-1}\theta = \theta$.

8. Determine all ideals in the ring of integers.

9. Prove the remaining identities in the corollary to Proposition 9 and prove Proposition 10.

10. Interpret the operations $A + B$, $A \cap B$, AB and $A \mathbin{.\cdot} B$ for ideals in the ring of integers.

11. Let G be an additive subgroup of the ring R. With each subgroup A of R associate the subgroup $A^c = (G \mathbin{.\cdot} A) \mathbin{.\cdot} G$. Show that ^{c} is a closure operation on the lattice of subgroups.

12. Show that the class of modular lattices may be equationally defined.

1.3 Modules, direct products, and direct sums

A *right R-module* A_R consists of an additive Abelian group A, a ring R, and a mapping $A \times R \to A$, denoted by juxtaposition, such that

$$(a + b)r = ar + br, \qquad a(r + s) = ar + as,$$

$$a(r \cdot s) = (ar)s, \qquad a1 = a,$$

for all $a, b \in A$ and $r, s \in R$. A left R-module $_RA$ is defined symmetrically.

Examples

1. If R is a field, A_R is what is usually called a vector space.

2. If $R = Z$, the ring of integers, A_R is essentially just A, since multiplication by a positive integer reduces to repeated addition. Thus Z-modules and additive Abelian groups may be regarded as the same objects.

3. If $A = R$ and the mapping $A \times R \to A$ is taken to be multiplication, that is $ar = a \cdot r$, then we have a right module R_R.

4. Let F be the set of endomorphisms of the additive Abelian group A, written on the right. We obtain a ring $(F,0,1,-,+,*)$ upon defining

$$a0 = 0, \qquad a1 = a, \qquad a(-f) = -(af),$$

$$a(f + g) = af + ag, \qquad a(f * g) = (af)g,$$

for any $a \in A$ and $f, g \in F$. Moreover we have the mapping $(a, f) \rightarrow af$ of $A \times F$ into A. Since f is a homomorphism, $(a + b)f = af + bf$, hence we have a right module A_F.

PROPOSITION 1. *Let* $\Gamma : R \rightarrow F$ *be a homomorphism of the ring R into the ring F of right endomorphisms of the additive Abelian group A, then putting* $ar = a(\Gamma r)$, *for all $a \in A$ and $r \in R$, we obtain a right R-module A_R, and every right R-module may be obtained in this way.*

   Proof. We have

$$(a + b)r = (a + b)\Gamma r = a\Gamma r + b\Gamma r = ar + br,$$

since Γr is a homomorphism;

$$a(r + s) = a\Gamma(r + s) = a(\Gamma r + \Gamma s) = a\Gamma r + a\Gamma s = ar + as,$$

since Γ is a homomorphism and by definition of $+$ in F;

$$a(r \cdot s) = a\Gamma(r \cdot s) = a(\Gamma r * \Gamma s) = (a\Gamma r)\Gamma s = (ar)s,$$

since Γ is a homomorphism and by definition of $*$ in F;

$$a1_R = a\Gamma 1_R = a1_F = a,$$

since Γ is a homomorphism. (To clarify the last equation, we have distinguished between the elements 1_R of R and 1_F of F, the latter being the identity automorphism of A.)

   Conversely, let A_R be any right R-module, then we define $\Gamma : R \rightarrow F$ by $a(\Gamma r) = ar$ and readily verify that Γ is a ring homomorphism.

   An R-module A_R may be regarded as a system $(A, 0, -, +, R)$, where $(A, 0, -, +)$ is an Abelian group and each element of R is a unary operation on A, subject to the identities $(a + b)r = ar + br$ and so on. We may have infinitely many operations (if R has infinite cardinality) and infinitely many identities. The just mentioned equation represents a set of identities, one for each element r of R. At any rate, for a given R, the class of right R-modules is an equationally defined class of algebras, and Propositions 1 to 5 of the last section immediately become applicable to modules, provided the words "ring" and "subring" are replaced by "module" and "submodule." A submodule B of A is of course a subgroup of A which is closed under the new operations, that is $br \in B$ for all $b \in B$ and $r \in R$. Moreover, Propositions 6 to 8 of Section 1.2 also remain valid for modules, provided "ideal" is replaced by "submodule." Thus the module analogs of Propositions 1 and 8 coincide. It would be tedious to restate and reprove these modified propositions, and we shall refrain from doing so.

   By a homomorphism (R-homomorphism) $\phi : A_R \rightarrow B_R$ we understand of course a group homomorphism of A into B which satisfies the extra condition $\phi(ar) = (\phi a)r$, for all $a \in A$ and $r \in R$. The set of these homomorphisms is usually denoted by $\text{Hom}_R(A,B)$. This is given the structure of an Abelian group by defining 0, $-$, and $+$ thus:

$$0a = 0, \qquad (-\phi)a = -(\phi a), \qquad (\phi + \psi)a = \phi a + \psi a.$$

When we deal with homomorphisms of left R-modules we prefer to write them on the right, and the extra condition then becomes $(ra)\phi = r(a\phi)$.

This is as good a place as any to illustrate *Zorn's Lemma*, which asserts:

If every simply ordered subset of a nonempty ordered set $(S, \le)$ has an upper bound in S, then S has at least one maximal *element m, maximal in the sense that $m \le s$ implies $m = s$, for all $s \in S$.*

This statement is part and parcel of most mathematicians' equipment and is well known to be equivalent to the *principle of well-order*, which asserts that every set can be well-ordered, and to the *axiom of choice*, which asserts that the Cartesian product of a nonempty family $\{S_i \mid i \in I\}$ of nonempty sets is nonempty, that is to say that there exists a function $f : I \to \bigcup_{i \in I} S_i$ such that $f(i) \in S_i$ for all $i \in I$. (Here I is any index set.)

PROPOSITION 2. *Let T be any subset of the module A_R. Then any submodule B of A_R which has no element in common with T except possibly 0 is contained in a submodule M which is maximal with respect to this property.*

This proposition remains valid if "module" and "submodule" are replaced by "ring" and "ideal," respectively.

Proof. Consider the set of all submodules of A_R which contain B and whose intersection with T is contained in the zero submodule. The submodule B is a member of this set. These submodules may be ordered by inclusion, and if $\{B_i \mid i \in I\}$ is any simply ordered family of submodules in the set then their least upper bound $\bigcup_{i \in I} B_i$ is also in the set. The conditions of Zorn's Lemma are now satisfied.

The submodules of R_R are called *right ideals*. A right ideal is called *proper* if it is not R, that is if it does not contain 1. Taking $T = \{1,0\}$ (or $T = \{1\}$), we thus have:

COROLLARY. *Every proper (right) ideal in a ring is contained in a maximal proper (right) ideal.*

The *direct product* $R = \prod_{i \in I} R_i$ of a family of rings is their Cartesian product with operations defined componentwise. Thus, if $r \in R$, that is $r : I \to \bigcup_{i \in I} R_i$ with $r(i) \in R_i$ for all $i \in I$, we define $-r$ by $(-r)(i) = -r(i)$, and similarly for the other ring operations.

It is easily seen that any equation valid in each of the R_i remains valid in R. For example, assume that all R_i are commutative, then $r(i)s(i) = s(i)r(i)$ for all r, $s \in R$ and $i \in I$, and this implies that $rs = sr$. We can now see why the class of fields cannot be equationally defined. For if this were so, the direct product of fields would be a field, contrary to fact. For example, if F is a field, $F \times F$ has the zero-divisor $(1,0) \neq (0,0)$, hence is not a field.

If R is the direct product of rings R_i $(i \in I)$, let $e_i \in R$ be defined by $e_i(j) = 1$ if $j = i$, $= 0$ if $j \neq i$. It is immediately verified that the e_i are *central*, or lie in the *center* of R, that is $e_i r = r e_i$ for all $r \in R$. Moreover the e_i form a system of *orthogonal idempotents*, in the sense that $e_i^2 = e_i$ and $e_i e_j = 0$ when $i \neq j$. (An *idempotent* is an element e such that $e^2 = e$.)

If e is any central idempotent in R, we can write every element r of R in the form

$$r = er + (1 - e)r, \quad \text{where} \quad er \in eR \quad \text{and} \quad (1 - e)r \in (1 - e)R.$$

Moreover, this is the only way in which r can be written as a sum of elements of eR and $(1 - e)R$, since $r = ex + (1 - e)y$ implies $er = ex$ and $(1 - e)r = (1 - e)y$. We say that R is the "direct sum" of the ideals eR and $(1 - e)R$, and it follows from what has been said that R is isomorphic to the direct product $eR \times (1 - e)R$. We observe that eR is a ring with unity element e, but it is not a subring of R except when $e = 1$. (This is a consequence of our definition of subring: A subring of R must contain 1, hence cannot be a proper ideal, that is an ideal $\neq R$.) In fact, an ideal of R is a ring (in our sense) if and only if it is a "direct summand." For let K be an ideal with unity element e (we must distinguish this notationally from the unity 1 of R) then $K = eR$ and $e^2 = e$.

There is no difficulty in extending the above remarks to any finite set of orthogonal idempotents. First let us call a sum $\sum_{i \in I} K_i$ of subgroups K_i of an additive Abelian group *direct* if 0 cannot be written nontrivially as a sum of elements of the K_i, that is $0 = \sum_{i \in I} k_i$ $(k_i \in K_i)$ implies that all $k_i = 0$.

PROPOSITION 3.   *The following statements are equivalent:*
   (a) *R is isomorphic to a finite direct product of rings R_i $(i = 1, 2, \ldots, n)$.*
   (b) *There exist central orthogonal idempotents $e_i \in R$ such that* $1 = \sum_{i=1}^{n} e_i$ *and* $e_i R \cong R_i$.
   (c) *R is a finite direct sum of ideals $K_i \cong R_i$.*
   Proof (sketched). $(a) \Rightarrow (b) \Rightarrow (c) \Rightarrow (a)$.

The direct product of a family of R-modules $\{A_i \mid i \in I\}$ is defined in exactly the same way as the direct product of rings (or as for any other kind of algebraic systems for that matter). If $A = \prod_{i \in I} A_i$, we have canonical epimorphisms $\pi_i : A \to A_i$ and monomorphisms $\kappa_i : A_i \to A$ defined by

$$\pi_i a = a(i), \qquad \kappa_i(a_i)(j) = \begin{cases} a_i & \text{if } j = i \\ 0 & \text{if } j \neq i. \end{cases}$$

Clearly then

$$\pi_j \circ \kappa_i = \begin{cases} 1 & \text{if } j = i \\ 0 & \text{if } j \neq i. \end{cases} \tag{1}$$

(Here 1 is the identity mapping of A_i.) It may be noted that the π_i also exist for rings, but that the κ_i are no longer homomorphisms for rings, since they do not map 1 onto 1.

We now introduce the (external) *direct sum* of modules:

$$A = \sum_{i \in I}^{*} A_i \subset \prod_{i \in I} A_i,$$

which consists of all $a \in \prod_{i \in I} A_i$ for which $a(i) = 0$ for all but a finite number of $i \in I$. It is immediate that A is also an R-module. In particular, a finite direct sum is the same as a finite direct product. For this reason we write "$A \times B$" for the external direct sum of two modules, but wish to warn the reader that most authors write "$A \oplus B$."

Canonical epimorphisms and monomorphisms are defined for direct sums in exactly the same way as for direct products. In addition to (1) we now also have

$$\sum_{i \in I} (\kappa_i \circ \pi_i) a = a, \tag{2}$$

for any $a \in A$. Indeed, the sum on the left side is $\sum_{i \in I} \kappa_i a(i)$, which applied to $j \in I$ yields $a(j)$. When we have a finite direct sum, this may also be written

$$\sum_{i=1}^{n} \kappa_i \circ \pi_i = 1,$$

where the right side denotes the identity automorphism of A_R.

If we write $\varepsilon_i = \kappa_i \circ \pi_i \in \operatorname{Hom}_R(A, A)$, then (1) and (2) may be rewritten as

$$\varepsilon_i \circ \varepsilon_j = \begin{cases} \varepsilon_i & \text{if } i = j \\ 0 & \text{if } i \neq j \end{cases} \tag{3}$$

and

$$\sum_{i \in I} \varepsilon_i a = a, \tag{4}$$

for all $a \in A$. We say that the ε_i form a *complete system of orthogonal idempotent endomorphisms* of A_R.

PROPOSITION 4.   *The following statements are equivalent:*

(a) A_R is isomorphic with the (external) direct sum of modules $(A_i)_R$, $i \in I$.

(b) A_R has a complete system of orthogonal idempotent endomorphisms $\{\varepsilon_i \mid i \in I\}$ and $\varepsilon_i A \cong A_i$.

(c) A_R is the (internal) direct sum of submodules $B_i \cong A_i$.

Proof (sketched). $(a) \Rightarrow (b) \Rightarrow (c) \Rightarrow (a)$.

EXERCISES

1. Show that in any right R-module A_R, $0r = 0$, $(-a)r = -(ar)$, $a0 = 0$, $a(-r) = -(ar)$, for all $a \in A$ and $r \in R$.

2. In the last part of Proposition 1, verify in detail that Γ is a homomorphism.

3. Verify that $\mathrm{Hom}_R(A,B)$ is an Abelian group.

4. If $Z(n)$ is the ring of integers modulo n, show that $Z(n)$ is isomorphic to the direct product of all $Z(p^r)$, where p^r is the highest power of the prime p dividing n.

5. Prove that if a ring is a sum of ideals, then it is a finite sum.

6. Let Q be the field of rationals, Q_p the subring of Q consisting of those rationals whose denominators are powers of the prime p. Show that the Abelian group Q/Z is the direct sum of the groups Q_p/Z.

7. If $R = S \times T$, show that $S \times 0$ is an ideal of R and that $R/(S \times 0) \cong T$.

8. Prove that the sum $\sum_{i \in I} B_i$ of submodules of A_R is direct if and only if, for all $i \in I$,

$$B_i \cap \sum_{j \neq i} B_j = 0.$$

9. Write out in detail the proofs of Propositions 3 and 4.

1.4   Classical isomorphism theorems

In order to make these notes self-contained, we shall present here the classical isomorphism theorems which are usually stated for groups with operators. While these theorems are valid for an even wider class of algebraic systems, we shall restrict attention to (right) R-modules. This is the case we are mainly interested in, and some of the proofs are a little simpler than in the general situation.

We begin with a restatement of Proposition 7 of Section 1.2 for modules instead of rings:

PROPOSITION 1. *If $\phi \in \operatorname{Hom}_R (A,B)$ then $\phi A \cong A/\phi^{-1}0$.*
ϕA and $\phi^{-1}0$ are usually called the *image* and *kernal* of ϕ, respectively.

PROPOSITION 2. *Let C be a submodule of A_R. Every submodule of A/C has the form B/C where $C \subset B \subset A$, and $A/B \cong (A/C)/(B/C)$.*
Proof. Let $\pi : A \to A/C$ be the canonical epimorphism. Any submodule B' of $\pi A = A/C$ has an inverse image $B = \pi^{-1}B'$ in A, hence $B' = \pi B$. Clearly $C = \pi^{-1}0 \subset B$, and so we may write $\pi B = B/C$. Now let $\pi' : \pi A \to \pi A/\pi B$ be the canonical epimorphism, then $\pi' \circ \pi : A \to \pi A/\pi B$, and the kernel of this mapping is

$$(\pi' \circ \pi)^{-1}0 = \pi^{-1}(\pi B) = B.$$

The result now follows from Proposition 1.

PROPOSITION 3. *If B and C are submodules of A then $(B + C)/B \cong C/(B \cap C)$.*
Proof. Consider the canonical epimorphism $\pi : B + C \to (B + C)/B$ and monomorphism $\kappa : C \to B + C$. Then $\pi \circ \kappa$ has kernel $B \cap C$ and image $\pi C = \pi B + \pi C = \pi(B + C)$. The result now follows from Proposition 1.

LEMMA 1 (Zassenhaus). *If $B' \subset B \subset A$ and $C' \subset C \subset A$, then*

$$(B' + (B \cap C))/(B' + (B \cap C')) \cong (C' + (B \cap C))/(C' + (B' \cap C)).$$

Proof. We prove that the left side is isomorphic with

$$(B \cap C)/((B' \cap C) + (B \cap C'))$$

by observing that

$$(B' + (B \cap C')) + (B \cap C) = B' + (B \cap C)$$

and

$$(B' + (B \cap C')) \cap (B \cap C) = (B' \cap C) + (B \cap C'),$$

by the modular law, and then applying Proposition 3. By symmetry, the right side is isomorphic to the same expression.

By a (finite) *chain* of submodules of A_R we understand a sequence

$$A_0 \subset A_1 \subset \cdots \subset A_m = A$$

of submodules, where each A_i is a submodule of A_{i+1}. We are interested in the corresponding factors A_{i+1}/A_i.

PROPOSITION 4 (Schreier). *Given two chains*

$$B = A_0 \subset A_1 \subset \cdots \subset A_m = A$$
$$B = B_0 \subset B_1 \subset \cdots \subset B_n = A$$

*then both chains can be refined so that the resulting chains have the same
length and isomorphic factors (not necessarily in the same order).*

Proof (Zassenhaus).   Between A_i and A_{i+1} insert

$$A_{i,j} = A_i + (A_{i+1} \cap B_j), \qquad (j = 0, \ldots, n)$$

and between B_j and B_{j+1} insert

$$B_{i,j} = B_j + (B_{j+1} \cap A_i), \qquad (i = 0, \ldots, m),$$

then

$$A_{i,j+1}/A_{i,j} \cong B_{i+1,j}/B_{i,j},$$

by the above lemma. ($A_i = A_{i,0}$ and $A_{i+1} = A_{i,n}$.)

A *composition series* of the module A_R is a chain

$$0 = A_0 \subset A_1 \subset \cdots \subset A_m = A \qquad (A_i \neq A_{i+1})$$

which cannot be properly refined. The following is immediate:

COROLLARY (Jordan-Hölder).   *Let*

$$0 = A_0 \subset A_1 \subset \cdots \subset A_m = A, \qquad 0 = B_0 \subset \cdots \subset B_n = A$$

*be two composition series of A. Then $m = n$ and there exists a permutation
p of the numbers $0, 1, \ldots, n - 1$ such that*

$$A_{i+1}/A_i \cong B_{p(i)+1}/B_{p(i)} \qquad (i = 0, 1, \ldots, n - 1).$$

A module is called *Artinian* (*Noetherian*) if every nonempty set of submodules has a minimal (maximal) element. This is the same as saying that
every descending (ascending) sequence of submodules becomes ultimately
stationary.

Indeed, suppose A is Noetherian, and let

$$A_1 \subset A_2 \subset \cdots$$

be an ascending sequence of submodules of A. This sequence must have
a maximal element A_n, hence

$$A_n = A_{n+1} = \cdots .$$

Conversely, assume every ascending sequence of submodules of A
becomes ultimately stationary. Consider any nonempty set of submodules
of A and suppose this set has no maximal element. Take any element A_1
in the set; since A_1 is not maximal, A_1 is properly contained in an element
A_2 of the set, etc. Thus we get an infinite ascending sequence

$$A_1 \subsetneq A_2 \subsetneq \cdots ,$$

contrary to assumption.

PROPOSITION 5. *A module is Noetherian if and only if every submodule is finitely generated.*

Proof. Let B be a submodule of a Noetherian module and consider the set of all finitely generated submodules of B. This set will have a maximal element C, hence $C + bR = C$ for any $b \in B$, and so $C = B$.

Conversely, assume the condition and consider an ascending sequence

$$A_1 \subset A_2 \subset \cdots$$

of submodules of the module A_R. Let B be the union of this sequence, then B is finitely generated by assumption. Now all generators of B must belong to one A_n, hence $A_n = A_{n+1} = \cdots$, that is to say the sequence is stationary from A_n on.

PROPOSITION 6. *Let B be a submodule of A_R. Then A is Artinian (Noetherian) if and only if B and A/B are Artinian (Noetherian).*

Proof. Assume A Artinian. Since every submodule of B is a submodule of A, B is Artinian. Since every submodule of A/B has the form C/B, where $B \subset C \subset A$, A/B is Artinian.

Conversely, assume that A/B and B are Artinian. Consider any descending sequence of submodules $A_1 \supset A_2 \supset \cdots$. Consider now the sequence of submodules of A/B:

$$(A_1 + B)/B \supset (A_2 + B)/B \supset \cdots$$

as well as the sequence of submodules of B:

$$A_1 \cap B \supset A_2 \cap B \supset \cdots.$$

By assumption, both these sequences are ultimately stationary, say after n steps. Then

$$A_n \cap B = A_{n+1} \cap B = \cdots$$

and

$$(A_n + B)/B = (A_{n+1} + B)/B = \cdots,$$

whence

$$A_n + B = A_{n+1} + B = \cdots.$$

Using the modular law, we now compute

$$A_n = A_n \cap (A_n + B) = A_n \cap (A_{n+1} + B)$$

$$= A_{n+1} + (A_n \cap B) = A_{n+1} + (A_{n+1} \cap B) = A_{n+1}.$$

COROLLARY. *A finite direct product of modules is Artinian (Noetherian) if and only if each factor is Artinian (Noetherian).*

Proof. It suffices to consider the product of two modules, say $A = B \times C$. But then $A/(0 \times C) \cong B$ and the above applies. Here and elsewhere $0 = \{0\}$ is the smallest subgroup of A.

PROPOSITION 7.   *A module has a composition series if and only if it is both Artinian and Noetherian.*

Proof. Assume A_R has a composition series of length n. By the corollary to Proposition 4, there is no chain of length $> n$. This implies that A is Artinian and Noetherian.

Conversely, assume that A is Artinian and Noetherian. Since A is Artinian, there exists a minimal submodule $A_1 \neq 0$, a minimal submodule A_2 properly containing A_1, and so on. Now the sequence $A_1 \subset A_2 \subset \cdots$ must break off, since A is Noetherian, hence $A_m = A$ for some m, and we have a composition series.

PROPOSITION 8.   *An endomorphism of an Artinian (Noetherian) module is an automorphism if and only if it is mono (epi).*

Proof. Let f be an endomorphism of the Artinian module A_R which is mono. Now $A \supset fA \supset f^2A \supset \cdots$, hence $f^nA = f^{n+1}A$ for some n. Take any $a \in A$, then $f^na = f^{n+1}b$ for some $b \in A$. Now f^n is mono, hence $a = fb$. Thus f is epi, hence an automorphism.

Next, let f be an endomorphism of the Noetherian module A_R which is epi. Now $0 \subset f^{-1}0 \subset f^{-2}0 \subset \cdots$, hence $f^{-n}0 = f^{-(n+1)}0$ for some n. Take any $a \in A$ and assume $fa = 0$. Now f^n is epi, hence $a = f^nb$ for some $b \in A$, and so $f^{n+1}b = 0$. But then $a = f^nb = 0$. Thus f is mono, hence an automorphism.

The following is known as *Fitting's Lemma:*

PROPOSITION 9.   *If f is an endomorphism of the Artinian and Noetherian module A_R then, for some n, $A = f^nA + f^{-n}0$ as a direct sum.*

Proof. The sequence $A \supset fA \supset f^2A \supset \cdots$ becomes stationary after n steps, say. Thus $f^nA = f^{n+1}A$. Therefore f^n induces an endomorphism on the Noetherian module f^nA which is epi, hence an automorphism. Thus $f^nA \cap f^{-n}0 = 0$. Now take any $a \in A$, then $f^na = f^{2n}b$ for some $b \in A$, hence $f^n(a - f^nb) = 0$. Writing $a = f^nb + (a - f^nb)$, we see that $A = f^nA + f^{-n}0$ as required.

A nonzero module is called *indecomposable* if it is not isomorphic to the direct product of nonzero modules, that is to say if it is not the direct sum of nonzero submodules. The following are corollaries to Fitting's lemma.

COROLLARY 1.   *If A_R is indecomposable, Artinian and Noetherian, then every endomorphism of A_R is either nilpotent or an automorphism.*

Proof. In view of Fitting's Lemma, either $f^n A = 0$ or $f^{-n} 0 = 0$. In the first case f is nilpotent, in the second case f^n is an automorphism, but then also f is an automorphism.

COROLLARY 2. *If A_R is indecomposable, Artinian and Noetherian, and $g = f_1 + \cdots + f_n$ is an automorphism, $f_i \in \mathrm{Hom}_R (A,A)$, then some f_i is an automorphism.*

Proof. First consider the case $n = 2$. Then $1 = g^{-1} f_1 + g^{-1} f_2$. By the above, $g^{-1} f_1$ is an automorphism or nilpotent. In the second case $g^{-1} f_2 = 1 - g^{-1} f_1$ is an automorphism. (For if $h^m = 0$ then $1 - h$ has inverse $1 + h + \cdots + h^{m-1}$.)

We now treat the general situation by induction. If f_1 is not an automorphism, then $g^{-1} f_1$ is not, hence $1 - g^{-1} f_1$ is. By inductional assumption, $g^{-1} f_i$ is an automorphism, for some $i \neq 1$, but then so is f_i.

If $A_1 \times A_2 \cong B_1 \times B_2$ and $A_1 \cong B_1$, can we deduce that $A_2 \cong B_2$? Not in general, for we may take A_2 and B_2 arbitrary, and $A_1 = B_1$, the direct product of countably many copies of $A_2 \times B_2$. However, the result holds when $A_1 \times A_2$ is Artinian and Noetherian. For the moment we require a weaker statement:

LEMMA 2. *Let λ be an isomorphism of the Artinian module $A = A_1 \times A_2$ onto $B = B_1 \times B_2$ such that $\lambda(a_1,0) = (\alpha a_1, \beta a_1)$, where α is an isomorphism of A_1 onto B_1, then $A_2 \cong B_2$.*

Proof. If $\beta A_1 = 0$, this is obvious, for then $A_2 \cong A/(A_1 \times 0) \cong \lambda A/(\alpha A_1 \times 0) = B/(B_1 \times 0) \cong B_2$. Our proof will therefore be complete if we can introduce another isomorphism $\mu : A_1 \times A_2 \to B_1 \times B_2$ such that $\mu(a_1,0) = (\alpha a_1,0)$. Indeed, if $\lambda(a_1,a_2) = (b_1,b_2)$, put $\mu(a_1,a_2) = (b_1, b_2 - \beta \alpha^{-1} b_1)$, then μ clearly satisfies this equation. To show that μ is an isomorphism it suffices to verify that it is mono. (For then $\lambda^{-1}\mu$ is mono, hence an automorphism.) Suppose therefore that $\mu(a_1,a_2) = 0$. Then $b_1 = 0 = b_2$, and so $a_1 = 0 = a_2$ since λ is mono. This completes the proof.

Our next result is usually ascribed to some combination of the following mathematicians: Krull, Remak, Schmidt, and Wedderburn.

PROPOSITION 10. *Let the Artinian and Noetherian module $A = A_1 \times A_2 \times \cdots \times A_m$ be isomorphic with $A' = A_1' \times A_2' \times \cdots \times A_n'$, where the A_i and A_j' are indecomposable modules. Then $m = n$ and, after some renumbering, $A_i \cong A_i'$.*

Proof. Let $\lambda : A \to A'$ be the given isomorphism and let κ_i, κ_j' and π_i, π_j' be the monomorphisms and epimorphisms canonically associated with the given direct products. Put $\alpha_i = \pi_1' \circ \lambda \circ \kappa_i$ and $\beta_i = \pi_i \circ \lambda^{-1} \circ \kappa_1'$.

Then $\sum_{i=1}^{m} \alpha_i \circ \beta_i = 1$, the identity automorphism of A_1'. By Corollary 2, one of the summands is an automorphism, say the first. Thus $\alpha_1 \circ \beta_1$ is an automorphism of A_1'. Therefore $\beta_1 \circ \alpha_1$ is not nilpotent, hence it is an automorphism of A_1, by Corollary 1. It follows that α_1 is an isomorphism of A_1 onto A_1'. Clearly $\lambda(a_1, 0, \ldots, 0) = (\alpha_1 a_1, *, \ldots, *)$. (Here $*$ denotes terms in which we are not interested.) By the lemma, $A_2 \times \cdots \times A_m \cong A_2' \times \cdots A_n'$. We repeat the same argument until only A_m is left on one side (we may assume $n \geq m$). But since A_m is indecomposable, $m = n$ and $A_m \cong A_n'$.

Lest some reader try to obtain the analog of Proposition 10 for rings, we hasten to point out that, if a ring is written as a direct sum of indecomposable ideals, then these are uniquely determined (not only up to isomorphism), in fact the ring will be the direct sum of all its indecomposable direct summands. We establish this in a number of steps.

PROPOSITION 11.   *The central idempotents of a ring R form a Boolean algebra $B(R)$.*

Proof.   Let B be the set of central idempotents of R, then $0 \in B$, if $e \in B$ so is $e' = 1 - e$, and if e and $f \in B$ then $ef \in B$. Clearly $(B, \cdot)$ is a semilattice. Moreover $ef' = 0$, that is $e(1 - f) = 0$, if and only if $ef = e$. According to our definition (in Section 1.1), $(B, 0, ', \cdot)$ is thus a Boolean algebra.

It should be noted that while the multiplication of $B(R)$, regarded as a Boolean ring, coincides with that of R, the addition does not in general. Indeed, let e and $f \in B(R)$, their sum in $B(R)$ is $ef' \vee fe'$, which after some computation becomes $e + f - 2ef = (e - f)^2$. Here $+$ denotes addition in R.

A minimal nonzero element of a Boolean algebra is called an *atom*.

LEMMA 3.   *If e is central idempotent in R then eR is indecomposable if and only if e is an atom of $B(R)$.*

Proof (sketched).   If e is not an atom then $e > f > 0$, hence $e = f + (e - f)$, where f and $e - f$ are orthogonal idempotents $\neq 0$. It follows that $eR = fR + (e - f)R$ as a direct sum of ideals.

Conversely, assume $eR = fR + gR$ as a direct sum of ideals, where f and g are nonzero central idempotents. It is easily shown that $fg = 0$ and $e = f + g$, hence that e is not an atom.

PROPOSITION 12.   *If R is a direct sum of indecomposable ideals then these are the only indecomposable direct summands of R.*

Proof.   We may assume that $R = e_1 R + \cdots + e_n R$ as a direct sum, where the e_i are central orthogonal idempotents and $1 = e_1 + \cdots + e_n$. We are told that the $e_i R$ are indecomposable, hence, by the lemma, that the e_i are atoms of $B(R)$. They are the only atoms; for suppose e is any atom, then $e = \sum_{i=1}^{n} e_i e = 0$, unless $e = e_i$ for some i. Therefore, by the lemma, the $e_i R$ are the only indecomposable direct summands of R.

The analog of Proposition 12 for indecomposable right ideals is false.

EXERCISES

1. If K is an ideal in the ring R, show that all ideals of R/K have the form J/K, where J is an ideal of R containing K, and that

$$R/J \cong (R/K)/(J/K).$$

2. If S is a subring of R and K is an ideal, show that

$$(S + K)/K \cong S/(S \cap K).$$

3. Show that an additive Abelian group (Z-module) has a composition series if and only if it is finite.

4. If $A_1 \times A_2 \cong B_1 \times B_2$ is Artinian and Noetherian and if $A_1 \cong B_1$, show that $A_2 \cong B_2$. (Use Proposition 10.)

5. Show that any Artinian or Noetherian module can be written as a direct sum of indecomposable modules.

6. Fill in the details in the proof of Lemma 3.

CHAPTER TWO

Selected Topics on Commutative Rings

2.1 Prime ideals in commutative rings

An element r of a ring is called a *unit* if $rs = 1 = sr$ for some $s \in R$, it is called a *zero-divisor* if $rs = 0$ or $sr = 0$ for some $s \neq 0$. Clearly no unit is a zero-divisor. A commutative ring is a *field* if $0 \neq 1$ and every nonzero element is a unit, it is an *integral domain* if $0 \neq 1$ and 0 is the only zero-divisor.

LEMMA 1. *An element of a commutative ring is a unit if and only if it lies in no proper ideal, and this is true if and only if it lies in no maximal (proper) ideal.*

Proof. Let r be an element, then $rs = 1$ for some element s if and only if the "principal" ideal rR generated by r contains 1, i.e., is improper. Moreover, every proper ideal is contained in a maximal proper ideal (Corollary of 1.3, Proposition 2).

NOTE. We shall henceforth say "maximal ideal" instead of "maximal proper ideal."

A proper ideal P in a ring is called *prime* if, for any two ideals A and B, $AB \subset P$ implies $A \subset P$ or $B \subset P$. Maximal ideals and prime ideals can also be characterized elementwise, as the next two propositions show:

PROPOSITION 1. *The proper ideal M of the commutative ring R is maximal if and only if*

$$\forall_{r \notin M} \exists_{x \in R} 1 - rx \in M.$$

Proof. The condition asserts that $M + rR$ contains 1, hence is improper, for any $r \notin M$. This is clearly equivalent to the maximality of M.

PROPOSITION 2. *The proper ideal P of the commutative ring R is prime if and only if, for all elements a and b, $ab \in P$ implies $a \in P$ or $b \in P$.*

27

Proof. Assume P prime and $ab \in P$. Then $(aR)(bR) \subset (ab)R \subset P$, hence $aR \subset P$ or $bR \subset P$, whence $a \in P$ or $b \in P$.

Conversely, assume the condition and $AB \subset P$. Suppose $A \not\subset P$, then $\exists_{a \in A} a \notin P$. Take any $b \in B$, then $ab \in P$, hence $b \in P$. Thus $B \subset P$, and so P is prime.

More important is the characterization of maximal and prime ideals by the factor rings which they determine.

PROPOSITION 3. *The ideal M of the commutative ring R is maximal if and only if R/M is a field.*

Proof. Let $\pi : R \to R/M$ be the canonical epimorphism, then R/M is a field if and only if every element πr, $r \notin M$, is a unit, i.e., $\pi r \, \pi x = 1$ for some $x \in R$, i.e., $1 - rx \in M$ for some $x \in R$, that is M is maximal, by Proposition 1.

PROPOSITION 4. *The ideal P of the commutative ring R is prime if and only if R/P is an integral domain.*

Proof. Let $\pi : R \to R/P$ be as above, then R/P is an integral domain if and only if $\pi r_1 \, \pi r_2 = 0$ implies $\pi r_1 = 0$ or $\pi r_2 = 0$, that is $r_1 r_2 \in P$ implies $r_1 \in P$ or $r_2 \in P$, that is P is prime, by Proposition 2.

PROPOSITION 5. *Every maximal ideal in a commutative ring is prime.*

Proof. Since no unit is a zero-divisor, every field is an integral domain. The result now follows from the last two propositions.

A prime ideal need not be maximal, as is shown by the zero ideal in the ring of integers. On the contrary, this particular ideal is a *minimal prime* ideal. The existence of minimal prime ideals is assured by the following (upon taking $A = 0$):

PROPOSITION 6. *If the ideal A is contained in the prime ideal B, then there exist minimal elements in the set of all prime ideals P such that $A \subset P \subset B$.*

Proof. In view of Zorn's lemma, it suffices to show that every family $\{P_i \,|\, i \in I\}$ of prime ideals between A and B which is simply ordered by inclusion has an inf in the set. Let $P = \bigcap_{i \in I} P_i$, we shall prove that P is prime. Suppose $ab \in P$, $a \notin P$. Then $a \notin P_i$ for some i. Now for any $j \in I$, $P_j \subset P_i$ or $P_i \subset P_j$. In the first case, $a \notin P_j$, hence $b \in P_j$. In the second case $b \in P_i \subset P_j$. Thus $b \in P$.

The intersection of all maximal ideals of a commutative ring R is called the *radical* of R, the intersection of all prime ideals of a ring R is called the *prime radical* of R. Clearly, the prime radical is always contained in the radical. The next two propositions will show how these two radicals may be characterized by elements.

PROPOSITION 7.   *The radical of R consists of all elements $r \in R$ such that $1 = rx$ is a unit for all $x \in R$.*

Proof. The element r belongs to the radical of R if and only if, for every maximal ideal M and for every element x, $1 - rx \notin M$. This is the same as saying that, for every element x, $1 - rx$ belongs to no maximal ideal, that is that $1 - rx$ is a unit, by Lemma 1.

An element r is called *nilpotent* if $r^n = 0$ for some natural number n.

PROPOSITION 8.   *The prime radical of a commutative ring R consists of all nilpotent elements of R.*

Proof. If r is nilpotent, then for any prime ideal P we have $r^n = 0 \in P$, hence $r \in P$, and therefore r belongs to the prime radical.

Conversely, suppose r is not nilpotent, then the set $T = \{1, r, r^2, \ldots\}$ does not contain 0. Let P be an ideal of R maximal with respect to the property that it does not meet T. Now let a,b be elements of R outside P. Then by maximality of P, we have $r^m \in P + aR$, $r^n \in P + bR$, hence $r^{m+n} \in (P + aR)(P + bR) \subset P + abR$. Since $r^{m+n} \notin P$, we see that $ab \notin P$. Moreover $1 \notin P$, hence P is prime. Since $r \notin P$, r does not lie in the prime radical.

If we study the second part of the above proof, we see that the essential properties of the set T were the following:

(a) If t_1, $t_2 \in T$ then $t_1 t_2 \in T$.
(b) $1 \in T$.
(c) $0 \notin T$.

Since 1 may be regarded as an empty product, (a) and (b) together mean that T is closed under finite products. We may therefore extract the following result from the above proof, which we record for future reference:

LEMMA 2.   *If T is a subset of a commutative ring which is closed under finite products and does not contain 0, then any ideal maximal in the set of ideals not meeting T is a prime ideal.*

A commutative ring R is called *semiprimitive* if its radical is 0, that is if $r \neq 0$ implies that, for some $x \in R$, $1 - rx$ is not a unit. (We shall avoid the overworked word "semisimple.") A commutative ring R is called *semiprime* if its prime radical is 0, that is if it has no nonzero nilpotent elements. From now on let Rad R and rad R denote the radical and prime radical of R, respectively. Clearly rad $R \subset$ Rad R.

PROPOSITION 9.   *R/Rad R is semiprimitive, R/rad R is semiprime.*

Proof. (a) Let $\pi : R \to R/\text{Rad } R$ canonically. An element πr of πR belongs to the radical of πR only if $1 - \pi r \, \pi x = \pi(1 - rx)$ is a unit for all $\pi x \in \pi R$, that is for all $x \in R$. But then $1 = \pi(1 - rx)\ \pi y = \pi((1 - rx)y)$ for some $y \in R$, that is $1 - (1 - rx)y \in \text{Rad } R$, hence $(1 - rx)y$ is a unit, and therefore $1 - rx$ is a unit. This being the case for all $x \in R$, we conclude that $r \in \text{Rad } R$, hence that $\pi r = 0$.

(b) Let $\pi : R \to R/\text{rad } R$ canonically, and assume that $(\pi r)^n = 0$, that is $\pi(r^n) = 0$, that is $r^n \in \text{rad } R$. Then $(r^n)^k = 0$ for some k, hence

$$r \in \text{rad } R,$$

and so $\pi r = 0$.

We call R a *subdirect product* of a family of rings $\{S_i \mid i \in I\}$ if there is a monomorphism

$$\kappa : R \to S = \prod_{i \in I} S_i$$

such that $\pi_i \circ \kappa$ is epi for all $i \in I$, where $\pi_i : S \to S_i$ canonically.

PROPOSITION 10.   *R is a subdirect product of the rings S_i, $i \in I$, if and only if $S_i \cong R/K_i$, K_i an ideal of R, and $\bigcap_{i \in I} K_i = 0$.*

Proof.   First, assume that R is a subdirect product of the S_i, and let κ and π_i be as in the above definition. Since $\pi_i \circ \kappa : R \to S_i$ is epi, we may write $S_i \cong R/K_i$, where K_i is the kernel of $\pi_i \circ \kappa$. Moreover, the kernel of κ consists of all $r \in R$ for which $(\pi_i \circ \kappa)r = \pi_i(\kappa r) = 0$, for all $i \in I$, that is $r \in \bigcap_{i \in I} K_i$. Since κ is mono, this intersection will be 0.

Conversely, assume that R satisfies the condition. Define $\kappa : R \to \prod_{i \in I} R/K_i$ by taking $\pi_i(\kappa r)$ to be the canonical image of r in R/K_i, then κ has kernel $\bigcap_{i \in I} K_i = 0$.

COROLLARY 1.   *A commutative ring is a subdirect product of fields (integral domains) if and only if it is semiprimitive (semiprime).*

COROLLARY 2.   *A commutative ring is semiprime if and only if it is isomorphic to a subring of a direct product of integral domains.*

Proof.   That a semiprime ring has the indicated property is an immediate consequence of the above. It also follows from the above that a direct product of integral domains is semiprime. Finally we observe that any subring of a commutative semiprime ring is semiprime, since a nilpotent element of the subring is surely a nilpotent element of the full ring.

COROLLARY 3.   *A commutative ring is semiprime if and only if it is isomorphic to a subring of a direct product of fields.*

Proof.   Any integral domain can be embedded in a field, e.g., its field of quotients. (See Section 2.3.)

A ring R is called *subdirectly irreducible* if the intersection of all nonzero ideals is not 0. This is equivalent to saying that whenever R is expressed as a subdirect product, one of the factors of this product is isomorphic to R.

PROPOSITION 11 (Birkhoff).   *Every ring is a subdirect product of subdirectly irreducible rings.*

Proof.   With any element $r \neq 0$ of R we associate an ideal K_r which is chosen maximal in the set of ideals contained in $R - \{r\}$. Since $r \notin K_r$, it follows that $\bigcap_{r \neq 0} K_r = 0$. Moreover, R/K_r is subdirectly irreducible. For consider all ideals of R which contain K_r properly. Each of these ideals contains r, in view of the maximality of K_r. Therefore their intersection contains r, hence contains K_r properly.

EXERCISES

1. Prove that a commutative ring is a field (integral domain) if and only if 0 is a maximal (prime) ideal.

2. If r is nilpotent, show that $1 - r$ is a unit.

3. Show that an ideal P in a commutative ring is prime if and only if its complementary set $R - P$ is closed under finite products.

4. Determine all prime and maximal ideals as well as both radicals of $Z(n)$, the ring of integers modulo n.

5. If K is an ideal of R, show that there is a one to one correspondence between the prime ideals of R containing K and those of R/K.

6. Show that the set of zero-divisors of a commutative ring contains at least one prime ideal.

7. Prove that in a subdirectly irreducible ring the zero-divisors form an ideal.

8. Generalize Proposition 11 to other algebraic systems.

9. Let R be a commutative ring, and suppose that the ideal A of R is contained in a finite union of prime ideals $\bigcup_{i=1}^{n} P_i$. Show that A is contained in at least one of the P_i. (*Hint:* Otherwise, by induction, one may assume that $A \cap P_j \not\subset \bigcup_{i \neq j} P_i$ for all j. Let a_j be an element of the left but not of the right side, then the element $a_1 + a_2 a_3 \cdots a_n$ is in A but not in any P_i.)

10. Let C be a subset of a commutative ring whose complement is closed under finite products and such that, for all $c \in C$, $cR \subset C$. Show that C is a union of prime ideals.

11. Let N be the prime radical of the commutative ring R and put $N^{+} = \{r \in R \mid \exists_{s \notin N} rs \in N\}$. Show that N is the intersection of all minimal prime ideals of R and that N^{+} is their union.

2.2 Prime ideals in special commutative rings

Let us see what the above notions amount to in the case of a Boolean ring. A subset F of a Boolean algebra (see Section 1.1) $(S,0,',\wedge)$ is called a *filter* if

$$0' \in F, \tag{1}$$

$$a, b \in F \Rightarrow a \wedge b \in F, \tag{2}$$

$$(a \in F \quad \& \quad a \leq b) \Rightarrow b \in F. \tag{3}$$

A filter is *proper* if moreover $0 \notin F$. (In books on topology "filter" is used to mean "proper filter.") A maximal proper filter is called an *ultrafilter*. We shall be concerned with filters of the dual Boolean algebra $(S,1,',\vee)$, call them *dual filters* for short.

PROPOSITION 1. *If a Boolean algebra is regarded as a ring, the dual filters are precisely the ideals, hence the dual ultrafilters are precisely the maximal ideals.*

Proof.   Let K be a dual filter, then $0 \in K$, by the dual of (1). If $a \in K$ and $s \in S$, then $as \leq a$, hence $as \in K$ by the dual of (3). If $a, b \in K$, then $a + b = ab' \vee ba' \in K \vee K \subset K$, by the result just proved and the dual of (2). Thus K is an ideal.

Conversely, assume K is an ideal. Then $0 \in K$, and if $b \leq a$ and $a \in K$ then $b = ab \in K$. If a and $b \in K$ then $a \vee b = (a'b')' = a + b - ab \in K$. Thus K is a dual filter. (Recall that $a' = 1 - a$.)

PROPOSITION 2.   *The following statements concerning the Boolean ideal K are equivalent:*

  (a) *K is maximal.*
  (b) *K is prime.*
  (c) *For every element s, either $s \in K$ or $s' \in K$ but not both.*

Proof.   Recall that (a) $\Rightarrow$ (b). Now suppose K is a prime ideal. Since K is proper, $s + s' = 1 \notin K$, hence not both s and s' belong to K. But one or the other must, since $ss' = 0 \in K$ and K is prime. Thus (b) $\Rightarrow$ (c).

Assume (c). Then K is proper, since $0 \in K$ and therefore $1 = 0' \notin K$. If $s \notin K$, then $s' \in K$, hence $1 = s' + s \in K + sS$, and so K is maximal. Thus (c) $\Rightarrow$ (a).

COROLLARY 1.   *The following statements concerning the Boolean ring S are equivalent:*

  (a) *S is a field.*
  (b) *S is an integral domain.*
  (c) *S has exactly two elements: 0 and 1.*

Up to isomorphism there is only one two-element Boolean ring. We may represent this as the ring of integers modulo 2. We may also represent it as the set of all subsets of a one-element set.

COROLLARY 2. *A Boolean ring is semiprimitive. Thus an element of a Boolean ring is 0 if and only if it is mapped onto 0 by every homomorphism of the ring into the two-element Boolean ring.*

More general than Boolean rings are the *regular* rings introduced by von Neumann, in which it is assumed that for every element a there exists an element a' such that $aa'a = a$. In the commutative case, this may of course be written $a^2a' = a$.

PROPOSITION 3. *In a commutative regular ring we have the following properties:*
(1) *Every nonunit is a zero-divisor.*
(2) *Every prime ideal is maximal.*
(3) *Every principal ideal is a direct summand.*
   Proof. (1) If a is not a zero-divisor, we may deduce from $a(a'a - 1) = 0$ that $a'a = 1$.
   (2) Let P be any prime ideal, $a \notin P$. Then $a'a - 1 \in P$, hence $1 \in P + aR$, therefore P is maximal.
   (3) Put $a'a = e$, then e is an idempotent and $aR = eR$. We recall that $R = eR + (1 - e)R$ is a direct sum.

PROPOSITION 4. *Every commutative regular ring is semiprimitive.*
   Proof. If $a \neq 0$ then $1 - aa'$ is a zero-divisor, hence not a unit.
   We shall now show that there exist semiprime rings which are not regular. A commutative ring is called *local* if it has exactly one maximal ideal M. Of course M is then the radical. Now, in any integral domain, 0 is a prime ideal, hence the prime radical. We shall thus be served by any local integral domain which is not a field.
   Example. Consider the ring of formal power series

$$a(x) = a_0 + a_1x + a_2x^2 + \cdots$$

over the field F. When $a(x) \neq 0$ and $b(x) \neq 0$ then $a(x)b(x) \neq 0$, as is shown by the first nonvanishing coefficients. Thus we do have an integral domain.
   We observe that $a(x)$ is a unit if and only if $a_0 \neq 0$. Therefore

$$a(x) \in \text{Rad } R \Leftrightarrow \forall_{b(x)} 1 - a(x)b(x) \text{ is a unit,}$$
$$\Leftrightarrow \forall_{b(x)} 1 - a_0b_0 \neq 0$$
$$\Leftrightarrow a_0 = 0,$$

and so Rad $R = xR$, the principal ideal generated by x. Now suppose $c(x) \notin xR$, then $c_0 \neq 0$, hence $c(x)R = R$. Therefore xR is a maximal ideal; and, being the radical, it is the only maximal ideal of R. Thus R is local.

Local rings may be characterized in different ways as we shall now see.

PROPOSITION 5. *Let R be a commutative ring. The following conditions are equivalent:*

(1) *R has a unique maximal ideal M.*

(2) *All nonunits of R are contained in a proper ideal M.*

(3) *The nonunits form an ideal M.*

Proof. (1) $\Rightarrow$ (2). Any nonunit is contained in some maximal ideal, hence in M.

(2) $\Rightarrow$ (3). Since a proper ideal contains only nonunits, M is the set of all nonunits.

(3) $\Rightarrow$ (1). Since a proper ideal contains only nonunits, every proper ideal is contained in M. M itself is proper, since $1 \notin M$.

Even more special than local rings are rings with a unique prime ideal. We shall call such rings *fully primary*. (These rings are usually just called "primary," but we shall reserve this term for a more general situation, in which 0 would be a primary ideal according to the usual terminology.)

PROPOSITION 6. *Let R be a commutative ring. The following conditions are equivalent:*

(1) *Every zero-divisor is nilpotent.*

(2) *R has a minimal prime ideal P, and this contains all zero divisors.*

We shall call such a ring *primary*.

Proof. Assume (1). Then the zero-divisors form an ideal P, and P will be prime. P is the ideal of nilpotent elements, hence the prime radical, and so is contained in every prime ideal. Thus (1) implies (2).

Assume (2). Let r be an element which is not nilpotent, and let T be the set of all elements of the form sr^k with $s \notin P$ and $k \geq 0$ any natural number. Clearly T contains 1 and r and is closed under finite products. However T does not contain 0; for if so, $sr^k = 0$, $r^k \neq 0$, hence s would be a zero-divisor and so would be contained in P. Therefore $R - T$ contains some prime ideal. On the other hand, $R - T$ is contained in the minimal prime ideal P, hence $R - T = P$. Since $r \in T$, therefore $r \notin P$. Thus (2) implies (1).

We now obtain a number of different characterizations of fully primary rings.

PROPOSITION 7.   *Let R be a commutative ring. The following conditions are equivalent:*
(1) *R has a unique prime ideal P.*
(2) *R is local and Rad R = rad R.*
(3) *Every nonunit is nilpotent.*
(4) *R is primary and all nonunits are zero-divisors.*
Proof.   Clearly (1) $\Rightarrow$ (2).

Assume (2), then every nonunit is in rad R, hence is nilpotent. Thus (2) $\Rightarrow$ (3).

Assume (3), then every nonunit is a zero-divisor and every zero-divisor is nilpotent. Thus (3) $\Rightarrow$ (4).

Assume (4), then the zero-divisors form the smallest prime ideal P of R. If $r \notin P$, r is not a zero-divisor, hence a unit by assumption. Thus P is maximal and so is the only prime ideal. Thus (4) $\Rightarrow$ (1).

This may be the place to take a closer look at subdirectly irreducible rings. These are the rings with a smallest nonzero ideal J. Clearly J is generated by any nonzero element of J, hence subdirectly irreducible commutative rings are characterized by the property

$$\exists_{0 \neq j \in R} \forall_{0 \neq a \in R} \exists_{r \in R} j = ar.$$

If K is any subset of the commutative ring R, we write $K^* = \{r \in R \mid rK = 0\}$ and call this the *annihilator* of K. We abbreviate $(K^*)^*$ as K^{**}. K^* is always an ideal.

PROPOSITION 8 (McCoy).   *Let R be a subdirectly irreducible commutative ring with smallest nonzero ideal J. Then the annihilator J^* of J is the set of all zero-divisors, J^* is a maximal ideal, and $J^{**} = J$.*
Proof.   If r is a zero-divisor, then $r^* \neq 0$, hence r^* contains J, and so $r \in J^*$. Thus J^* is the set of all zero-divisors.

Clearly $1 \notin J^*$. Suppose $r \notin J^*$, then $rj \neq 0$ for some $j \in J$, hence $J = rjR$. In particular, $j = rjx$ for some $x \in R$. Thus $(1 - rx)j = 0$, and so $1 - rx \in J^*$. Therefore J^* is maximal.

Now clearly $J \subset J^{**}$, we will show that also $J^{**} \subset J$. Let $0 \neq a \in J^{**}$, then $J \subset aR$, hence $0 \neq ar \in J$ for some $r \in R$, and $r \notin J^*$. By the above, $1 - rx \in J^*$ for some $x \in R$, hence $a(1 - rx) = 0$, and so $a = arx \in J$. Therefore $J^{**} = J$.

COROLLARY.   *If R is subdirectly irreducible and semiprime, then R is a field.*
Proof. $J^2 \neq 0$, hence $J \not\subset J^*$. Therefore $J^* = 0$, hence R is a field.

McCoy has also given necessary and sufficient conditions for a commutative ring to be subdirectly irreducible. The following is a different characterization:

PROPOSITION 9.   *A commutative ring is subdirectly irreducible if and only if it contains an element j such that jR has nonzero intersection with all nonzero ideals and its annihilator j* is a maximal ideal.*

Proof. If R has smallest nonzero ideal J, then, for any $0 \neq j \in J$, $J = jR$, and $j^* = J^*$ is maximal by Proposition 8. The other condition is obvious.

Conversely, assume the conditions. If $a \neq 0$, then $aR \cap jR \neq 0$, hence $0 \neq ar = js$ for some $r, s \in R$. Thus $s \notin j^*$, hence $1 - st \in j^*$ for some $t \in R$. Therefore $j = jst = art$, hence $jR \subset aR$, as required.

EXERCISES

1. Which of the properties "semiprime," "semiprimitive," and "regular" are preserved by passing to subrings, factor rings, and direct products?

2. Show that the ring of $n \times n$ matrices over a field is a regular ring.

3. Show that in a regular ring R there exists for each element r an element r^- such that $rr^-r = r$ and $r^-rr^- = r^-$. If R is commutative, show that r^- is uniquely determined by r.

4. Show that in a commutative regular ring there exists for each element r a unit u such that $rur = r$.

5. Show that a ring is regular if and only if every principal right ideal is a direct summand (as a right module).

6. Show that in a commutative regular ring every finitely generated ideal is principal.

7. Show that a commutative ring is local if and only if, for any elements r and s, $r + s = 1$ implies that r or s is a unit.

8. Let Z^p be the ring of rational numbers with denominators not divisible by p, p any prime number. Show that Z^p is local.

9. If M is a maximal ideal in the commutative ring R, n any positive integer, show that R/M^n has a unique prime ideal.

2.3   The complete ring of quotients of a commutative ring

There are several ways of constructing the rational numbers from the integers, some of which go back to Euclid's theory of proportions. We shall briefly sketch two such methods:

Method 1.   This method is used in many elementary textbooks. One considers pairs of integers (a,b), $b \neq 0$. These pairs are divided into equivalence classes in such a way that (a,b) and (c,d) are equivalent if and only if $ad = bc$. Operations are then introduced which will turn the set of these equivalence classes into a field which extends the ring of integers. In a variation of this method one defines the ratio a/b outright as the set of all pairs (x,y) such that $ay = bx$ and proceeds from there.

Method 2.   The fraction $4/6$ may be regarded as a partial endomorphism of the additive group of integers; its domain is the ideal $6Z$ and it sends $6z$ onto $4z$, where $z \in Z$, the ring of integers. Similarly the fraction $6/9$ has domain $9Z$ and sends $9z$ onto $6z$. These two fractions are equivalent in the sense that they agree on the intersection of their domains, the ideal $18Z$, since both send $18z$ onto $12z$. Ratios are then defined as equivalence classes of fractions. In a variation of this method one picks one "irreducible" fraction from each equivalence class, thus the above mentioned class contains the irreducible fraction $2/3$.

Both methods may be applied to any integral domain to construct its "field of quotients." The first method may be applied to any commutative ring to construct its "classical ring of quotients," provided only non-zerodivisors are admitted as denominators. The second method may also be applied to any commutative ring to construct its "complete ring of quotients," provided only certain ideals are admitted as domains. As we shall see, the "complete ring of quotients" may be larger than the "classical ring of quotients."

An ideal D in a commutative ring R will be called *dense* if, for all $r \in R$, $rD = 0$ implies $r = 0$. Here are some properties of dense ideals:

(1) *R is dense.*
(2) *If D is dense and $D \subset D'$ then D' is dense.*
(3) *If D and D' are dense, so are DD' and $D \cap D'$.*
(4) *If $R \neq 0$ then 0 is not dense.*

Here is a proof of (3), the other properties being obvious: Let $rDD' = 0$, then, for any $d \in D$, $rdD' = 0$, and so $rd = 0$, since D' is dense. Thus $rD = 0$, hence $r = 0$, since D is dense. Therefore DD' is dense. But $DD' \subset D \cap D'$, hence the latter is also dense by (2).

By a *fraction* we mean an element $f \in \mathrm{Hom}_R(D,R)$, where D is any dense ideal. Thus f is a group homomorphism of D into R such that $f(dr) = (fd)r$ for any $d \in D$ and $r \in R$. We define $-f \in \mathrm{Hom}_R(D,R)$ by $(-f)d = -(fd)$. We also introduce fractions $0, 1 \in \mathrm{Hom}_R(R,R)$, by writing $0r = 0$, $1r = r$, for all $r \in R$. Addition and multiplication of fractions $f_i \in \mathrm{Hom}_R(D_i,R)$, $i = 1, 2$, are defined thus:

$$f_1 + f_2 \in \mathrm{Hom}_R(D_1 \cap D_2, R), \qquad (f_1 + f_2)d = f_1d + f_2d,$$
$$f_1f_2 \in \mathrm{Hom}_R(f_2^{-1}D_1, R), \qquad (f_1f_2)d = f_1(f_2d).$$

Here $f_2^{-1}D_1 = \{r \in R \mid f_2r \in D_1\}$ is dense since it clearly contains D_2D_1.

Clearly then the fractions form an additive Abelian semigroup $(F,0,+)$ with zero, and an Abelian semigroup $(F,1,\cdot)$ with 1. They do not yet form a ring, since $f + (-f) \neq 0$ for example. (The left side has domain D, the right side has domain R.)

We shall write $f_1 \, \theta \, f_2$ to mean that f_1 and f_2 agree on the intersection of their domains, that is $f_1 d = f_2 d$ for all $d \in D_1 \cap D_2$.

LEMMA 1. $f_1 \, \theta \, f_2$ *if and only if* f_1 *and* f_2 *agree on some dense ideal.*

Proof. If $f_1 \, \theta \, f_2$ then f_1 and f_2 agree on $D_1 \cap D_2$. Conversely, assume they agree on the dense ideal D'. Take $d \in D_1 \cap D_2$ and $d' \in D'$, then

$$(f_1 d)d' = f_1(dd') = f_2(dd') = (f_2 d)d'.$$

Therefore $(f_1 d - f_2 d)D' = 0$, but D' is dense, hence $f_1 d = f_2 d$. Therefore $f_1 \, \theta \, f_2$.

LEMMA 2. θ *is a congruence relation on the system* $(F,0,1,-,+,\cdot)$.

Proof. Clearly θ is reflexive and symmetric. Now suppose $f_1 \, \theta \, f_2$ and $f_2 \, \theta \, f_3$. Then f_1 agrees with f_2 on $D_1 \cap D_2$ and f_2 agrees with f_3 on $D_2 \cap D_3$, hence f_1 agrees with f_3 on $D_1 \cap D_2 \cap D_3$. But this is a dense ideal, hence $f_1 \, \theta \, f_3$ by Lemma 1. Thus θ is an equivalence relation. To show that it is a congruence relation we must verify that it preserves the various operations. For example, let $f_1 \, \theta \, f_3$, $f_2 \, \theta \, f_4$, then $f_1 + f_2$ and $f_3 + f_4$ are both defined and agree on the dense ideal $D_1 \cap D_2 \cap D_3 \cap D_4$. Hence $(f_1 + f_2) \, \theta \, (f_3 + f_4)$.

PROPOSITION 1.   *If* R *is a commutative ring, the system*

$$(F,0,1,-,+,\cdot)/\theta = Q(R)$$

is also a commutative ring. It extends R *and will be called its* complete ring of quotients.

Proof. By Lemma 2, F/θ satisfies all the identities that F satisfies. To show that it is a commutative ring, it only remains to show that $\theta f + \theta(-f) = \theta 0$ and the distributive law.

Now $f + (-f)$ agrees with 0 on D, the domain of f, hence $(f + (-f)) \, \theta \, 0$. Moreover $f_1(f_2 + f_3)$ and $(f_1 f_2) + (f_1 f_3)$ both agree on $D_1 D_2 D_3$, hence the relation θ holds between them.

Finally, with every $r \in R$ we may associate the fraction $r/1$ with domain R, which sends any $s \in R$ onto rs. The mapping $r \to \theta(r/1)$ is easily seen to be a homomorphism. It is mono, since $r/1$ agrees with $0/1$ on some dense ideal D only when $rD = 0$, that is $r = 0$. We shall call the mapping $r \to \theta(r/1)$ the *canonical monomorphism* of R into $Q(R)$.

More generally, with any non-zero-divisor d of R we associate the dense ideal dR. If $r \in R$, we have a *classical fraction* $r/d \in \operatorname{Hom}_R(dR,R)$ defined by $(r/d)(ds) = rs$, for any $s \in R$. We state without proof:

PROPOSITION 2.   *The equivalence classes $\theta(r/d)$, $r \in R$, d not a zero-divisor, form a subring of $Q(R)$, which is called the* classical ring of quotients *of R and is denoted by $Q_{cl}(R)$.*

We observe that $\theta(r_1/d_1) = \theta(r_2/d_2)$ if and only if r_1/d_1 agrees with r_2/d_2 on $D_1 D_2$, hence if and only if $r_1 d_2 = r_2 d_1$. Therefore $Q_{cl}(R)$ agrees with the classical ring of quotients constructed by Method 1 above.

A fraction is called *irreducible* if it cannot be extended to a larger domain.

PROPOSITION 3.   *Every equivalence class of fractions contains exactly one irreducible fraction, and this extends all fractions in the class.*

Proof.   The fractions in an equivalence class form an ordered set, if $f_1 \le f_2$ means that $D_1 \subset D_2$. Consider a simply ordered family of fractions $\{f_i \mid i \in I\}$ in the equivalence class. Let $D = \bigcup_{i \in I} D_i$ and define $f \in \mathrm{Hom}_R(D, R)$ by $fd = f_i d$ when $d \in D_i$. (If also $d \in D_j$, then $f_i d = f_j d$, since f_i and f_j agree on $D_i \cap D_j$.) Then f is an upper bound to the simply ordered family. By Zorn's lemma, the equivalence class contains at least one irreducible fraction. The result will now follow from the fact that any two equivalent fractions have a common extension. Indeed, let $f_1 \,\theta\, f_2$, and define $f \in \mathrm{Hom}_R(D_1 + D_2, R)$ by $f(d_1 + d_2) = f_1 d_1 + f_2 d_2$. (To verify that this makes sense, we must show that $d_1 + d_2 = 0$ implies $f_1 d_1 + f_2 d_2 = 0$. But if $d_1 = -d_2 \in D_1 \cap D_2$ then $f_1 d_1 = f_2 d_1 = -f_2 d_2$.)

PROPOSITION 4.   *The following statements concerning the commutative ring R are equivalent:*

(1) *Every irreducible fraction has domain R.*

(2) *For every fraction f there exists an element $s \in R$ such that $fd = sd$ for all $d \in D$, the domain of f.*

(3) *$Q(R) \cong R$ canonically.*

Under any of these conditions we call R *rationally complete.*

Proof.   Assume (1) and let f be any fraction, f' its irreducible extension. By (1), f' has domain R. Put $f'1 = s$, then $fd = f'd = f'(1d) = (f'1)d = sd$, for all $d \in D$. Therefore (2).

Assume (2) and consider any element θf of $Q(R)$. By (2), $f \,\theta\, (s/1)$, in the notation of the proof of Proposition 1. Thus $\theta f = \theta(s/1)$, the canonical image of $s \in R$ in $Q(R)$. It follows that the canonical monomorphism of R into $Q(R)$ is an isomorphism.

Assume (3) and let f be any irreducible fraction. Then $\theta f = \theta(s/1)$ for some $s \in R$. Now $s/1$ is irreducible, hence, by Proposition 3, $f = s/1$, and so f has domain R.

PROPOSITION 5.   *If R is any commutative ring, then $Q(R)$ is rationally complete.*

Before proving this, we make some preliminary remarks. In order to prevent the notations from growing out of hand, we shall identify R with its canonical image in $Q(R)$. Thus we write $\theta(r/1) = r$. For any $q \in Q(R)$, put $q^{-1}R = \{r \in R \mid qr \in R\}$. This will be a dense ideal; for if $q = \theta f$, f a fraction with domain D, then

$$qd = \theta f \theta(d/1) = \theta(f(d/1)) = \theta(fd/1) = fd,$$

for all $d \in D$, hence $qD \subset R$ and so $D \subset q^{-1}R$.

Proof. Let ϕ be any fraction over $Q(R)$, K its domain. Put $D = \{r \in K \mid \phi r \in R\}$ and define $f \in \mathrm{Hom}_R(D,R)$ by $fd = \phi d$. We claim that (a) D is a dense ideal and (b) for any $k \in K$, $\phi k = (\theta f)k$. The result will then follow by Proposition 4, condition (2).

(a) Assume $r \in R$ and $rD = 0$. Take any $k \in K$, then $\phi k \in Q(R)$. Put $D' = k^{-1}R \cap (\phi k)^{-1}R$, this is a dense ideal and $kD' \subset R$, $(\phi k)D' \subset R$. Therefore $\phi(kD') \subset R$, and so $kD' \subset D$. Thus $(rk)D' = r(kD') \subset rD = 0$, hence $rk = 0$. Therefore $rK = 0$, but K is dense, hence $r = 0$.

(b) Let $k \in K$ and take $d' \in D'$ as above. Then $(\phi k)d' = \phi(kd') = f(kd') = (\theta f)(kd')$, in view of the above remarks. Therefore $\phi k - (\theta f)k$ annihilates the dense ideal D' of R, hence it is 0. (Indeed, any element of $Q(R)$ which annihilates a dense ideal of R is zero.)

If S is any commutative ring, we may call a subgroup D of S *dense*, even if it is not an ideal, provided $sD = 0$ implies $s = 0$, for all $s \in S$. Now suppose R is a subring of S, then S is called a *ring of quotients* of R if and only if, for all $s \in S$, $s^{-1}R = \{r \in R \mid sr \in R\}$ is dense in S. Thus S is a ring of quotients of R if and only if, for all s and $t \in S$, $t \neq 0$ implies $t(s^{-1}R) \neq 0$, in other words

$$\forall_{s \in S} \forall_{0 \neq t \in S} \exists_{r \in R}(sr \in R \quad \& \quad tr \neq 0).$$

This definition is due to Utumi.

The following proposition will show that R, $Q_{\mathrm{cl}}(R)$ and $Q(R)$ are all rings of quotients of R, as has been anticipated by our terminology. In fact R is the smallest and $Q(R)$ the largest ring of quotients, in a sense that will be made precise.

PROPOSITION 6.   *Let R be a subring of the commutative ring S. Then the following three statements are equivalent:*

(1) *S is a ring of quotients of R.*

(2) *For all $0 \neq s \in S$, $s^{-1}R$ is a dense ideal of R and $s(s^{-1}R) \neq 0$.*

(3) *There exists a monomorphism of S into $Q(R)$ which induces the canonical monomorphism of R into $Q(R)$.*

Proof. Clearly (1) implies (2). Now suppose (2). The mapping $d \to sd$, $d \in s^{-1}R$, is a fraction $\hat{s}$. The mapping $s \to \theta\hat{s}$ is easily seen to be a homomorphism of S into $Q(R)$, which clearly induces the canonical monomorphism $r \to \theta\hat{r} = \theta(r/1)$. Its kernel consists of all $s \in S$ for which $\theta\hat{s} = 0$, that is $\hat{s} \, \theta \, 0$, that is $s(s^{-1}R) = 0$, that is $s = 0$. Hence it is mono. Thus (2) implies (3).

Finally, suppose (3). We may as well assume that $R \subset S \subset Q(R)$. If $s = \theta f \in S$, then $s^{-1}R$ contains D, the domain of f. Now let $t \in S$ and assume that $t(s^{-1}R) = 0$. Putting $t = \theta f'$, we obtain $f'D = 0$, hence $f' \, \theta \, 0$, hence $t = 0$. Thus (3) implies (1), and our cyclical proof is complete.

From the last part of the above proof we deduce:

COROLLARY.   *If S is a ring of quotients of the commutative ring R and D is a dense ideal in R then D is dense in S.*

PROPOSITION 7.   *Up to isomorphism over R, $Q(R)$ is the only rationally complete ring of quotients of the commutative ring R.*

Proof.   Let S be any ring of quotients of R. In view of the last proposition, we may as well write $R \subset S \subset Q(R)$. For any $q \in Q(R)$, put $D = \{s \in S \mid qs \in S\}$. Then D contains $q^{-1}R$, hence is dense in S. But D is an ideal, hence the mapping $d \to qd$, $d \in D$, is a fraction over S. Now assume that S is rationally complete, then there is an $s \in S$ such that $qd = sd$ for all $d \in D$. Since $q^{-1}R \subset D$ is dense in $Q(R)$, we conclude that $q = s$. Therefore $Q(R) = S$.

For completeness we also state the following:

PROPOSITION 8.   *If $\{R_i \mid i \in I\}$ is a family of commutative rings, then*

$$Q(\textstyle\prod_{i \in I} R_i) \cong \prod_{i \in I} Q(R_i).$$

We shall omit the proof of this for the moment, as we shall have to establish it later anyway, without the restriction that the rings be commutative.

EXERCISES

1. Prove Proposition 2.
2. Give another proof of Proposition 3, without using Zorn's lemma, by constructing a fraction whose domain is the sum of the domains of all fractions in the equivalence class.
3. If $R \subset S \subset T$, show that T is a ring of quotients of R if and only if S is a ring or quotients of R and T is a ring of quotients of S.

4. Show that S is a ring of quotients of R if and only if, for every R-submodule D of S containing R and every $\phi \in \mathrm{Hom}_R(D,S)$, $\phi R = 0$ implies $\phi = 0$.

5. Show that for every ring of quotients S of R there is exactly one homomorphism of S into $Q(R)$ which induces the canonical monomorphism on R.

6. If f is an irreducible fraction over R and $q = \theta f$ is its equivalence class, show that $q^{-1}R$ is the domain of f.

7. For a commutative ring R, show that $R = Q_{\mathrm{cl}}(R)$ if and only if every nonunit is a zero-divisor.

8. For which commutative rings does every equivalence class of classical fractions contain a unique irreducible classical fraction?

2.4   Rings of quotients of commutative semiprime rings

With any subset K of a commutative ring R we associate its *annihilator* $K^* = \{r \in R \mid rK = 0\}$. Clearly K^* is an ideal of R. Usually K itself will be an ideal. An ideal K is dense if and only if $K^* = 0$. We note that for subgroups K_1 and K_2 of R, $(K_1 + K_2)^* = K_1{}^* \cap K_2{}^*$. We write $(K^*)^*$ as K^{**}.

LEMMA 1.   *For any ideal K in a commutative semiprime ring we have*

$$K \cap K^* = 0, \qquad K + K^* \text{ dense.}$$

Proof. $(K \cap K^*)^2 \subset K^*K = 0$, hence $K \cap K^* = 0$. Also

$$(K + K^*)^* = K^* \cap K^{**} = 0,$$

by the result just proved.

PROPOSITION 1.   *If R is a commutative ring then $Q(R)$ is regular if and only if R is semiprime.*

Proof.   If $Q(R)$ is regular then it is semiprime, hence so is any subring of $Q(R)$ (which is commutative), in particular R.

Now assume R semiprime. It will follow that $Q(R)$ is regular if for each fraction f over R there exists a fraction f' such that $ff'f \theta f$. Let f be a fraction with domain D and kernel $K \subset D$. Then the restriction of f to $D \cap K^*$ is a monomorphism, since $D \cap K^* \cap K = 0$. Let $E = f(D \cap K^*)$, and define $f' \in \mathrm{Hom}_R(E + E^*, R)$ by putting $f'(fd) = d$ for all $fd \in E$ and $f'r = 0$ for all $r \in E^*$. Then $ff'fd = fd$ when $d \in D \cap K^*$. But this equation also holds trivially when $d \in K \subset D$. Hence $ff'f - f$ annihilates $K + (D \cap K^*)$, which, by the modular law, is the same as

$D \cap (K + K^*)$, the intersection of two dense ideals, hence dense. There-fore $ff'f\theta f$.

LEMMA 2.   *In any commutative ring we have:*

$$K \subset J \Rightarrow J^* \subset K^*. \tag{1}$$

$$K \subset K^{**}. \tag{2}$$

$$K^{***} = K^*. \tag{3}$$

Proof. (1) is obvious. (2) follows from $KK^* = K^*K = 0$. From (1) and (2) follows $K^{***} \subset K^*$; and $K^* \subset K^{***}$ is a special case of (2).

The ideals of the form K^* are called *annihilator ideals.* Thus J is an annihilator ideal if and only if $J = K^*$ for some subset K of R, and this is the same as saying that $J^{**} = J$, in view of (3).

PROPOSITION 2.   *The annihilator ideals in a commutative semiprime ring form a complete Boolean algebra* $B^*(R)$, *with intersection as inf and* $*$ *as complementation.*

Proof. Any intersection of annihilator ideals is an annihilator ideal, since $\bigcap_{i \in I} K_i^* = (\sum_{i \in I} K_i)^*$. Hence these ideals form a complete semi-lattice with intersection as inf. To show that they form a Boolean algebra, it remains to verify that

$$J \cap K^* = 0 \Leftrightarrow J \subset K$$

for annihilator ideals J and K.

Indeed, if $J \subset K$, then $J \cap K^* \subset K \cap K^* = 0$. Conversely, if $J \cap K^* = 0$, then $JK^* = 0$, hence $J \subset K^{**} = K$.

LEMMA 3.   *If* M_R *is an R-submodule of* $Q(R)$ *and if* $q(M \cap R) = 0$, $q \in Q(R)$, *then* $qM = 0$.

Proof. Assume $q(M \cap R) = 0$. Let $m \in M$, $D = m^{-1}R$, then $mD \subset M \cap R$, hence $qmD = 0$. Since D is dense, $qm = 0$. Thus $qM = 0$.

PROPOSITION 3.   *The mapping* $K \to K \cap R$ *is an isomorphism of* $B^*(Q(R))$ *onto* $B^*(R)$.

Proof. Let K be an annihilator ideal in $Q(R)$, say the annihilator of $M \subset Q(R)$. Then $K \cap R = \{r \in R \mid rM = 0\} = (M \cap R)^*$, by the lemma. Thus $K \cap R \in B^*(R)$.

The mapping is a Boolean homomorphism, since it sends 0 onto 0, $K_1 \cap K_2$ onto $(K_1 \cap R) \cap (K_2 \cap R)$, and the "complement" (annihilator) of M onto $(M \cap R)^*$, the "complement" of $M \cap R$.

The mapping is mono, since $K \cap R = 0$ implies $K = 0$, by the lemma. It is epi; for let $J \subset R$, then $J^* = K \cap R$, where $K = \{q \in Q(R) \mid qJ = 0\}$ is an annihilator ideal in $Q(R)$.

PROPOSITION 4. *If R is commutative semiprime and rationally complete, every annihilator of R is a direct summand.*

Proof. Let K be an annihilator ideal. Consider the mapping $f \in \operatorname{Hom}_R(K + K^*, R)$ defined by $f(a + b) = a$, where $a \in K$ and $b \in K^*$. Now $K + K^*$ is dense, R is rationally complete, hence there is an element $e \in R$ such that $a = f(a + b) = e(a + b)$. Then $e^2(a + b) = ea = fa = a = e(a + b)$, hence $e^2 - e$ annihilates the dense ideal $K + K^*$ and so $e^2 = e$. Moreover $K = eK \subset eR$, and similarly $K^* \subset (1 - e)R$, hence $eR \subset ((1 - e)R)^* \subset K^{**} = K$. Thus $K = eR$ is a direct summand.

COROLLARY 1. *If R is commutative semiprime and rationally complete then $B^*(R) \simeq B(R)$, the Boolean algebra of central idempotents of R.*

Proof. Associate eR with $e \in B(R)$. The details are left as an exercise.

COROLLARY 2. *If R is commutative semiprime then $B^*(R) \simeq B^*(Q(R)) \simeq B(Q(R))$.*

LEMMA 4. *If R is a Boolean ring then $Q(R)$ is a Boolean ring.*

Proof. Let f be any fraction over R, D its domain. Then f^2 is defined on D^2, and this is the same as D. (Indeed, $D^2 \subset D$, and $d \in D$ implies $d = d^2 \in D^2$.) Now $f^2 d = f(fd^2) = f((fd)d) = (fd)^2 = fd$, for any $d \in D$, hence $f^2 \theta f$. Therefore $(\theta f)^2 = \theta f$, and so $Q(R)$ is Boolean.

To investigate the relationship between the Boolean rings R and $Q(R)$ we shall make a small detour.

Let $(S, \leq)$ be any ordered set. With any subset X of S we associate $X^\vee = $ set of all upper bounds of X and $X^\wedge = $ set of all lower bounds of X. Write $(X^\vee)^\wedge = X^{\vee\wedge}$.

LEMMA 5.

$$X \subset Y \Rightarrow (Y^\vee \subset X^\vee \quad \& \quad Y^\wedge \subset X^\wedge). \tag{1}$$

$$X \subset X^{\vee\wedge}, \qquad X \subset X^{\wedge\vee}. \tag{2}$$

$$X^{\vee\wedge\vee} = X^\vee, \qquad X^{\wedge\vee\wedge} = X^\wedge. \tag{3}$$

$${}^{\vee\wedge} \text{ is a closure operation (and so is } {}^{\wedge\vee}). \tag{4}$$

The proof of this will be an exercise.

We call Y a *lower set* if $Y = X^\wedge$ for some X. In view of (3), this is the same as saying that $Y = Y^{\vee\wedge}$.

PROPOSITION 5. *The lower sets of $(S, \leq)$ form a complete lattice $D(S)$. The canonical mapping $\mu : S \to D(S)$ defined by $\mu x = \{x\}^{\vee\wedge}$ has the property that $x \leq y$ if and only if $\mu x \subset \mu y$, thus $(D(S), \subset)$ may be regarded as an extension of $(S, \leq)$. Moreover each element of $D(S)$ is the sup and inf of subsets of μS.*

$D(S)$ is called the *Dedekind-MacNeille completion* of S.

Proof. Clearly $x \leq y$ implies $\{y\}^\vee \subset \{x\}^\vee$ hence $\mu x \subset \mu y$, by (1). Conversely, assume $\mu x \subset \mu y$, then $\{y\}^\vee \subset \{x\}^\vee$ by (3). This means that, for all $t \in S$, $y \leq t \Rightarrow x \leq t$. But $y \leq y$, hence $x \leq y$.

Next we show that any lower set $X = \sup \{\mu s \mid \mu s \subset X\}$. Indeed, $\mu s \subset X$ means $X^\vee \subset \{s\}^\vee$, that is $s \in X$. Now surely X is an upper bound of the indicated set. Suppose the lower set Y is also an upper bound, then $\mu s \subset X$ implies $\mu s \subset Y$, that is $s \in X$ implies $s \in Y$, that is $X \subset Y$. Therefore X is the least upper bound.

Finally we show that any lower set $X = \inf \{\mu s \mid X \subset \mu s\}$. Indeed $X \subset \mu s$ means $\{s\}^\vee \subset X^\vee$, that is, for all $t \in S$, $s \leq t$ implies $t \in X^\vee$. This entails $s \in X^\vee$, but also conversely $s \in X^\vee$ and $s \leq t$ implies $t \in X^\vee$, by transitivity of $\leq$. Now X is clearly a lower bound of the indicated set. Suppose the lower set Y is also a lower bound, then $X \subset \mu s$ implies $Y \subset \mu s$, that is $s \in X^\vee$ implies $s \in Y^\vee$, that is $X^\vee \subset Y^\vee$, that is $Y \subset X$. Therefore X is the greatest lower bound.

PROPOSITION 6.   *The lower sets of a Boolean algebra, regarded as a ring R, are its annihilator ideals, that is $D(R) = B^*(R)$.*

Proof. If K is any subset of R, the set of its upper bounds is given by

$$K^\vee = \{r \in R \mid \forall_{k \in K} rk = k\} = \{r \in R \mid 1 - r \in K^*\},$$

and the set of all lower bounds of $K^\vee$ is given by

$$K^{\vee\wedge} = \{s \in R \mid \forall_{r \in K^\vee} sr = s\} = \{s \in R \mid sK^* = 0\} = K^{**}.$$

Thus $K = K^{\vee\wedge}$ if and only if $K = K^{**}$.

COROLLARY.   *If R is a Boolean ring, then its Dedekind-MacNeille completion is isomorphic over R to its complete ring of quotients.*

Proof. $D(R) = B^*(R) \simeq B(Q(R)) = Q(R)$.

The isomorphism is of course such that R, regarded as a subset of $D(R)$, is carried elementwise into R, regarded as a subset of $Q(R)$.

We are now in a position to give an example of a ring R for which the complete ring of quotients differs from the classical ring of quotients. Indeed, if R is a Boolean ring, we have $r(1 - r) = 0$ for all $r \in R$, hence 1 is the only regular element. Therefore $Q_{cl}(R) = R$. But we have just shown that $Q(R) \simeq D(R)$, and it is easy to construct Boolean algebras which are not complete. For example, the set of all finite and cofinite sets of natural numbers forms such a Boolean algebra; its completion is of course the set of all sets of natural numbers.

EXERCISES

1. Let R and S be sets, θ a binary relation between them (that is essentially a subset of $R \times S$). For any subsets X of R and Y of S write

$$X^* = \{s \in S \mid \forall_{x \in X} x \,\theta\, s\},$$

$$Y^+ = \{r \in R \mid \forall_{y \in Y} r \,\theta\, y\}.$$

Show that $X \subset X^{*+}$,

$$X_1 \subset X_2 \Rightarrow X_2^* \subset X_1^*,$$

$$X^{*+*} = X^*,$$

and dually $Y \subset Y^{+*}$, etc.

2. In the notation of the above exercise show that $X \to X^{*+}$ and $Y \to Y^{+*}$ are closure operations on the sets of all subsets of R and S, respectively. Show that the lattice of closed subsets of R is isomorphic to the dual of the lattice of closed subsets of S.

(Such a situation is called a *polarity*. This chapter contains two examples of polarities in which $R = S$. In the first example $r \,\theta\, s$ means $rs = 0$, in the second example it means $r \leq s$.)

3. If K is an ideal in a semiprime ring, K^* its annihilator, show that K^* is the intersection of all prime ideals P such that $K \not\subset P$.

4. If f' is constructed as in the proof of Proposition 1, show that not only $ff'f \theta f$ but also $f'ff' \theta f'$.

5. If R is a semiprime ring and a subring of the commutative ring S, show that S is a ring of quotients of R if and only if $s(s^{-1}R) \neq 0$ for all nonzero elements s of S.

6. Let R be commutative, semiprime, and rationally complete. If K is any ideal of R (not just a dense ideal) and $\phi \in \mathrm{Hom}_R(K,R)$, show that there exists an element $r \in R$ such that $\phi k = rk$ for all $k \in K$. (This property of R is called *self-injectivity* and will be discussed later.)

7. If R is commutative, semiprime, and rationally complete, show that $R = S \times T$, where S is a direct product of fields and $B(T)$ has no atoms.

8. Show that the Dedekind-MacNeille completion of an ordered set $(S, \leq)$ can be characterized abstractly, up to isomorphism over S, as any complete lattice extending S, every element of which can be expressed both as an inf and as a sup of elements in S.

2.5 Prime ideal spaces

A *topological space* is a system (X,T), where T is a set of subsets of X which is closed under union and finite intersection. The elements of T are called *open sets*. Thus we have the following:

(1) *Any union of open sets is open. (In particular, the empty set is open.)*

(2) *If V_1 and V_2 are open, so is $V_1 \cap V_2$.*

(3) *X is open.*

A topological space is called *compact* if any family of open sets which covers the space contains a finite subfamily which already covers the space. A set is called *closed* if its complement is open. The *closure* of a set is the intersection of all closed sets containing it.

In what follows, Π will be any set of prime ideals of the commutative ring R. The examples we have in mind are

(a) the set of all prime ideals, and

(b) the set of all maximal ideals of R.

(See, however, the proof of Proposition 4.) We shall endow Π with a topology, which is attributed by some authors to Stone and by others to Zariski.

PROPOSITION 1. Π *becomes topological space, if as open sets we take all sets of the form*

$$\Gamma A = \{P \in \Pi \mid A \not\subseteq P\},$$

where A is any subset of R. If Π contains all maximal ideals, then Π is compact.

It does not matter if we insist that A be an ideal of R, for always $\Gamma A = \Gamma A'$, where A' is the intersection of all prime ideals of Π containing A, hence an ideal. We note that

$$\Gamma A = \bigcup_{a \in A} \Gamma a;$$

thus the sets Γa form a *basis* of the open sets of Π, in the sense that they are open and every open set is a union of basic open sets.

Proof.   First

$$\bigcup_{i \in I} \Gamma A_i = \{P \in \Pi \mid \exists_{i \in I} A_i \not\subseteq P\}$$
$$= \{P \in \Pi \mid \textstyle\sum_{i \in I} A_i \not\subseteq P\}$$
$$= \Gamma(\textstyle\sum_{i \in I} A_i).$$

Second

$$\Gamma A \cap \Gamma B = \{P \in \Pi \mid A \not\subseteq P \ \ \& \ \ B \not\subseteq P\}$$
$$= \{P \in \Pi \mid AB \not\subseteq P\}$$
$$= \Gamma(AB).$$

Third

$$\Gamma R = \{P \in \Pi \mid R \not\subseteq P\} = \Pi.$$

Finally, suppose

$$\Pi = \bigcup_{i \in I} \Gamma A_i = \Gamma(\textstyle\sum_{i \in I} A_i).$$

Then $\sum_{i \in I} A_i$ is contained in no maximal ideal and so contains 1. But then $1 \in \sum_{i \in F} A_i$, where F is a finite subset of I, hence

$$\Pi = \Gamma(\textstyle\sum_{i \in F} A_i) = \bigcup_{i \in F} \Gamma A_i.$$

This completes our proof.

Γ was a mapping from the set of subsets of R into the set of subsets of Π. We now introduce a mapping Δ which goes the other way, by putting

$$\Delta V = \bigcap_{P \in V} P,$$

for any subset V of Π. In particular $\Delta\Pi$ will be the prime radical or radical of R, depending on whether Π is the set of all prime ideals or only of all maximal ideals of R.

Note that for any subset A of R, ΓA is an open set, and for any subset V of Π, ΔV is an intersection of prime ideals. What happens if we apply both Γ and Δ?

The union of all open sets contained in a set V is called the *interior* of V. We find it convenient to speak also of the *exterior* of V, and by this we mean the interior of the complement of V.

PROPOSITION 2. *For any subset V of Π, $\Gamma\Delta V$ is the exterior of V. If $\Delta\Pi = 0$ then, for any subset A of R, $\Delta\Gamma A$ is the annihilator A^* of A.*

Proof. First

$$P' \in \Gamma\Delta V \Leftrightarrow \Delta V \not\subseteq P'$$

$$\Leftrightarrow \exists_{r \in R} \forall_{P \in V}(r \in P \quad \& \quad r \notin P')$$

$$\Leftrightarrow \exists_{r \in R}(P' \in \Gamma r \quad \& \quad \forall_{P \in V} P \not\subseteq \Gamma r),$$

and this means that there exists a basic open set Γr containing P' and not meeting V, which is the same as saying that P' belongs to the exterior of V.

Second

$$r \in \Delta\Gamma A \Leftrightarrow \forall_{P \in \Pi}(A \not\subseteq P \Rightarrow r \in P)$$

$$\Leftrightarrow \forall_{P \in \Pi} rA \subset P$$

$$\Leftrightarrow rA \subset \Delta\Pi$$

$$\Leftrightarrow rA = 0.$$

A subset of a topological space is called a *regular open* set if it is the interior of its closure. This is easily seen to be the same as saying that it is the interior of some closed set, hence that it is the exterior of some open set. The regular open sets form a complete Boolean algebra with finite intersection as finite inf and exterior as complement. The 0-element of this Boolean algebra is the empty set.

The exterior of the exterior of a regular open set V is V. The annihilator of the annihilator of an annihilator ideal A is A. Hence the mappings Γ and $\Delta\Gamma\Delta$ are inverses of one another, assuming of course that $\Delta\Pi = 0$. Moreover, Γ is a Boolean homomorphism, as is easily verified, hence we have the first part of the following:

PROPOSITION 3.   *If Π is a prime ideal space of the commutative ring R such that $\Delta\Pi = 0$, Γ is an isomorphism of the complete Boolean algebra of annihilator ideals of R onto the complete Boolean algebra of regular open sets of Π. Moreover, if Π contains all maximal ideals of R, Γ induces an isomorphism of the Boolean algebra of direct summands of R onto the Boolean algebra of the (simultaneously) closed and open sets in Π.*

Proof. It remains to prove the second statement. Since R is a commutative semiprime ring, direct summands may be characterized as those annihilator ideals A for which $A + A^* = R$. Since Π contains all maximal ideals, this is equivalent to $\Gamma(A + A^*) = \Gamma R$, that is $\Gamma A \cup \Gamma\Delta\Gamma A = \Pi$. Now $\Gamma\Delta\Gamma A$ is the exterior of ΓA, hence an annihilator ideal is a direct summand if and only if the associated regular open set ΓA is the complement of its exterior, that is to say ΓA is both open and closed.

COROLLARY (Stone).   *If Π is the set of all prime (= maximal) ideals of the Boolean ring R, then R is isomorphic to the algebra of closed and open subsets of Π. Moreover, its Dedekind-MacNeille completion is isomorphic to the algebra of regular open subsets of Π.*

Proof. $R = B(R)$, $D(R) \cong B^*(R)$.

The above gives a representation of a Boolean ring as an algebra of subsets of the set Π. We may ask how to characterize the algebra of all subsets of some set. Clearly, this algebra must be *complete* (Dedekind complete or rationally complete) and *atomic*: For every element r there exists an *atom* (minimal nonzero element) a such that $a \leq r$.

PROPOSITION 4.   *A Boolean algebra is isomorphic to the algebra of all subsets of a set if and only if it is complete and atomic.*

Proof. It remains to establish the sufficiency of the conditions. We shall apply Proposition 3 to a space Π, which is not in general the set of all prime ideals.

With each atom a we associate the ideal a^*. Clearly $1 \notin a^*$. Suppose $r \notin a^*$, then $0 \neq ar \leq a$, hence $ar = a$, and so $1 - r \in a^*$. Therefore a^* is a maximal ideal.

Let Π be the set of all maximal ideals of the form a^*, where a is any atom of R. If $r \neq 0$, then there exists an atom $a \leq r$, so that $ar = a \neq 0$, hence $r \notin a^*$, and so $r \notin \Delta\Pi$. Thus $\Delta\Pi = 0$, and the first part of Proposition 3 applies.

If a is any atom, Γa is the set of all b^* where b is an atom such that $a \notin b^*$, that is $ab \neq 0$, that is $a = ab = b$. Hence $\Gamma a = \{a^*\}$.

Thus every point in Π is open. (One says that Π has the *discrete* topology.) It readily follows that every subset of Π is a regular open set, hence $D(R) \simeq B^*(R)$ is isomorphic to the algebra of all subsets of Π. Since R is complete, $D(R) = R$ and our proof is finished.

Note that, while every subset of Π is closed and open, we could not have applied the second part of Proposition 3 (or its corollary), since Π does not necessarily contain all maximal ideals. In fact, if Π did contain all maximal ideals it would be a finite set; for a compact discrete space is always finite.

Since the completeness of R only entered the above proof at the end, we can extract a little more information from it.

COROLLARY. *If R is any atomic Boolean algebra, its completion is isomorphic to the algebra of all sets of atoms of R.*

EXERCISES

1. Show that the interior of any closed set is the interior of its own closure.

2. Prove that the regular open sets in any topological space form a Boolean algebra.

3. Prove directly that every finite Boolean algebra is isomorphic to the algebra of all subsets of a finite set.

4. Show that in a complete Boolean algebra

$$a \wedge \sup_{i \in I} b_i = \sup_{i \in I}(a \wedge b_i),$$

for any elements a and b_i $(i \in I)$.

5. Give a direct proof of Proposition 4, by associating with every element $r \in R$ the set of all atoms a such that $a \leq r$.

CHAPTER THREE

Classical Theory of Associative Rings

3.1 Primitive rings

From now on R will be an associative ring with 1, not necessarily commutative. A module A_R is called *irreducible* if it has exactly two submodules. These submodules must be A and 0, and the definition is meant to imply that $A \neq 0$. Let M be any right ideal of R, then R/M is an irreducible right R-module if and only if M is a maximal (proper) right ideal. On the other hand, M_R is irreducible if and only if M is a minimal nonzero right ideal, *minimal* right ideal for short.

An element r of the ring R is called *right invertible* in R if there exists an element $s \in R$ such that $rs = 1$. It is called a *unit* if it is both right invertible and left invertible; it is easily verified that the two "inverses" are then the same.

PROPOSITION 1. *The following conditions concerning the ring R are equivalent:*

(1) *0 is a maximal right ideal.*
(2) *R is irreducible as a right R-module.*
(3) *Every nonzero element is right invertible.*
(4) *Every nonzero element is a unit.*
(1')–(3') *Conditions (1) to (3) with "right" replaced by "left."*
Under these conditions R is called a *division ring*.

Proof. The equivalence of (1) to (3) is obvious, and also the fact that $(4) \Rightarrow (3)$. The equivalence with (1') to (3') will follow from the symmetry of (4). Thus it remains to show that $(3) \Rightarrow (4)$.

Assume (3) and let $0 \neq r \in R$, then $rs = 1$ for some $s \in R$. Now $0 \neq s$, hence $st = 1$ for some $t \in R$. But

$$t = 1t = (rs)t = r(st) = r1 = r,$$

hence $sr = 1$, and so r is also left invertible.

A ring is called *simple* if it has exactly two ideals, that is if 0 is a maximal ideal. If M is any ideal of R, R/M is a simple ring if and only if M is a maximal ideal. Clearly every division ring is simple. A commutative ring is simple if and only if it is a division ring, that is if and only if it is a field. It is now fashionable to embed the study of simple rings in that of a somewhat larger class of rings.

An ideal P in the ring R is called (right) *primitive* if it is the largest ideal contained in some maximal right ideal M, thus

$$P = R \cdot M = \{r \in R \mid Rr \subset M\}.$$

This definition is not symmetrical, and it is known that right primitivity does not imply left primitivity. Nonetheless, the attribute "right" is usually omitted. A ring is called (right) *primitive* if 0 is a primitive ideal. It easily follows that, for any ideal P, R/P is a primitive ring if and only if P is a primitive ideal. A commutative ring is primitive if and only if it is a field. Clearly every simple ring is a primitive ring, and every maximal ideal is a primitive ideal.

In a moment we shall state another characterization of primitive rings, which is sometimes taken as their definition. To do this we need one more concept. A module A_R is called *faithful* if, for any $0 \neq r \in R$, $Ar \neq 0$. This means that the canonical representation of R by endomorphisms of the additive group A is mono.

PROPOSITION 2 (Jacobson). *The ring R is primitive if and only if there exists a faithful irreducible module A_R.*

Proof. Assume R is a primitive ring. Then there exists a maximal right ideal M such that $R \cdot M = 0$. Put $A = R/M$ then we have an irreducible module A_R. Suppose $r \in R$ and $Ar = 0$, then $Rr \subset M$ and so $r \in R \cdot M = 0$. Thus A_R is faithful.

Conversely, assume that R has a faithful irreducible module A_R. Let $0 \neq a \in A$, then $0 \neq aR \subset A$ and so $aR = A$. The mapping $r \to ar$ is thus an epimorphism of R onto A. Let M be its kernel, then $R/M \cong A$, an irreducible R-module, hence M is a maximal right ideal. Now $r \in R \cdot M$ if and only if $Rr \subset M$, that is $Ar = 0$, that is $r = 0$, since A_R is faithful. Thus $R \cdot M = 0$ and so R is primitive.

It is possible to push the structure of primitive rings a little further.

LEMMA 1 (Schur). *If A_R is an irreducible module, then its ring of endomorphisms $D = Hom_R(A,A)$ is a division ring.*

Proof. Let $0 \neq d \in D$, then $0 \neq dA \subset A$, hence $dA = A$. Also $d^{-1}0 \neq A$, hence $d^{-1}0 = 0$. Thus d is an automorphism of A, hence a unit of D. (The reader will recall that $d^{-1}0 = \{a \in A/da = 0\}$.)

Note that we write the endomorphisms of $d \in D$ on the left of the right module A_R. Thus the fact that d is an R-endomorphism is expressed by the "associativity" condition

$$d(ar) = (da)r \qquad (d \in D, \qquad a \in A, \qquad r \in R).$$

(We assume of course in addition that d is an endomorphism of the additive group of A.) Thus A becomes not only a left module $_D A$, but a so-called *bimodule*. The same associativity condition assures that we have a representation of R by endomorphisms of $_D A$; and, if A_R is moreover a faithful module, then R may be regarded as a subring of $E = \mathrm{Hom}_D(A,A)$. Since D is a division ring, A is also called a *vector space*, and E is called the ring of *linear transformations* of this vector space. How densely is R embedded in E? The following is due to Jacobson (Density Theorem):

PROPOSITION 3. *Let R be a primitive ring with faithful irreducible module A_R, then $D = \mathrm{Hom}_R(A,A)$ is a division ring, and R is canonically embedded in $E = \mathrm{Hom}_D(A,A)$ so that, for every $e \in E$ and every finitely generated submodule G of $_D A$, there exists an element $r \in R$ such that $G(e - r) = 0$.*

Proof. We write $G^r = \{r \in R \mid Gr = 0\}$ and $S^l = \{a \in A \mid aS = 0\}$, for any subset S of R. We prove by induction on the number of generators of G that (i) $\exists_{r \in R} G(e - r) = 0$ and (ii) $G^{rl} = G$.

Clearly the results hold when $G = 0$. Assume the results for G and consider $G + Da$, $a \notin G$. Now $G(e - r) = 0$, we seek $s \in R$ such that $(G + Da)(e - r - s) = 0$, that is $Da(e - r) = (G + Da)s$. Putting $b = a(e - r)$, it clearly suffices that $Gs = 0$ and $as = b$, and this will follow if $aG^r = A$. Indeed, if this were not so, then $aG^r = 0$, hence $a \in G^{rl} = G$, a contradiction. Thus (i) holds for $G + Da$.

It remains to show that $G + Da = (G + Da)^{rl} = (G^r \cap a^r)^l$. Clearly, $LHS \subset RHS$. Now suppose $b \in RHS$, that is $br = 0$ whenever $Gr = 0$ and $ar = 0$. Consider the mapping $ar \to br$ of aG^r into bG^r. Since A_R is irreducible, either $aG^r = 0$ or $aG^r = A$. In the first case $bG^r = 0$ and so $b \in G^{rl} = G \subset LHS$. In the second case there exists $d \in D$ such that $br = dar$ for all $r \in G^r$, hence $b - da \in G^{rl} = G$, and so $b \in G + Da$ as required. Thus (ii) holds for $G + Da$.

The above result can be given a topological interpretation. If $\{X_i \mid i \in I\}$ is a family of topological spaces, one introduces a *product topology* into $X = \prod_{i \in I} X_i$, by taking as basic open sets all sets of the form $\bigcap_{i \in F} \pi_i^{-1} V_i$, where $\pi_i : X \to X_i$ canonically, V_i is any basic open set of X_i and F is a finite subset of I. In particular, let all X_i have the discrete topology, in which all sets are open. Then the product topology on X is not the discrete topology on X but has basic open sets $V = \bigcap_{i \in F} \pi_i^{-1} x_i$, where $x_i \in X_i$. It is easily seen that

$$V = \{x \in X \,|\, \forall_{i \in F} x(i) = x_i\},$$

where $x(i) = \pi_i x$. One calls this the *finite* topology on X.

Now $E = \text{Hom}_D(A,A)$ is a subset of the set of all functions of A into A, that is of $\prod_{a \in A} A$. As such it is a topological space whose open sets are obtained from those of $\prod_{a \in A} A$ by intersecting with E. (Actually, it is a topological ring, but this is a matter we shall not consider now.) The basic open sets of E have the form

$$V = \{e \in E \,|\, \forall_{i \in F} a_i e = b_i\},$$

where F is a finite set of indices and $a_i, b_i \in A$. A subset of a topological space is called *dense* if its closure is the whole space, i.e., if it meets every nonempty open set. Proposition 3 now gives rise to the following:

COROLLARY. *A primitive ring is a dense subring of the ring of all linear transformations of a vector space.*

Proof. Let V be any nonempty basic open set of E, then $\exists_{e \in E} \forall_{i \in F} a_i e = b_i$. By Proposition 3, we can find $r \in R$ such that $\forall_{i \in F} a_i r = a_i e = b_i$, hence $b \in R \cap V$, and thus R meets V.

An ideal P of R is called *prime* if it is proper (that is $P \neq R$) and $AB \subset P$ implies $A \subset P$ or $B \subset P$, for any ideals A and B of R. R is called a *prime* ring if 0 is a prime ideal. The ideal P is a prime ideal if and only if the ring R/P is a prime ring. A commutative ring is prime if and only if it is an integral domain.

PROPOSITION 4. *The proper ideal P of R is prime if and only if, for any elements a and b of R, $aRb \subset P$ implies $a \in P$ or $b \in P$.*

Proof. If P is prime and $aRb \subset P$, then $(RaR)(RbR) \subset P$, hence $a \in RaR \subset P$ or $b \in RbR \subset P$. Here RaR is the *principal* ideal generated by a and consists of all finite sums of elements of the form ras, where r and $s \in R$.

Conversely, assume the condition and $AB \subset P$. Suppose $A \nsubseteq P$, then there exists $a \in A$ such that $a \notin P$. But, for any $b \in B$, $aRb \subset P$, hence $b \in P$. Thus $B \subset P$, and our proof is complete.

COROLLARY. *R is a prime ring if and only if $1 \neq 0$ and, for all $a \neq 0$ and $b \neq 0$ in R, there exists $r \in R$ such that $arb \neq 0$.*

PROPOSITION 5. *Every primitive ideal (ring) is prime.*

Proof. Let P be a primitive ideal of R, then $P = R \cdot M$, where M is a maximal right ideal. Now let A and B be ideals of R such that

$AB \subset P \subset M$. Since $M \subset M \,.\, B \subset R$, we have $M \,.\, B = M$ or $M \,.\, B = R$. In the first case, $A \subset M \,.\, B = M$, and therefore $A \subset P$. In the second case, $B \subset (M \,.\, B)B \subset M$, and therefore $B \subset P$. Thus P is prime. (See the end of Section 1.2 for the definition of the symbols "$.$" and "$\cdot$".)

EXERCISES

1. Show that the ring of linear transformations of a finite dimensional vector space is simple.

2. If M is a maximal right ideal of R, and if s is an element of R not in M, show that $s^{-1}M = \{r \in R \mid sr \in M\}$ is also a maximal right ideal and that $R/s^{-1}M \cong R/M$.

3. If M is a maximal right ideal of R, show that the associated primitive ideal $R \cdot M$ is the intersection of all $s^{-1}M$, where s ranges over all elements of R not in M.

4. Show that a dense subring of the ring of linear transformations of a vector space is primitive.

5. Show that R is a prime ring if and only if $1 \neq 0$ and $AB \neq 0$ for any two nonzero right ideals A and B of R.

6. Show that a prime ring with a minimal right ideal is (right) primitive.

7. Show that an ideal P of R is a maximal right ideal (maximal ideal, primitive ideal, prime ideal) if and only if R/P is a division ring (simple ring, primitive ring, prime ring).

8. If R is primitive and e is any idempotent in R, show that eRe is primitive. (*Hint:* If R is a dense subring of the ring of linear transformations of the vector space $_DV$, then eRe is a dense subring of the ring of linear transformations of Ve.)

9. A module M_R is called *subdirectly irreducible* if it contains a smallest nonzero submodule A. Show that $A^r = \{x \in R \mid Ax = 0\}$ is a primitive ideal of R.

3.2 Radicals

We define the *prime radical* as the intersection of all prime ideals of R, and we denote it by rad R. We wish to characterize this internally. An element a of R will be called *strongly nilpotent* provided every sequence $a_0, a_1, a_2, \ldots$, such that

$$a_0 = a, \qquad a_{n+1} \in a_n R a_n$$

is ultimately zero. Clearly, every strongly nilpotent element is *nilpotent*, in the sense that $a^n = 0$ for some natural number n. If R is commutative, every nilpotent element is strongly nilpotent.

PROPOSITION 1. *The prime radical of R is the set of all strongly nilpotent elements.*

Proof. Assume a is not in rad R, then there exists a prime ideal P such that $a_0 = a \notin P$. Hence $a_0 R a_0 \not\subset P$, and so there is an $a_1 \in a_0 R a_0$ such that $a_1 \notin P$. Continuing in this manner, we find $a_{n+1} \in a_n R a_n$ such that $a_{n+1} \notin P$. Thus, for all natural numbers n, $a_n \notin P$, hence $a_n \neq 0$, and so a is not strongly nilpotent.

Conversely, assume that a is not strongly nilpotent. Then there exists a sequence $a_0, a_1, a_2, \ldots$, such that $a_0 = a$, $a_{n+1} \in a_n R a_n$, and all $a_n \neq 0$. Let T be the set of all a_n, then $0 \notin T$. Consider an ideal P which is maximal in the set of ideals not meeting T. If we can show that P is prime, it will follow from $a \notin P$ that $a \notin$ rad R.

Now suppose A and B are ideals of R such that $A \not\subset P$ and $B \not\subset P$. By maximality of P, $A + P$ and $B + P$ meet T, hence $a_i \in A + P$ and $a_j \in B + P$. Let $m = \max(i,j)$, then

$$a_{m+1} \in a_m R a_m \subset (A + P)(B + P) \subset AB + P.$$

But $a_{m+1} \notin P$, hence $AB \not\subset P$. P is proper (since $a \notin P$), hence P is prime.

An ideal is called *nilpotent* if some power of it is zero.

PROPOSITION 2. *The following conditions concerning the ring R are equivalent:*

   (1) *0 is the only nilpotent ideal of R.*
   (2) *0 is an intersection of prime ideals, that is rad $R = 0$.*
   (3) *For any ideals A and B of R, $AB = 0 \Rightarrow A \cap B = 0$.*

Under these conditions R is called *semiprime*.

Proof. Assume (1) and let $a_0 = a \neq 0$. Then $R a_0 R$ is not nilpotent, hence we can pick $a_1 \in a_0 R a_0$ such that $a_1 \neq 0$. Continuing in this way, we see that a is not strongly nilpotent, hence that $a \notin$ rad R. Thus (1) $\Rightarrow$ (2).

Assume (2) and let $AB = 0$. Then $AB \subset P$, for any prime ideal P, hence A or $B \subset P$, therefore $A \cap B \subset P$. Thus $A \cap B \subset$ rad $R = 0$, and so (2) $\Rightarrow$ (3).

Assume (3) and let $A^n = 0$. But then $A = A \cap \cdots \cap A = 0$. Thus (3) $\Rightarrow$ (1).

COROLLARY. *The prime radical of R is the smallest ideal K such that R/K is semiprime.*

Proof. The canonical one-to-one correspondence between the ideals of R/K and the ideals of R containing K associates prime ideals with prime ideals: If $K \subset P \subset R$, then P/K is prime if and only if P is prime. Therefore R/K is semiprime if and only if K is the intersection of prime ideals of R. Clearly rad R is the smallest such ideal K.

The intersection of all maximal ideals of R does not seem to be an important concept. However, the intersection of all maximal right ideals is called the (*Perlis-*)*Jacobson radical* or just the *radical* of R. The apparent asymmetry in this definition will be removed later. Let us recall now that there always are plenty of maximal (proper) right ideals, in fact every proper right ideal is contained in at least one such. We denote the radical of R by Rad R. Recall that an element r of R is right invertible if $rs = 1$ for some $s \in R$, that is to say if rR is not a proper right ideal.

PROPOSITION 3.   *The radical of R is the set of all $r \in R$ such that $1 - rs$ is right invertible for all $s \in R$.*

Proof. $r \in$ Rad R if and only if, for all maximal right ideals M, $r \in M$, that is $1 \notin M + rR$. Thus $r \in$ Rad R if and only if, for all $s \in R$, $1 - rs$ belongs to no maximal right ideal, i.e., is right invertible.

A ring will be called *semiprimitive* if its radical is 0. (Jacobson calls such a ring "semisimple," but this term is used for a more restricted class of rings by other authors.)

PROPOSITION 4.   *The radical is an ideal and $R/$Rad R is semiprimitive.*

Proof.   To see that Rad R is an ideal, we need only show that it is a left ideal, that is that for all $r \in$ Rad R, and for all s, $t \in R$, $1 - trs$ has a right inverse. Since $rs \in$ Rad R, it suffices to show that $1 - tr$ is right invertible. Now $1 - rt$ is right invertible, hence there exists an element u in R such that $(1 - rt)u = 1$, that is $1 + rtu = u$. Therefore

$$(1 - tr)(1 + tur) = 1 + tur - t(1 + rtu)r = 1,$$

and so $1 - tr$ is right invertible as required.

Now let $\pi : R \to R/$Rad R canonically, and suppose $\pi r \in$ Rad (πR), then $r \in M$, for every maximal right ideal M of R containing Rad R. But every maximal right ideal contains Rad R, and so $r \in$ Rad R, hence $\pi r = 0$.

PROPOSITION 5.   *The radical is the largest ideal K such that, for all $r \in K$, $1 - r$ is a unit.*

Proof.   By Proposition 3, the radical contains every such ideal K. Since the radical is an ideal, it only remains to show that $1 - r$ is a unit for any $r \in$ Rad R. We already know that $(1 - r)u = 1$ for some $u \in R$.

Thus $1 - u = -ru \in \text{Rad } R$, hence u has a right inverse v. Thus $v = (1 - r)uv = 1 - r$, and so $u(1 - r) = 1$.

In view of the symmetry of Proposition 5, we immediately have the following:

COROLLARY.   *The radical is the intersection of all maximal left ideals.*

The radical may also be regarded as the intersection of certain two-sided ideals.

PROPOSITION 6.   *The radical of R is the intersection of all primitive ideals.*

Proof.   The radical is an ideal, hence $r \in \text{Rad } R$ if and only if $Rr \subset M$ for all maximal right ideals M, that is $r \in R \cdot. M = P$ for all primitive ideals P.

The following obvious result will be stated without proof.

PROPOSITION 7.   *R is semiprime (semiprimitive) if and only if it is a subdirect product of prime (primitive) rings.*

EXERCISES

1. Let S be a subset of R such that $1 \notin S$ and, for any a and $b \notin S$, there exists $r \in R$ such that $arb \notin S$. If furthermore $0 \in S$, show that any ideal which is maximal in the set of ideals contained in S is prime.

2. If A is any ideal and r is any element of the semiprime ring R, show that $Ar = 0$ if and only if $rA = 0$.

3 (Tominaga). Show that the ideals K for which R/K is semiprime form a complete distributive lattice.

4. If K and P are ideals such that $K \subset P \subset R$, show that P/K is prime if and only if P is prime.

5. Show that a ring R is a subdirect product of division rings (simple rings, primitive rings, prime rings) if and only if $\bigcap_{i \in I} P_i = 0$, where $\{P_i \mid i \in I\}$ is the set of all ideals which are maximal right ideals (maximal ideals, primitive ideals, prime ideals).

6. (Chinese remainder theorem.) Let $P_1, P_2, \ldots, P_n$ be a finite set of ideals in R such that $P_i + P_j = R$ whenever $i \neq j$. Show that, for any set of elements $a_1, a_2, \ldots, a_n \in R$, there exists an element $r \in R$ such that $r - a_i \in P_i$, for $i = 1, 2, \ldots, n$.

7. If the intersection of all maximal ideals of R is 0, show that R is a dense subring of a product of simple rings, dense in the finite topology.

8 (Eckmann). Call a right ideal A of R *small* if, for every right ideal B,

$$A + B = R \Rightarrow B = R.$$

Show that A is small if and only if $A \subset \text{Rad } R$.

9. Let R be the ring of all 2×2 matrices with entries in the ring A. Show that Rad R consists of all matrices with entries in Rad A.

10 (McCoy). Let $R[x]$ be the ring obtained from any ring R by adjoining an indeterminate x which commutes with all elements of R, and let $\pi : R[x] \to R$ be the canonical epimorphism such that $\pi f(x) = f(0)$. Show that, for any prime ideal P of R, $\pi^{-1}P$ is a prime ideal of $R[x]$ and $\pi^{-1}P \cap R = P$. Also show that, for any prime ideal P' of $R[x]$, $P' \cap R$ is a prime ideal of R. Deduce that rad $(R[x]) \cap R = $ rad R.

11 (Amitsur, McCoy). Show that rad $(R[x]) = ($rad $R)[x]$, the set of polynomials in x with coefficients in rad R. [*Hint:* Let $f(x) = a_0 x^n + \cdots + a_n \in$ rad $(R[x])$, P any prime ideal of R. Then $f(x) \in \pi^{-1}P$, hence $a_n \in P \subset \pi^{-1}P$, hence $a_0 x^n + \cdots + a_{n-1}x \in \pi^{-1}P$. Put $g(x) = a_0 x^{n-1} + \cdots + a_{n-1}$, then $xg(x)$ is strongly nilpotent, hence so is $g(x)$. Therefore $a_{n-1} \in P$, etc.]

12. If $r \in R \cap$ Rad $(R[x])$, show that r is nilpotent. (*Hint:* $1 - rx$ is a unit.)

13 (Amitsur). Let R have characteristic 0, i.e., $na = a + a + \cdots + a \neq 0$, for all $n \geq 1$, if $a \neq 0$. Prove that $R \cap$ Rad $(R[x]) \neq 0$ if Rad $(R[x]) \neq 0$. [*Hint:* Let $f(x)$ be a polynomial of minimal degree in Rad $(R[x])$. The radical is invariant under all automorphisms of $R[x]$, hence $f(x + 1) \in$ Rad $(R[x])$, and so $f(x + 1) - f(x) = 0$ by minimality.]

14 (Amitsur). Let R have characteristic 0, and put $N = R \cap$ Rad $(R[x])$. Show that Rad $(R[x]) = N[x]$. [*Hint:* Putting $S = R/N$, verify that Rad $(S[x]) \cong$ Rad $(R[x])/N[x]$ and deduce Rad $(S[x]) \cap S = 0$.]

3.3 Completely reducible modules

One may define the *radical* Rad A of any module A_R as the intersection of all maximal (proper) submodules. There need not be any such submodules, in which case Rad $A = A$. (Of course, if $A_R = R_R$, this situation does not arise, since we always assume that $1 \in R$.) Dually one defines the *socle* Soc A of A_R as the sum of all minimal (nonzero) submodules of A, that is all submodules of A which are irreducible. If there are no such submodules, Soc $A = 0$.

PROPOSITION 1. *The socle of A_R is the direct sum of a subfamily of the family of all irreducible submodules of A_R. It is invariant under every endomorphism of A_R.*

Proof. Let $\{A_i \mid i \in I\}$ be the family of all irreducible submodules of A. For the purpose of this proof only, let us call a subset J of the index set I *direct* if $\sum_{j \in J} A_j$ is a direct sum. Consider a family $\{J_k \mid k \in K\}$ of direct sets which is simply ordered under inclusion and let J be its union. We claim that J is direct. For suppose $\sum_{j\in J} a_j = 0$, where $a_j \in A_j$ and $\{j \in J \mid a_j \neq 0\}$ is finite. This finite set will lie in some J_k, but J_k is direct, hence all $a_j = 0$. Thus J is direct.

We may apply Zorn's Lemma and obtain a maximal direct set $J \subset I$. Now suppose A_i is an irreducible submodule of A not contained in $\sum_{j\in J} A_j$. Then $A_i \cap \sum_{j\in J} A_j = 0$. Suppose $a_i + \sum_{j\in J} a_j = 0$, where $a_i \in A_i$ and $a_j \in A_j$. Then $a_i = 0 = \sum_{j\in J} a_j$, and so all $a_j = 0$, since J is direct. Thus $J \cup \{i\}$ is also direct, contradicting the maximality of J. Therefore Soc $A = \sum_{j\in J} A_j$ is a direct sum.

Finally, let $e \in \operatorname{Hom}_R(A,A)$. Then eA_i is a homomorphic image of A_i, hence 0 or irreducible. In either case, $eA_i \subset \operatorname{Soc} A$, and therefore $e \operatorname{Soc} A \subset \operatorname{Soc} A$.

COROLLARY. *The following conditions concerning the module A_R are equivalent:*
  (1) $A = \operatorname{Soc} A$.
  (2) *A is the sum of minimal submodules.*
  (3) *A is isomorphic to a direct sum of irreducible modules.*
  Under these conditions A_R is said to be *completely reducible.*

It is immediate that every submodule and every factor module of a completely reducible module is completely reducible.

Following R. E. Johnson, we call a submodule of a module A_R *large* if it has nonzero intersection with every nonzero submodule of A_R. The following lemma ensures that there are plenty of large submodules.

LEMMA 1. *If B is a submodule of A and C is maximal among the submodules of A such that $B \cap C = 0$, then $B + C$ is large.*
  Proof. Assume $(B + C) \cap D = 0$, then also $B \cap (C + D) = 0$, since $B \cap C = 0$. (For $b = c + d$ implies $d = b - c = 0$, hence $b = c = 0$.) By maximality of C, $D \subset C$, hence $D = (B + C) \cap D = 0$.

We recall that the lattice $L(A)$ of submodules of A is complemented if every submodule B of A has a complementary submodule B' such that $B \cap B' = 0$ and $B + B' = A$.

LEMMA 2. *If $L(A)$ is complemented then so is $L(B)$ for any submodule B of A.*
  Proof. Let $C \subset B$, then C has a complement C' in A. Now $C' \cap B$ is its complement in B, for

$$C \cap (C' \cap B) = (C \cap C') \cap B = 0 \cap B = 0$$

and

$$C + (C' \cap B) = (C + C') \cap B = A \cap B = B$$

by the modular law.

LEMMA 3.   *If $L(A)$ is complemented then Rad $A = 0$.*

Proof.   Let $0 \neq a \in A$ and let M be maximal among the submodules of A such that $a \notin M$. We will show that M is a maximal submodule of A.

Indeed, suppose $M \subset N \subset A$. Since $a \notin M$ and $N \cap (M + N') = M$, by the modular law, therefore $a \notin N$ or $a \notin M + N'$. Hence, by maximality of M, either $M = N$ or $N' = 0$, i.e., $N = A$.

PROPOSITION 2.   *The following conditions concerning the module A are equivalent:*

(1) *A is completely reducible.*

(2) *A has no proper large submodule.*

(3) *$L(A)$ is complemented.*

Proof.   Assume (1). A large submodule of A has nonzero intersection with every nonzero submodule of A, hence contains every irreducible submodule of A, hence contains Soc $A = A$. Thus $(1) \Rightarrow (2)$.

Assume (2). Let B be any submodule of A. By Lemma 1 we have $C \subset A$ such that $B \cap C = 0$ and $B + C$ is large. By (2), $B + C = A$. Thus $(2) \Rightarrow (3)$. (See Secton 1.3, Proposition 2.)

Assume (3). Then $A = \text{Soc } A + C$, $\text{Soc } A \cap C = 0$. By Lemma 2, $L(C)$ is complemented. Hence, by Lemma 3, Rad $C = 0$. Suppose $0 \neq c \in C$, then there exists a maximal submodule of C not containing c. Its complement in C would be irreducible, a contradiction. Thus $C = 0$ and so $(3) \Rightarrow (1)$.

If A_R is any right R-module, $E = \text{Hom}_R(A,A)$ its ring of endomorphisms, then we have also a left module $_EA$. In fact, $e(ar) = (ea)r$, for all $e \in E$, $a \in A$, and $r \in R$, and in this situation one speaks of a bimodule $_EA_R$.

Let A_i be any irreducible R-submodule of A. We write EA_i for the submodule of A generated by all ea_i with $e \in E$ and $a_i \in A_i$. Then EA_i is an E-R-submodule of A. Now, for any $e \in E$, eA_i is a homomorphic image of A_i, hence $eA_i = 0$ or $eA_i \cong A_i$, and so eA_i is either 0 or irreducible.

LEMMA 4.   *If A_R is completely reducible then EA_i is the sum of all irreducible submodules of A_R which are isomorphic to A_i. EA_i is called a homogeneous component of A_R.*

Proof.   Consider any irreducible submodule $A_k \cong A_i$. Now $L(A_R)$ is complemented, hence $A = A_i + A_i'$ and $A_i \cap A_i' = 0$, for some submodule A_i' of A. Define $e \in E$ by letting e induce the given isomorphism of A_i onto A_k and putting $eA_i' = 0$. Then $A_k = eA_i \subset EA_i$.

PROPOSITION 3.   *Let A_R be the direct sum of a finite number of irreducible submodules A_j, $j \in J$, and let $E = Hom_R(A,A)$. Then every E-R-submodule of A is the (direct) sum of some of the homogeneous components EA_j.*

Proof. Let B be any such E-R-submodule and let $e_j = e_j^2 \in E$ be such that $e_j A = A_j$, $\sum_{j \in J} e_j = 1$. Then $e_j B \subset A_j$, hence $e_j B = 0$ or $e_j B = A_j$. Let J' be the set of all $j \in J$ for which the second alternative holds, then

$$B = \sum_{j \in J} e_j B = \sum_{j \in J'} A_j.$$

Now, for any $j \in J'$, $EA_j \subset EB \subset B$, hence $B = \sum_{j \in J'} EA_j$. But the EA_j are minimal submodules of the bimodule $_E B_R$. Applying Proposition 1 to the bimodule $_E B_R$, we see that B is also a direct sum of some of the EA_j.

EXERCISES

1. Give a simpler proof of Proposition 1 in the case when I is a finite set.

2. If π is an epimorphism of C onto A, and if B is a large submodule of A, show that $\pi^{-1}B$ is a large submodule of C.

3. If $A \subset B \subset C$, show that A is a large submodule of C if and only if A is a large submodule of B and B is a large submodule of C.

4. If B and C are large submodules of A, show that $B \cap C$ is large.

5. If R is a commutative ring, show that every dense ideal is large, and that conversely every large ideal is dense if and only if R is semiprime.

6. Show that the ring of endomorphisms of a completely reducible module is isomorphic to the direct product of the endomorphism rings of its homogeneous components.

7 (Sandomierski-Kasch). Show that the intersection of all large submodules of A is the socle of A. Dualize this result.

3.4   Completely reducible rings

We now turn our attention to the ring R regarded as a right R-module R_R.

PROPOSITION 1 (Brauer).   *If K is any minimal right ideal of R, then either $K^2 = 0$ or $K = eR$, where $e^2 = e \in K$.*

Proof. Assume $K^2 \neq 0$, then $kK \neq 0$ for some $k \in K$, hence $kK = K$. Consider $k^{-1}0 = \{r \in R \mid kr = 0\}$, then $k^{-1}0 \cap K \neq K$, hence $= 0$. Now $ke = k$ for some $e \in K$. Thus $k(e^2 - e) = 0$, and so $e^2 - e \in k^{-1}0 \cap K = 0$. Therefore $e^2 = e$, and this $\neq 0$, since $k \neq 0$. Now $0 \neq eR \subset K$, hence $eR = K$.

COROLLARY.   *Every minimal right ideal of a semiprime ring R has the form eR, where $e^2 = e \in R$.*

LEMMA 1.   *If $e^2 = e \in R$ and $f \in R$, then there is a group isomorphism $\text{Hom}_R(eR, fR) \cong fRe$. Moreover, if $f = e$, this is a ring isomorphism.*

Proof. Consider a typical element fre of fRe and define $\phi \in \text{Hom}_R(eR, fR)$ by $\phi(er') = (fre)(er') = frer'$, for any $r' \in R$. Clearly, $\phi = 0$ implies $fre = 0$. Moreover, any $\phi \in \text{Hom}_R(eR, fR)$ can be obtained in this way. Indeed, putting $\phi e = fr$, we have $\phi(er') = \phi(e^2 r') = (\phi e)(er') = frer'$. This shows the first statement. The second statement is an easy consequence and is left as an exercise.

Let $e^2 = e \in R$, then eRe is a ring with unity e. By Lemma 1, $eRe \cong \text{Hom}_R(eR, eR)$. When eR is irreducible, we conclude by Schur's Lemma that eRe is a division ring. The converse of this inference is also valid, provided R is semiprime.

PROPOSITION 2.   *If R is semiprime and $e^2 = e \in R$, then eR is a minimal right ideal if and only if eRe is a division ring.*

Proof. It remains to show the "if" part. Assume that eRe is a division ring, and let $r \in R$ such that $er \neq 0$. Since R is semiprime, we have $erRer \neq 0$, hence $erse \neq 0$ for some $s \in R$. Let ete be the inverse of $erse$, then $ersete = e$. Thus $erR = eR$, and so eR is irreducible.

COROLLARY.   *If R is semiprime and $e^2 = e \in R$, then eR is a minimal right ideal if and only if Re is a minimal left ideal.*

PROPOSITION 3.   *If $e^2 = e \in R$ and $f^2 = f \in R$, then $eR \cong fR$ if and only if there exist $u, v \in R$ such that $vu = e$ and $uv = f$.*

Proof. Assume $eR \cong fR$. Let $u = fue$ correspond to the given isomorphism $eR \to fR$, and let $v = evf$ correspond to the inverse isomorphism $fR \to eR$. Then clearly $vu = e$ and $uv = f$.

Conversely, assume $vu = e$ and $uv = f$. Then $ue = u(vu) = (uv)u = fu$, and similarly $vf = ev$. Thus the mappings $er \to uer = fur$ and $fr' \to vfr' = evr'$ give such a pair of inverse isomorphisms.

COROLLARY.   *If $e^2 = e \in R$ and $f^2 = f \in R$, then $eR \cong fR$ if and only if $Re \cong Rf$.*

Proof. This follows immediately from the symmetry of the pair of conditions $vu = e$ and $uv = f$.

PROPOSITION 4.   *If R is semiprime then R_R and $_R R$ have the same socles. Moreover, they have the same homogeneous components, and these are minimal ideals.*

Proof. In view of the above, the socle S of R_R is $\sum eR$, where e ranges over all idempotents of R for which eRe is a division ring. Similarly, the socle S' of $_R R$ is $\sum Re$. Now S is an ideal (by Proposition 1 of the preceding section), hence $S' \subset S$. Similarly $S \subset S'$.

Next, consider any homogeneous component H of S. H has the form $\sum eR$, where e ranges over all idempotents of R for which eR is isomorphic to a given minimal right ideal $fR, f^2 = f \in R$. Since $eR \cong fR \Leftrightarrow Re \cong Rf$, by the above corollary, $H' = \sum Re$ is a corresponding homogeneous component of S'. One proves that $H = H'$ in the same way as one proved that $S = S'$.

Let K be any nonzero ideal of R contained in H, then K_R is completely reducible. An irreducible submodule of K_R will be a minimal right ideal eR of R, $e^2 = e$. If $fR \cong eR$, then $f = uv = uev$ as above, hence $fR = u(eR) \subset uK \subset K$. Thus $H \subset K$, and therefore H is minimal as a nonzero two-sided ideal.

PROPOSITION 5. *The following statements concerning the ring R are equivalent:*

(1) *Every right R-module is completely reducible.*
(2) *R_R is completely reducible.*
(3) *Every left R-module is completely reducible.*
(4) *$_R R$ is completely reducible.*

Under these conditions we call R *completely reducible.* (Bourbaki calls such a ring "semisimple.")

Proof. Clearly $(1) \Rightarrow (2)$. Now assume (2) and let B_R be any right R-module. Since R is the sum of irreducible right ideals A_i $(i \in I)$, $B = \sum_{b \in B} bR$ is the sum of submodules bA_i, and each of these is either 0 or irreducible, since it is the homomorphic image of A_i under the mapping $r \to br$ of R into B. Therefore B_R is completely reducible. Thus $(1) \Leftrightarrow (2)$, and similarly $(3) \Leftrightarrow (4)$.

Again assume (2). Then R is semiprime, in view of Lemma 3 of Section 3.3. By Proposition 4, R_R and $_R R$ have the same socle. Since R_R is completely reducible, its socle is R. Therefore $_R R$ is also completely reducible. Thus $(2) \Rightarrow (4)$ and, by symmetry, $(4) \Rightarrow (2)$.

We recall that a *vector space* is a module over a division ring.

COROLLARY. *A vector space is completely reducible.*

Proof. If R is a division ring, R_R is irreducible, hence (2) holds trivially.

Thus a vector space is a direct sum of copies of R_R. The number of these is called the *dimension* of the vector space.

If V_R is a finite dimensional vector space over the division ring R, the ring $\text{Hom}_R(V,V)$ of endomorphisms of V_R is well known to be isomorphic to the ring of $n \times n$ matrices over R, where n is the dimension of V_R.

LEMMA 2. *Let R be a prime ring and assume that the socle S_R of R_R is not zero. Let $e^2 = e \in R$ such that eR is a minimal right ideal of R. Then $\text{Hom}_R(S,S)$ is isomorphic to the ring of linear transformations $\text{Hom}_{eRe}(Re,Re)$.*

Note that Re is a right eRe-module, hence a vector space.

Proof. Since a homogeneous component H of S is a direct summand of S, and since R is prime, we have $S = H$. Let S be written as a direct sum of minimal right ideals e_iR, where $i \in I$, and $e_iR \cong eR$ say, the e_i and e being idempotent elements of R. We may assume that e is one of the e_i. By Proposition 3, there exist $u_i, v_i \in R$ such that $v_iu_i = e$ and $u_iv_i = e_i$. We compute

$$u_iev_i = u_iv_iu_iv_i = e_i{}^2 = e_i.$$

Now consider any $\phi \in \text{Hom}_R(S,S)$. Observing that $Re \subset S$, we define $\phi' \in \text{Hom}_{eRe}(Re,Re)$ by

$$\phi'(re) = \phi(re) = \phi(re^2) = \phi(re)e.$$

Consider any $s = \sum e_ir_i = \sum u_iev_ir_i \in S$, then

$$\phi s = \sum \phi(u_ie)v_ir_i = \sum \phi'(u_ie)v_ir_i.$$

From this formula it is easily inferred that the correspondence $\phi \to \phi'$ is an isomorphism.

The next proposition is a variation of a classical result in the theory of rings.

PROPOSITION 6 (Wedderburn-Artin). (a) *A ring R is completely reducible if and only if it is isomorphic to a finite direct product of completely reducible simple rings.* (b) *A ring R is completely reducible and simple if and only if it is the ring of all linear transformations of a finite dimensional vector space.*

Proof. (a) Let R be completely reducible, thus a direct sum of minimal right ideals. Now 1 must belong to a finite sum of these, hence R is a direct sum of finitely many minimal right ideals. Therefore R is the direct sum of finitely many homogeneous components; these are minimal ideals by Proposition 4. (For R is semiprime, by Lemma 3 of Section 3.3.)

By Section 1.3, Proposition 3, there exist central orthogonal idempotents $c_i \in R$ such that $1 = \sum_{i=1}^m c_i$, and c_iR is the i-th homogeneous component. Clearly, c_iR is a ring with unity c_i (however, in our terminology, not a subring of R, except when $c_i = 1$), and R is isomorphic to the direct product of the rings $c_i R$.

Let $H = c_i R$ be any homogeneous component of R. It is easily seen that the ideals (right ideals) of H are precisely the ideals (right ideals) of R which are contained in H. Since H is a minimal ideal of R, it is therefore a simple ring. Now H is a direct sum of finitely many right ideals of R, and these are minimal right ideals of H. Therefore H is also completely reducible.

Conversely, assume that R is a direct sum of ideals, each of which is completely reducible as a ring. The same argument shows that R is completely reducible.

(b) Let R be completely reducible and simple, hence prime. Let eR be a minimal right ideal of R, $e^2 = e \in R$. Now R_R is its own socle, hence

$$R \cong \mathrm{Hom}_R(R,R) \cong \mathrm{Hom}_{eRe}(Re,Re),$$

by Lemma 2. $(Re)_{eRe}$ is a vector space, hence completely reducible. To verify that it is finite dimensional, it suffices to show that it is Noetherian.

Let $\{K_i \mid i \in I\}$ be a family of submodules of $(Re)_{eRe}$. Then $K_i R$ is a family of submodules of $(ReR)_R$. Since R_R is Noetherian, so is $(ReR)_R$, hence the latter family has a maximal element $K_m R$. Now suppose $K_m \subset K_i$, then $K_m R \subset K_i R$, hence $K_m R = K_i R$. Since $K_i = K_i eRe = K_i Re$, we may deduce that $K_m = K_i$. Therefore K_m is a maximal element of the former family. Thus $(Re)_{eRe}$ is indeed Noetherian.

Finally, we assume that $R = \mathrm{Hom}_D(V,V)$, where V_D is a vector space with basis $v_1, \ldots, v_n$. Let $e_{ij} \in R$ be defined by $e_{ij} v_j = v_i$, $e_{ij} v_k = 0$ for $k \neq j$, and consider $A_i = \sum_{j=1}^{n} e_{ij} D = \{r \in R \mid rV \subset v_i D\}$. Clearly A_i is a right ideal of R. Now let $0 \neq a \in A_i$, then $a = \sum_{j=1}^{n} e_{ij} d_j$, $d_j \in D$, where some $d_k \neq 0$. Then $a e_{k1} = e_{i1} d_k$, hence $e_{i1} = a e_{k1} d_k^{-1} \in aR$, and so $A_i \subset aR$. Thus A_i is irreducible.

Since clearly $R = \sum_{i,j} e_{ij} D = \sum_i A_i$, it follows that R is completely reducible. To see that R is simple, one assumes that $0 \neq r \in R$ and shows similarly that $RrR = R$. We shall omit the details.

EXERCISES

1. If the ring R is a direct sum of the irreducible right ideals $A_j (j \in J)$, show that every ideal of R is a sum of some of the RA_j.

2. If R is semiprime, show that the homogeneous components of the socle of R are precisely the ideals eR, where e is any atom of the Boolean algebra of central idempotents of R.

3. If D is a division ring and V_D has dimension n, show that $\text{Hom}_D(V,V) \cong D_n$, the ring of $n \times n$ matrices over D.

4. If a module M_R is completely reducible and equal to the homogeneous component EA, where A_R is a minimal submodule, show that $E = \text{Hom}_R(M,M)$ is isomorphic to the ring of all "column-finite" matrices over the division ring $D = \text{Hom}_R(A,A)$.

5. Use the preceding exercise to give another proof of the Wedderburn-Artin Theorem.

6. Show that R is completely reducible if and only if no maximal right ideal is large.

7. Show that the ring of all 2×2 matrices over an infinite field has an infinite number of distinct minimal right ideals.

8. If D and D' are division rings and $D_n \cong D'_{n'}$ (see Exercise 3 above), show that $D \cong D'$ and $n = n'$.

3.5 Artinian and Noetherian rings

A ring is called *right Artinian* (*Noetherian*) if the right module R_R is Artinian (Noetherian).

PROPOSITION 1. *The radical of a right Artinian ring is nilpotent.*

Proof. Among the powers of Rad R there is a smallest, say $B = (\text{Rad } R)^n$. Then $B^2 = B$. Assume that $B \neq 0$ and let A be minimal in the set of right ideals contained in B such that $AB \neq 0$. Then $aB \neq 0$ for some $a \in A$. Now $aB \subset A \subset B$, $(aB)B = aB^2 = aB \neq 0$, hence $aB = A$. Therefore $ab = a$ for some $b \in B$. Now $b \in B \subset \text{Rad } R$, hence there exists $c \in R$ such that $(1 - b)c = 1$, hence $a = a(1 - b)c = 0$. This is a contradiction, and so $B = 0$, as required.

COROLLARY 1. *In a right Artinian ring, the radical is the largest nilpotent ideal.*

Proof. Any nilpotent ideal is contained in the prime radical rad R, and this is contained in Rad R.

COROLLARY 2. *If R is right Artinian then Rad $R = $ rad R.*

We recall that a *regular* ring is a ring in which for every element a there exists an element a' such that $aa'a = a$. Putting $e = aa'$, we see that $e^2 = e$ and that $aR = eR$, hence that every principal right ideal is a direct summand. Conversely, this property implies that the ring is regular. For from $aR = eR$ we deduce that $e = aa'$ for some $a' \in R$, hence that $aa'a = ea = a$.

LEMMA (von Neumann). *In a regular ring every finitely generated right ideal is principal.*

Proof. It suffices to consider a right ideal $aR + bR$. Now $aR = eR$, where $e^2 = e$, and $bR \subset ebR + (1 - e)bR$. Therefore $aR + bR = eR + (1 - e)bR = eR + fR$, where $f^2 = f$ and $ef = 0$. Put $g = f(1 - e)$, then

$$gf = f(1 - e)f = f(f - ef) = f^2 = f,$$

$$g^2 = gf(1 - e) = f(1 - e) = g,$$

$$eg = 0 = ge.$$

Now $g \in fR$ and $f \in gR$, hence $fR = gR$. Therefore $aR + bR = eR + gR$. We claim that this is the same as $(e + g)R$. Indeed, $er + gr' = (e + g)(er + gr')$, hence $eR + gR \subset (e + g)R$, and the converse is obvious. Thus $aR + bR = (e + g)R$, as required.

PROPOSITION 2. *The following statements concerning the ring R are equivalent:*

  (1) *R is completely reducible.*
  (2) *R is right Artinian and regular.*
  (3) *R is right Artinian and semiprimitive.*
  (4) *R is right Artinian and semiprime.*
  (5) *R is right Noetherian and regular.*

Note that the word "right" in conditions (2) to (5) can be replaced by "left," since condition (1) is symmetrical.

Proof. Since every regular ring is semiprimitive (for $1 - aa'$ is a zero-divisor for every $a \neq 0$) and every semiprimitive ring is semiprime, therefore $(2) \Rightarrow (3) \Rightarrow (4)$.

Assume (1), then R is a direct sum of finitely many minimal right ideals $A_1, \ldots, A_n$. We thus have a composition series

$$A_1 \subset A_1 + A_2 \subset \cdots \subset R$$

of R_R, hence R is right Artinian and right Noetherian. Moreover, every right ideal is a direct summand, in particular every principal right ideal, hence R is regular. Thus $(1) \Rightarrow (2)$ and $(1) \Rightarrow (5)$.

Assume (4). By Proposition 1, the intersection of all maximal right ideals is 0. Since R is right Artinian, already a finite number of these have zero intersection:

$$M_1 \cap M_2 \cap \cdots \cap M_n = 0.$$

We may assume that M_i does not contain $A_i = \bigcap_{j \neq i} M_j$ (or else M_i could have been omitted in the first place). Therefore $M_i + A_i = R$.

On the other hand, $M_i \cap A_i = 0$, hence $A_i \cong R/M_i$, and this is an irreducible right R-module. Thus $A_i = e_i R$, $e_i^2 = e_i \in R$, and $M_i = (1 - e_i)R$. Let $e = \sum_{i=1}^n e_i$, then

$$e - 1 = (e_i - 1) + \sum_{j \neq i} e_j \in M_i + M_i,$$

for $j \neq i \Rightarrow e_j \in A_j \subset M_i$. Therefore $e - 1 \in \bigcap_{i=1}^n M_i = 0$. Therefore $1 = \sum_{i=1}^n e_i$, and so $R = \sum_{i=1}^n A_i$ is completely reducible. Thus (4) $\Rightarrow$ (1).

Assume (5). Since R is right Noetherian, every right ideal is finitely generated. Since R is regular, every finitely generated right ideal is principal, by the above lemma, hence a direct summand. Therefore every right ideal is a direct summand, hence R_R is completely reducible. Thus (5) $\Rightarrow$ (1).

PROPOSITION 3. *If R is right Artinian then any right R-module is Noetherian if and only if it is Artinian.*

Proof. Let $N = \text{Rad } R$, then $N^p = 0$ for some positive integer p, by Proposition 1. Now consider any Artinian right R-module A_R. This has a chain of submodules

$$A \supset AN \supset AN^2 \supset \cdots \supset AN^p = 0$$

with factor modules $F_k = AN^{k-1}/AN^k$, $k = 1, \ldots, p$. Now F_k is annihilated by N, hence may be regarded as an R/N-module. By Proposition 2, R/N is completely reducible, hence F_k is completely reducible as an R/N-module and therefore also as an R-module. Being Artinian, F_k is the direct sum of a finite number of irreducible R-modules, hence F_k is also Noetherian.

Thus

$$AN^{p-1}(= F_p) \quad \text{and} \quad AN^{p-2}/AN^{p-1}(= F_{p-1})$$

are Noetherian, hence so is AN^{p-2}. Continuing in this fashion, we see that A is Noetherian.

Interchanging the words "Artinian" and "Noetherian" in this proof we get the converse result.

COROLLARY. *Every right Artinian ring is right Noetherian.*

The ring of integers shows that the converse of this does not hold.

PROPOSITION 4. *In a right Noetherian ring the prime radical is the largest nilpotent right ideal.*

Proof. Let R be right Noetherian, N any maximal nilpotent right ideal, say $N^k = 0$. In view of the binomial theorem,

$$(N^k = 0 \quad \& \quad N'^{k'} = 0) \Rightarrow (N + N')^{k+k'} = 0.$$

Therefore N is the largest nilpotent right ideal. Being nilpotent, N is contained in rad R. Now suppose A is any right ideal such that $A^m \subset N$, m some positive integer. Then A is nilpotent, hence $A \subseteq N$. Thus R/N is semiprime, and so $N = $ rad R, by the corollary to Proposition 2 of Section 3.2.

A subset of a ring is called *nil* if every element is nilpotent. We know from Proposition 1 of Section 3.2 that the prime radical of any ring is nil.

PROPOSITION 5 (Levitzki). *In a right Noetherian ring the prime radical is the largest nil left ideal.*

Proof (Utumi). Let R be right Noetherian, N any nil left ideal in R. We claim that $N \subset$ rad R.

First let us assume that R is semiprime; we shall show that $N = 0$. Otherwise pick $n \in N$, $n \neq 0$, so that $n^{\mathrm{r}} = \{s \in R \mid ns = 0\}$ is maximal. Consider any $x \in R$ such that $xn \neq 0$, and let $k = k(x)$ be the smallest positive integer for which $(xn)^k = 0$. Then $k > 1$ and $(xn)^{k-1} \neq 0$. Now any right annihilator of n also annihilates $(xn)^{k-1}$, hence $n^{\mathrm{r}} = ((xn)^{k-1})^{\mathrm{r}}$, by maximality of n^{r}. Therefore $xn \in n^{\mathrm{r}}$, that is $nxn = 0$. Thus $nRn = 0$, and so $n = 0$, since R is semiprime.

Next consider the general situation where R is no longer assumed to be semiprime. The canonical image of N in the right Noetherian ring $R/$rad R is zero by the above, hence $N \subset$ rad R, as was to be proved.

COROLLARY. *In a right Noetherian ring every nil ideal is nilpotent.*

The following important result is known as the *Hilbert Basis Theorem*.

PROPOSITION 6. *Let $R[x]$ be the ring obtained from R by adjoining an indeterminate x which commutes with all elements of R. Then $R[x]$ is right Noetherian if R is.*

Proof. If K is any right ideal of $R[x]$, let K_i be the set of all r in R for which there exists a polynomial with leading term rx^i in K. Then K_i is a right ideal of R and $K_i \subset K_{i+1}$. Since R is right Noetherian, there exists an n such that $K_n = K_{n+1} = \cdots$. Let $K_i = \sum_{j=1}^{m(i)} b_{ij}R$; we claim that the polynomials $p_{ij}(x)$ corresponding to $b_{ij}(i \leq n)$ form a basis of K.

Suppose not every polynomial in K can be expressed as a linear combination of the $p_{ij}(x)$, then among these "bad" polynomials we can pick one with minimal degree m, say $g(x) = c\, x^m + \cdots$. First assume $m \leq n$. Since $c \in K_m$, we may write $c = \sum_j b_{mj} c_{mj}$. Now

$$g(x) - \sum_j p_{mj}(x)\, c_{mj}$$

is in K and has degree less than m (if any), and this leads to a contradiction. Finally, when $m > n$, we have $c \in K_n$ and proceed similarly, using n in place of m.

COROLLARY. *Let* $R[x_1, x_2, \ldots, x_n]$ *be the ring obtained from R by adjoining n indeterminates* x_i *which commute with all elements of R and with each other. Then this is right Noetherian if R is.*

EXERCISES

1. Show that every factor ring of a right Noetherian (Artinian) ring is right Noetherian (Artinian).

2. Show that a finite direct product of right Noetherian (Artinian) rings is right Noetherian (Artinian).

3. If R contains a division ring D as a subring so that R_D is finite dimensional, show that R is right Artinian.

4. If R is right Noetherian (Artinian) then every finitely generated right R-module is right Noetherian (Artinian).

5. Show that a right Artinian ring without zero-divisors is a division ring.

6. If R is isomorphic to the ring A_n of all $n \times n$ matrices over the ring A, show that R contains elements $e_{ij}(i, j = 1, \ldots, n)$ such that $e_{ij}e_{kl} = e_{il}$ if $j = k$, $= 0$ otherwise. Show that, without loss in generality, one may assume that $ae_{ij} = e_{ij}a$ for all $a \in A$. Verify that $e_{11}Re_{11} \cong A$.

7. If K is any right ideal of $R = A_n = \sum_{i,j} e_{ij}A$, show that $e_{11}K$ is a submodule of the free A-module $e_{11}R = \sum_j e_{ij}A$. If L is any A-submodule of $e_{11}R$, show that $\sum_i e_{i1}L$ is a right ideal of R. Verify that these correspondences yield a lattice isomorphism between the lattice of right ideals of R and the lattice of A-submodules of $e_{11}R$.

8. Show that A_n is right Noetherian (Artinian) if and only if A is right Noetherian (Artinian). (*Hint:* Use Exercises 2 and 7.)

9. Prove that all (two-sided) ideals of A_n have the form $K_n = \sum_{i,j} e_{ij}K$, where K is an ideal of A. Show that $K \to K_n$ is a lattice isomorphism which also preserves multiplication of ideals. Hence show that K_n is prime if and only if K is prime, and deduce that rad $(A_n) =$ (rad $A)_n$.

10. Show that the ideal K_n of A_n is primitive if and only if K is primitive in A, and deduce that Rad $(A_n) = ($Rad $A)_n$. (*Hint:* Use Exercise 8 of Section 3.1. Also, if K is primitive, it is the largest two-sided ideal contained in some maximal right ideal M of A. Then $M' = \sum_i e_{i1}M + \sum_i e_{i2}A + \cdots + \sum_i e_{in}A$ is a maximal right ideal of A_n, in view of Exercise 7 above, and K_n is the largest two-sided ideal contained in M'.)

11 (Small). Show that the ring of all 2 × 2 matrices

$$\begin{pmatrix} a & b \\ 0 & c \end{pmatrix}$$

where a is an integer and b and c are rationals is right Noetherian but not left Noetherian.

12 (Small). Show that the ring of all 2 × 2 matrices

$$\begin{pmatrix} a & b \\ 0 & c \end{pmatrix}$$

where a is rational and b and c are reals is right Artinian but not left Artinian.

3.6 On lifting idempotents

A fundamental tool in the classical theory of nonsemiprimitive Artinian rings is the technique of lifting idempotents.

In what follows, N will be an ideal of R, usually assumed to be contained in the radical of R. We say that idempotents modulo N can be *lifted* provided for every element u of R such that $u^2 - u \in N$ there exists an element $e^2 = e \in R$ such that $e - u \in N$. In other words, if u is an idempotent modulo N then there should exist an idempotent of R to which it is congruent modulo N.

The following result is classical. We recall that an ideal is called *nil* if every element is nilpotent.

PROPOSITION 1. *Let N be a nil ideal of R. Then idempotents modulo N can be lifted.*

Proof. Let $u^2 - u \in N$. Put $e = u + x(1 - 2u)$, where x is an element of R, as yet to be determined, which is assumed to commute with u. After a little computation we see that the equation $e^2 = e$ is equivalent to the equation

$$(x^2 - x)(1 + 4n) + n = 0,$$

where $n = u^2 - u \in N$. This has a formal solution

$$x = \tfrac{1}{2}(1 - (1 + 4n)^{-1/2})$$

$$= \frac{1}{2}\left(2n - \binom{4}{2}n^2 + \binom{6}{3}n^3 - \cdots\right).$$

Since n is nilpotent, this formula actually defines x as a polynomial expression in n, hence in u, with integer coefficients. It follows that x

does commute with u as anticipated. Therefore $e = u + x(1 - 2u)$ is a solution of the equation $e^2 = e$. Moreover, $x \in nR \subset N$, and so $e - u \in N$ as required.

COROLLARY.   *In any ring idempotents modulo the prime radical can be lifted.*

Usually one wants to lift not only one idempotent but a whole set of mutually orthogonal idempotents. To this purpose we find the following very useful.

LEMMA 1.   *Assume that idempotents can be lifted modulo $N \subset \text{Rad } R$. If g is a given idempotent of R, and u is an idempotent modulo N such that ug and $gu \in N$, then there exists an idempotent e of R such that $e - u \in N$ and $eg = ge = 0$.*

Proof.   Let $u^2 - u \in N, g^2 = g, ug$ and $gu \in N$. By assumption, we may lift u to $f = f^2$, thus $f - u \in N$. It follows that fg and $gf \in N$. In particular, $1 - fg$ has an inverse in R, and we may form

$$f' = (1 - fg)^{-1}f(1 - fg).$$

Clearly, this is an idempotent and $f'g = 0$. Multiplying by $1 - fg$ on the left, we see that $f' - f \in N$.

Now put $e = f' - gf' = (1 - g)f'$. Then clearly $ge = 0 = eg$, and $e \equiv (1 - g)f \equiv f \equiv u$ modulo N. Moreover, $e^2 = (1 - g)f'(1 - g)f' = (1 - g)f' = e$.

We recall that a set of idempotents is said to be *orthogonal* if the product of any two of them is zero.

PROPOSITION 2.   *Assume that idempotents can be lifted modulo $N \subset \text{Rad } R$. Then any finite or countable orthogonal set of nonzero idempotents modulo N can be lifted to an orthogonal set of nonzero idempotents of R.*

In other words, if $u_1, u_2, \ldots$ are elements of R such that $u_i \notin N$ and $u_i u_j - \delta_{ij} u_j \in N$, then we can find $e_1, e_2, \ldots$, such that $e_i \neq 0, e_i - u_i \in N$ and $e_i e_j = \delta_{ij} e_j$. Here

$$\delta_{ij} = \begin{cases} 1 & \text{if } i = j \\ 0 & \text{if } i \neq j \end{cases}$$

as usual.

Proof.   Suppose we have already lifted $u_1, u_2, \ldots, u_{k-1}$ to $e_1, e_2, \ldots, e_{k-1}$. Put $g = e_1 + \cdots + e_{k-1}$, then surely $u_k g$ and $gu_k \in N$. Hence, by the lemma, we can find an idempotent $e_k \equiv u_k$ modulo N which is orthogonal to g, hence to $e_1, e_2, \ldots, e_{k-1}$. Finally $e_k \neq 0$, since $u_k \notin N$.

Following Bass, we call the ring R *semiperfect* if idempotents modulo Rad R can be lifted and if $R/\text{Rad } R$ is completely reducible.

PROPOSITION 3.   *Any right Artinian ring is semiperfect.*

Remark. By symmetry, the same is true for any left Artinian ring.

Proof. Let R be right Artinian, then so is $R/\mathrm{Rad}\, R$ (see 3.5, Exercise 1). Being semiprimitive, it is therefore completely reducible (see Section 3.5, Proposition 2). Moreover idempotents modulo Rad R can be lifted, by Proposition 1, since the radical is nil (see Section 3.5, Proposition 1). A nonzero idempotent e of R is called *primitive* if it cannot be written as the sum of two orthogonal nonzero idempotents. This is easily seen to be equivalent to the fact that the right module eR is indecomposable, and by symmetry also that Re is indecomposable. We note that then $eRe \cong \mathrm{Hom}_R(eR, eR)$ is a ring whose only nonzero idempotent is e. For, if ere is idempotent for some $r \in R$, then so is $e - ere$, and, the latter being orthogonal to the former, we may conclude from the primitivity of e that ere is either 0 or e.

PROPOSITION 4.   *Any semiperfect ring contains a finite orthogonal set of primitive idempotents whose sum is 1.*

Proof. Assume for a moment that R is right Noetherian. Let e_1, $e_2, \ldots$, be an orthogonal set of nonzero idempotents of R. Among the right ideals e_1R, $e_1R + e_2R$, $\ldots$, there must be a maximal one, hence one readily sees that the set in question is finite. Thus any right Noetherian ring has a maximal orthogonal set of primitive idempotents.

We apply this observation to the ring R/N, where $N = \mathrm{Rad}\, R$. Let u_1, u_2, $\ldots$, u_n be a maximal orthogonal set of primitive idempotents modulo N. By Proposition 2, these can be lifted to an orthogonal set of nonzero idempotents e_1, e_2, $\ldots$, e_n of R. We claim that this set is again maximal and that the e_i are also primitive.

Indeed, assume that e is an idempotent orthogonal to all e_i, then it is orthogonal modulo N to all u_i. By maximality of the latter set, either $e \in N = \mathrm{Rad}\, R$ or $e - e_j \in N$ for some j. In the first case $1 - e$ has an inverse, hence from $e(1 - e) = 0$ we deduce that $e = 0$. In the second case we show similarly that $e = e_j$. Therefore the e_i form a maximal set.

Next, assume that a given e_i can be written as $e + f$, where e and f are orthogonal idempotents. Since u_i is primitive modulo Rad R, it follows that e or $f \in N$, hence again that e or $f = 0$. Thus each e_i is primitive.

Put

$$S = e_1R + e_2R + \cdots + e_nR = eR,$$

where $e = e_1 + e_2 + \cdots + e_n$ is an idempotent. It follows that $(1 - e)R$ contains no primitive idempotents, hence neither does $(1 - e)R/N$. Since R/N is completely reducible, it readily follows that $(1 - e)R/N = 0$, hence $1 - e \in N$, hence $e = 1$, and this completes the proof.

How unique are the primitive idempotents of Proposition 4? Surely, if $e_1, \ldots, e_n$ is an orthogonal set whose sum is 1, then so is $u^{-1}e_1u, \ldots, u^{-1}e_nu$, for any unit u. As we shall see presently, there are no other sets of primitive idempotents whose sum is 1.

EXERCISES

1. Assume that idempotents can be lifted modulo $N \subset \operatorname{Rad} R$. If $uu'u - u \in N$, show that there exist $v \equiv u$ and $v' \equiv u'$ modulo N such that $vv'v = v$.

2. Show that the idempotent $e \neq 0$ of R is primitive if and only if eRe contains no idempotents other than 0 and e.

3. Assume that idempotents can be lifted modulo $N \subset \operatorname{Rad} R$. Show that any primitive idempotent of R remains primitive modulo N.

4. If e is a primitive idempotent in a regular ring, show that eRe is a division ring.

3.7 Local and semiperfect rings

PROPOSITION 1. *Let R be a ring in which $0 \neq 1$. The following conditions are equivalent:*
  (1) *$R/\operatorname{Rad} R$ is a division ring.*
  (2) *R has exactly one maximal right ideal.*
  (3) *All nonunits of R are contained in a proper ideal.*
  (4) *The nonunits of R form a proper ideal.*
  (5) *For every element r of R, either r or $1 - r$ is a unit.*
  (6) *For every element r of R, either r or $1 - r$ is right invertible.*
  Remark.   Of course "right" may be replaced by "left" in (2) and (6).

If R satisfies one of these equivalent conditions, we shall call it a *local* ring. The term "completely primary" also appears in the literature, but "local" agrees with our usage in the commutative case. The cyclical proof of the equivalence of conditions (1) to (6) will be left as an exercise.

If e is an idempotent of the ring R, then eRe is also a ring with unity e.

LEMMA 1. *If e is an idempotent of R and $N = \operatorname{Rad} R$, then $\operatorname{Rad}(eRe) = eRe \cap N = eNe$.*

  Proof.   Assume $r = ere \in \operatorname{Rad}(eRe)$ and $x \in R$. Then $e - rxe$ has an inverse $e - y$ in eRe, where $y = eye$, thus $(e - rxe)(e - y) = e$. One easily computes that

$$(1 - rx)(1 - y) = 1 - rx(1 - e).$$

Multiplying this by $1 + rx(1 - e)$ on the right, one obtains 1, hence $1 - rx$ has a right inverse in R. Thus Rad $(eRe) \subseteq eRe \cap N$.

Next, assume that $r \in eRe \cap N$, then $r = ere \in eNe$. Thus $eRe \cap N \subseteq eNe$.

Finally, assume $r \in eNe \subseteq N$, and let $x = exe \in eRe$. Then $1 - rx$ has a right inverse $1 - y$ in R, whence

$$(e - rx)(e - eye) = e(1 - rx)(1 - y)e = e.$$

Thus $eNe \subseteq$ Rad (eRe), and our cyclical proof is complete.

PROPOSITION 2.   *If R is semiperfect and e is a primitive idempotent of R, then eRe is local.*

Proof.   Again let $N =$ Rad R. Consider any element $u \in eRe$, there exists $u' \in R$ such that $uu'u \equiv u$ modulo N, since R/N is a regular ring. As we can always replace u' by $eu'e$ in this, we may as well assume that $u' \in eRe$ also.

Now uu' is an idempotent modulo N orthogonal to $1 - e$. By Lemma 1 of the last section, we can lift it to an idempotent f of R orthogonal to $1 - e$. Thus $f \in eRe$, and f and $e - f$ are two orthogonal idempotents. Since e is primitive, one of them must be 0.

Assume that $u \notin N$. Since $fu \equiv uu'u \equiv u$ modulo N, it follows that $f \neq 0$. Therefore $f = e$, and so $uu' \equiv e$ modulo N. Similarly $u'u \equiv e$ modulo N, hence u is a unit of eRe modulo $N \cap eRe =$ Rad (eRe). Thus eRe is a local ring.

COROLLARY 1.   *A ring is local if and only if it is semiperfect and 1 is a primitive idempotent.*

It will be convenient to call the idempotent e itself *local* if eRe is a local ring. (Jacobson uses "completely primitive.") Clearly, every local idempotent is primitive; but the converse is not true. (For example, if R is the ring of integers, then 1 is a primitive idempotent which is not local.) In view of Proposition 4 of the last section we may assert the following.

COROLLARY 2.   *Any semiperfect ring contains a finite orthogonal set of local idempotents whose sum is 1.*

Before we consider the question to what extent these local idempotents are unique, we require two lemmas.

LEMMA 2.   *Let e be a local idempotent of the ring R and let π be the canonical epimorphism $R \rightarrow R/$Rad R. Then πeR is a minimal right ideal of πR.*

Proof.   Consider the right ideal $\pi(1 - e)R$ in πR. This is clearly a proper right ideal (otherwise $e \in$ Rad R, hence $e = 0$), therefore it will be contained in a maximal right ideal πM of πR. The result will follow if we show that $\pi M \cap \pi e R = 0$.

Indeed, suppose this is not so; then $(\pi M \cap \pi e R)^2 \neq 0$, since πR is semiprime. Therefore we can find $r \in R$ such that $\pi e r \in \pi M$ and $\pi e r e \neq 0$. Now $\pi e R e$ is a division ring, hence it contains an element πx such that $\pi e r e x = \pi e$. Therefore $\pi e \in \pi M$, and we obtain the contradiction that $\pi 1 = \pi e + \pi (1 - e) \in \pi M$. This completes the proof.

LEMMA 3.   *Let $u'u - e$ and $uu' - f \in \text{Rad } R$, where e and f are idempotents of R. Then there exist elements v and v' of R such that $v'v = e$ and $vv' = f$.*

   Proof.   Put $N = \text{Rad } R$. Since

$$fu \equiv uu'u \equiv ue \text{ modulo } N$$

and

$$eu' \equiv u'uu' \equiv u'f \text{ modulo } N,$$

we have

$$eu'fu \equiv u'fu \equiv u'ue \equiv e^2 \equiv e \text{ modulo } N.$$

Put

$$x = e - eu'fu \in N,$$

then

$$eu'fu = e(1 - x)$$

and $1 - x$ has an inverse $1 - y$. Since $xy = x + y$, we see that also $y \in N$. Put

$$v = fu(1 - y), \qquad v' = eu'f,$$

then

$$v'v = eu'fu(1 - y) = e(1 - x)(1 - y) = e,$$

hence

$$(vv')^2 = vev' = vv',$$

and so

$$(f - vv')^2 = f - fvv' - vv'f + vv' = f - vv'.$$

But

$$vv' = fu(1 - y)eu'f \equiv fueu'f \equiv fuu'f \equiv f$$

modulo N, hence $f - vv' \in N$. Since the radical contains no nonzero idempotents, it follows that $vv' = f$, and the proof is complete.

PROPOSITION 3.   *In any ring R, let*

$$\sum_{i=1}^{m} e_i = 1 = \sum_{j=1}^{n} f_j$$

be two representations of 1 as the sum of finite orthogonal sets of local idempotents. Then $m = n$, and there exists a unit v of R and a permutation p of the numbers 1 to m so that

$$ve_i = f_{p(i)}v \qquad (i = 1, 2, \ldots, m).$$

Proof. Let $\pi : R \to R/\mathrm{Rad}\; R$ be the canonical epimorphism, then

$$\sum_{i=1}^{m} \pi e_i R = \pi R = \sum_{j=1}^{n} \pi f_j R$$

as direct sums. By Lemma 2, the summands are irreducible right πR-modules. Applying the Jordan-Hölder Theorem (Corollary to Section 1.4, Proposition 4), we have $m = n$ and $\pi e_i R \cong \pi f_{p(i)} R$, for a suitable permutation p. Hence there exist elements πu_i and $\pi u_i'$ of πR such that $\pi e_i = \pi u_i' \pi u_i = \pi u_i' u_i$ and $\pi f_{p(i)} = \pi u_i u_i'$. (See Section 3.4, Proposition 3.) By Lemma 3, there exist elements v_i and v_i' of R such that $v_i' v_i = e_i$ and $v_i v_i' = f_{p(i)}$. It is easily verified that also

$$v_i' f_{p(i)} v_i = e_i, \qquad v_i e_i v_i' = f_{p(i)}.$$

Putting

$$v = \sum_{i=1}^{m} f_{p(i)} v_i e_i, \quad v' = \sum_{j=1}^{m} e_j v_j' f_{p(j)},$$

one readily computes $vv' = 1 = v'v$ and

$$v e_j = f_{p(j)} v_j e_j = f_{p(j)} v,$$

and the proof is complete.

COROLLARY (Azumaya).   *Let the S-module A_S be expressed in two different ways as a direct sum of submodules whose rings of endomorphisms are local,*

$$\sum_{i=1}^{m} A_i = A = \sum_{j=1}^{n} B_j.$$

Then $m = n$, and there exists a permutation p of the numbers 1 to m such that

$$A_i \cong B_{p(i)} \qquad (i = 1, 2, \ldots, m).$$

Proof. Let $R = \mathrm{Hom}_S(A,A)$, $e_i A = A_i$, $f_j A = B_j$. Then

$$\mathrm{Hom}_S(A_i, A_i) \cong e_i R e_i,$$

similar to Section 3.4, Lemma 1, and so on.

The reader will have no difficulty in convincing himself that the Krull-Schmidt Theorem (Section 1.4, Proposition 10) for modules is a special case of the above, in view of Fitting's Lemma (Section 1.4, Proposition 9). Thus it turns out that the Krull-Schmidt Theorem for modules is a consequence of the Jordan-Hölder Theorem.

We now return to the structure of semiperfect rings. In general, this is a little messy to describe, as is even the structure of right Artinian rings. However, the situation becomes quite neat when one assumes that $R/\mathrm{Rad}\; R$ is simple or prime. (These two properties are equivalent for completely reducible rings.)

PROPOSITION 4.   *Let R be semiperfect and $R/\mathrm{Rad}\ R$ prime. Then R is isomorphic to the ring of all endomorphisms of a finitely generated free S-module, where S is a local ring.*

Remark.   We have $R \cong \mathrm{Hom}_S(V, V)$, where V_S is isomorphic to a direct sum of n copies of S_S. Then clearly R is isomorphic to the ring of all $n \times n$ matrices with coefficients in S.

Proof.   Let $e_1, e_2, \ldots, e_n$ be an orthogonal set of local idempotents of R whose sum is 1. Let $\pi : R \to R/\mathrm{Rad}\ R$ canonically, then the $\pi e_i R$ are irreducible right πR-modules, by Lemma 2. Therefore $\pi R = \sum_{i=1}^n \pi e_i R$ coincides with its own socle. Let e be one of the e_i. Since the homogeneous component πReR is a direct summand of πR, and since πR is prime, therefore $\pi R = \pi ReR$.

Now by Section 3.3, Lemma 4, this is a direct sum of modules isomorphic to πeR. By the Jordan-Hölder Theorem, each $\pi e_i R \cong \pi eR$. Hence there exist elements u_i and v_i such that $\pi v_i \pi u_i = \pi e$ and $\pi u_i \pi v_i = \pi e_i$. (See Section 3.4, Proposition 3.) In view of Lemma 3 of the present section, we may as well assume that $v_i u_i = e$ and $u_i v_i = e_i$. By an argument that should now be familiar (see the proof of Section 3.4, Lemma 2) we see that $R \cong \mathrm{Hom}\ (R_R, R_R) \cong \mathrm{Hom}_{eRe}(Re, Re)$.

Because of the orthogonality of the e_i, $Re = \sum_{i=1}^n e_i Re$ is a direct sum of right eRe-modules. Moreover, $e_i re \to v_i e_i re = v_i u_i v_i re = ev_i re$ is easily seen to be an eRe-isomorphism between $e_i Re$ and eRe. Hence Re is a free eRe-module in n generators.

EXERCISES

1. Write out a cyclical proof of Proposition 1.
2. Write out a complete proof of the Corollary to Proposition 3.
3. Deduce the Krull-Schmidt Theorem from Azumaya's Theorem.
4. Let $N \subset \mathrm{Rad}\ R$ and $\pi : R \to R/N$ canonically. If e and f are idempotents of R, show that $eR \cong fR$ as R-modules if and only if $\pi eR \cong \pi fR$ as πR-modules.

Injectivity and Related Concepts

4.1 Projective modules

We recall that the (external) direct sum $A = \sum_{i \in I}^{*} A_i$ of a family of modules consists of all $a \in \prod_{i \in I} A_i$ such that $a(i) = 0$ for all but a finite number of i. The canonical mapping $\kappa_i : A_i \to A$ was defined by

$$(\kappa_i a_i)(j) = \begin{cases} a_i & \text{if } j = i \\ 0 & \text{if } j \neq i, \end{cases}$$

whence

$$\sum_{i \in I} \kappa_i a(i) = a.$$

PROPOSITION 1. *If A is the direct sum of a family of modules $\{A_i \mid i \in I\}$ with canonical mappings $\kappa_i : A_i \to A$ then, for every module B and for every family of homomorphisms $\phi_i : A_i \to B$, there exists a unique homomorphism $\phi : A \to B$ such that $\phi \circ \kappa_i = \phi_i$. Moreover, this property characterizes the direct sum up to isomorphism.*

The proposition is illustrated by the "commutative" diagram:

The dotted arrow represents the mapping whose existence is asserted.
  Proof. Define $\phi : A \to B$ by

$$\phi a = \sum_{i \in I} \phi_i a(i).$$

It is clear that ϕ is a homomorphism and that

$$(\phi \circ \kappa_j)a_j = \phi(\kappa_j a_j) = \sum_{i \in I} \phi_i((\kappa_j a_j)(i)) = \phi_j a_j.$$

Thus $\phi \circ \kappa_j = \phi_j$. If also $\psi \circ \kappa_j = \phi_j$, then

$$\psi a = \sum_{i \in I} \psi(\kappa_i a(i)) = \sum_{i \in I} \phi_i a(i) = \phi a,$$

hence $\psi = \phi$.

Conversely, assume that A' and $\kappa_i' : A_i \to A'$ satisfy the abstract conditions of Proposition 1. Taking $\phi_i = \kappa_i'$ and $B = A'$, we see that there exists $\kappa' : A \to A'$ such that $\kappa' \circ \kappa_i = \kappa_i'$. Similarly there exists $\kappa : A' \to A$ such that $\kappa \circ \kappa_i' = \kappa_i$. Therefore

$$\kappa \circ \kappa' \circ \kappa_i = \kappa \circ \kappa_i' = \kappa_i = 1_A \circ \kappa_i,$$

where 1_A is the identity mapping of A. By the uniqueness property, $\kappa \circ \kappa' = 1_A$. Similarly $\kappa' \circ \kappa = 1_{A'}$. Therefore κ is an isomorphism.

COROLLARY. *If A is isomorphic to the direct sum of modules A_i with canonical mappings $\kappa_i : A_i \to A$, then there exist mappings $\pi_i : A \to A_i$ (also called canonical) such that $\pi_i \circ \kappa_i = 1$ and $\pi_i \circ \kappa_j = 0$ when $i \neq j$.*

Incidentally, this implies that κ_i is mono and π_i is epi.

Proof. For fixed i consider the mapping $\delta_{ij} : A_j \to A_i$, where $\delta_{ij} = 1$ when $i = j$ and $\delta_{ij} = 0$ when $i \neq j$. Then there exists $\pi_i : A \to A_i$ such that, for all j, $\pi_i \circ \kappa_j = \delta_{ij}$. (Take $\phi_j = \delta_{ij}$ and $\phi = \pi_i$.)

A module M_R is called *free* if it has a *basis* $\{m_i \mid i \in I\}$, $m_i \in M$, such that every element $m \in M$ can be written uniquely in the form

$$m = \sum_{i \in I} m_i r_i$$

where $r_i \in R$ and all but a finite number of the r_i are 0. This implies that $\sum_{i \in I} m_i r_i = 0$ only when all $r_i = 0$. In particular, $m_i r = 0 \Rightarrow r = 0$, hence $m_i R \cong R$ as a right R-module. Moreover $M = \sum_{i \in I} m_i R$ is a direct sum, hence we have proved the first part of the following:

LEMMA.   *M_R is free if and only if it is isomorphic to a direct sum of copies of R_R.*

The converse proof is straightforward and will be omitted.

One of the most interesting facts about a free module M is that it is *projective* in the following sense: Let π be an epimorphism of some module B onto some module A, then any homomorphism $\phi : M \to A$ can be "lifted" to a homomorphism $\psi : M \to B$ such that $\pi \circ \psi = \phi$. This property is illustrated by the diagram:

PROPOSITION 2.   *Every free module is projective.*

Proof.   Let M_R be free with basis $\{m_i \mid i \in I\}$, and let $\phi \in \mathrm{Hom}_R(M,A)$. Also let $\pi \in \mathrm{Hom}_R(B,A)$ be epi, then for any $i \in I$ there exists $b_i \in B$ such that

$$\phi m_i = \pi b_i.$$

For any $m = \sum_{i \in I} m_i r_i$ we now define

$$\psi m = \sum_{i \in I} b_i r_i.$$

(Note that all but a finite number of $r_i = 0$.) To verify that ψ is single-valued, we assume that $m = 0$ and deduce that all $r_i = 0$, hence that $\sum_{i \in I} b_i r_i = 0$. It is readily seen that $\psi \in \mathrm{Hom}_R(M,B)$.

COROLLARY.   *R_R is projective.*

Proposition 2 could also have been proved by first showing the corollary and then using the preceding lemma together with the next result:

PROPOSITION 3.   *If M is the direct sum of a family of modules $\{M_i \mid i \in I\}$, then M is projective if and only if each M_i is projective.*

Proof.   Assume all M_i projective.   Let $\phi \in \mathrm{Hom}_R(M,A)$ and let $\pi \in \mathrm{Hom}_R(B,A)$ be epi. Then $\phi \circ \kappa_i : M_i \to A$ can be lifted to $\psi_i : M_i \to B$, such that $\pi \circ \psi_i = \phi \circ \kappa_i$. ($\kappa_i$ is the canonical mapping of M_i into M.) Now, by Proposition 1, there exists a unique ψ such that $\psi \circ \kappa_i = \psi_i$ for all $i \in I$. We shall not use the uniqueness of ψ, but that of ϕ such that

$\phi \circ \kappa_i = \pi \circ \psi_i$ for all $i \in I$. Since $\pi \circ \psi \circ \kappa_i = \pi \circ \psi_i$, we may deduce that $\pi \circ \psi = \phi$. Thus M is projective.

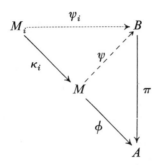

Conversely, assume M projective, and let $\phi_i : M_i \to A$ and $\pi_i : M \to M_i$ canonically. Then $\phi_i \circ \pi_i : M \to A$ can be lifted to $\psi : M \to B$ such that $\pi \circ \psi = \phi_i \circ \pi_i$. But $\pi_i \circ \kappa_i = 1$, hence $\pi \circ \psi \circ \kappa_i = \phi_i$, and so ϕ_i has been lifted to $\psi \circ \kappa_i$. Therefore M_i is projective.

PROPOSITION 4.   *Every module is isomorphic to a factor of a free module.*

Proof.   Let M_R be any right R-module. We may write $M = \sum_{i \in I} m_i R$; for example, the m_i may be all the elements of M. Let R^i_R be a copy of R_R, then we have a mapping $\phi_i : R^i \to M$ defined by $\phi_i r = m_i r$, hence a mapping $\phi : \sum^*_{i \in I} R^i \to M$ such that $\phi \circ \kappa_i = \phi_i$, where κ_i is the canonical mapping of R^i into the direct sum. The image of ϕ contains all $m_i R$, hence it contains $M = \sum_{i \in I} m_i R$. Thus ϕ is an epimorphism.

COROLLARY.   *Every module is isomorphic to a factor module of a projective module.*

We shall call an epimorphism $\pi : B \to M$ *direct* if there exists a homomorphism $\kappa : M \to B$ such that $\pi \circ \kappa = 1$. Note that κ is then a monomorphism. The reason for this terminology is the fact that $\kappa \circ \pi$ is then an idempotent endomorphism of B, whose image is isomorphic to $\pi B = M$. Thus M is isomorphic to a direct summand of B. (See Section 1.3.)

PROPOSITION 5.   *M is projective if and only if every epimorphism $\pi : B \to M$ is direct.*

This proposition is sometimes stated loosely thus: M is projective if and only if it is a direct summand of every module of which it is a factor module.

Proof.   Assume M projective, $\pi : B \to M$ an epimorphism. The identity mapping of M into M may be lifted to a mapping $\kappa : M \to B$, such that $\pi \circ \kappa = 1$.

Conversely, assume that every epimorphism $\pi : B \to M$ is direct. In view of the last corollary, we may take B projective, hence M is a direct summand of a projective module, hence M is projective, by Proposition 3.

COROLLARY. *M is projective if and only if it is isomorphic to a direct summand of a free module.*

Which rings R have the property that all R-modules are projective?

PROPOSITION 6. *Every R-module is projective if and only if R is completely reducible.*

Proof. Assume that every R-module is projective, then so is R/K for any right ideal K of R. By Proposition 5, the canonical epimorphism $\pi : R \to R/K$ is direct, in fact we have $\kappa : R/K \to R$ such that $\pi \circ \kappa = 1$. As has already been remarked, $\kappa \circ \pi$ is an idempotent endomorphism of R, whose image is isomorphic to $\pi R = R/K$. Its kernel is clearly $\pi^{-1}0 = K$, hence K_R is also a direct summand of R_R, in fact the complementary summand to $\kappa(\pi R)$. Thus every right ideal is a direct summand, hence R_R is completely reducible.

Conversely, assume that R is completely reducible. Let M be any right R-module and assume $\pi \in \mathrm{Hom}_R(B,M)$ is epi. Let $K = \pi^{-1}0$. Now B is completely reducible, hence B has a submodule K' such that $K + K' = B$ and $K \cap K' = 0$. Thus $M \cong B/K \cong K'$, a direct summand of B. Since we may assume that B is projective (even free), it follows that M is projective.

We are now ready to consider an example of a module which is projective but not free.

Example. Consider the ring R of all 2×2 matrices over a field F, say the field of reals. The matrices of the form

$$\begin{pmatrix} \alpha & \beta \\ 0 & 0 \end{pmatrix}$$

with $\alpha, \beta \in F$ form a right ideal in R, hence a right module M_R. By Proposition 6, M_R is projective. M has dimension 2 when regarded as a vector space over F. On the other hand, every free R-module, when regarded as a vector space over F, has a dimension which is a multiple of 4, the dimension of R_F. Therefore M_R is not free.

To get another kind of example, let us take $R = Z$, the ring of integers. The Z-modules are just Abelian groups. By the Corollary to Proposition 5, an Abelian group will be projective if and only if it is a direct summand of a free Abelian group. We shall see presently that any subgroup of a free Abelian group is free. It follows that an Abelian group is free if and only if it is projective.

PROPOSITION 7. *Let* $M = \sum_{i \in I} M_i$ *be a direct sum of submodules* M_i. *Assume that not only* M_i *but all submodules of each* M_i *are projective. Then any submodule N of M is isomorphic to a direct sum* $\sum_{i \in I} N_i$, *where* $N_i \subset M_i$, *for every* $i \in I$.

Note that we do not assert that N is equal to $\sum_{i \in I} N_i$.

Proof. We may as well take I to be the set of all ordinal numbers $< r$. For any ordinal $k \leq r$ put $M^k = \sum_{i < k} M_i$. The canonical mapping of $M^{k+1} = M^k + M_k$ onto M_k sends $N \cap M^{k+1}$ onto some submodule N_k of M_k. Now this submodule is assumed to be projective, hence it is isomorphic to a direct summand of $N \cap M^{k+1}$, in fact

$$N \cap M^{k+1} = (N \cap M^k) + N_k',$$

where $N \cap M^k \cap N_k' = 0$ and $N_k' \cong N_k$. We shall prove by transfinite induction that for all $i \leq r$

$$N \cap M^i = \sum_{j < i} N_j'$$

as a direct sum of submodules. This is trivially so for the first ordinal $i = 0$ and holds for $i = k + 1$ if it holds for $i = k$ by the above. Now let k be any limit ordinal and assume the result for all $i < k$, then

$$N \cap M^k = N \cap \bigcup_{i < k} M^i = \bigcup_{i < k} (N \cap M^i) = \bigcup_{i < k} \sum_{j < i} N_j' = \sum_{j < k} N_j'.$$

It is easily seen that the sum on the right-hand side is still direct. Our statement therefore holds for all $i \leq r$, in particular for $i = r$ as required.

COROLLARY. *If R is a commutative integral domain in which all ideals are principal then every submodule of a free R-module is free.*

Proof. A free module M is a direct sum of submodules $M_i \cong R_R$. Now any nonzero ideal of R is isomorphic to R as a right R-module. Hence all nonzero $N_i \cong R_R$, and so N is also free.

PROPOSITION 8. *Let* $M = \sum_{i \in I} M_i$ *be a direct sum of submodules* M_i. *Assume that every finitely generated submodule of each* M_i *is projective. Then any finitely generated submodule N of M is isomorphic to a direct sum* $\sum_{i \in F} N_i$, *where F is a finite subset of I and* $N_i \subset M_i$, *for every* $i \in F$.

Proof. Since N is finitely generated, it is already contained in some $\sum_{i \in F} M_i$, where F is a finite subset of I. To simplify the notation, let $M^n = \sum_{i=1}^n M_i$, N a finitely generated submodule of M^n. We shall prove by induction on n that

$$N = \sum_{i=1}^n N_i, \qquad N_i \subset M_i.$$

The result holds trivially for $n = 1$. Assume it for $n - 1$. The canonical mapping of $M^n = M^{n-1} + M_n$ onto M_n sends N onto a finitely generated submodule N_n of M_n. By assumption, N_n is projective, hence isomorphic to a direct summand $N_n{}'$ of N, in fact

$$N = (N \cap M^{n-1}) + N_n{}', \qquad N \cap M^{n-1} \cap N_n{}' = 0.$$

Thus $N \cap M^{n-1}$, being also a direct summand of N, is finitely generated. By inductional assumption, it has the form $\sum_{i=1}^{n-1} N_i$, hence $N \cong \sum_{i=1}^n N_i$.

It will be noted that the proof of Proposition 8 is very similar to that of Proposition 7. With a little trouble, we probably could have found a common proof for both.

EXERCISES

1. Show that M_R is projective if and only if there exist $m_i \in M$ and $f_i \in \operatorname{Hom}_R(M,R)$, i belonging to some index set I, such that, for any $m \in M$,

$$m = \sum_{i \in I} m_i(f_i m).$$

(It is understood of course that $f_i m = 0$ for all but a finite number of i.)

2. If M_R is finitely generated and projective, show that there exist $m_1, \ldots, m_n \in M$ and $f_1, \ldots, f_n \in \operatorname{Hom}_R(M,R)$ such that, for $m \in M$ and $f \in \operatorname{Hom}_R(M,R)$,

$$m = \sum_{i=1}^n m_i(f_i m), \qquad f = \sum_{i=1}^n (fm_i)f_i.$$

3. A ring is called *right hereditary* if every right ideal is projective. If R is right hereditary, show that every submodule of a free R-module is a direct sum of modules, each of which is isomorphic to a right ideal of R.

4. Show that a ring is right hereditary if and only if every submodule of a projective module is projective.

5. If R is completely reducible, show that every right R-module is a direct sum of right ideals of R.

6. A ring R is called *right semihereditary* if every finitely generated right ideal is projective. For example, any regular ring is both right and left semihereditary. State and prove the analog of Exercises 3 and 4 above.

7. Show that the ring A_n of all $n \times n$ matrices with entries in the ring A is regular if and only if A is regular. (*Hint:* One way, consider the element $e_{11}re_{11}$ corresponding to $r \in A_n$. The other way, utilize the lattice isomorphism of Section 3.5, Exercise 7, and observe that a finitely generated right ideal K of A_n is a direct summand if and only if $e_{11}K$ is a direct summand of the A-module $e_{11}A_n$.)

8 (Small). Show that the ring in Example 11 of Section 3.5 is right hereditary but not left hereditary.

4.2   Injective modules

It may come as a surprise to the reader that the direct product of modules may be characterized abstractly in a fashion quite "dual" to the direct sum. By "dual" is meant that all mappings are reversed and that "epi" is interchanged with "mono."

PROPOSITION 1.   *If A is the direct product of a family of modules $\{A_i \mid i \in I\}$ with canonical mappings $\pi_i : A \to A_i$ then for every module B and for every family of homomorphisms $\phi_i : B \to A_i$ there exists a unique homomorphism $\phi : B \to A$ such that $\pi_i \circ \phi = \phi_i$. Moreover, this property characterizes the direct product up to isomorphism.*

Proof. We recall that, for any $a \in A$, $\pi_i a = a(i) \in A_i$. Define $\phi : B \to A$ by

$$(\phi b)(i) = \phi_i b.$$

It is clear that ϕ is a homomorphism and that

$$(\pi_i \circ \phi)b = \pi_i(\phi b) = (\phi b)(i) = \phi_i b.$$

Thus $\pi_i \circ \phi = \phi_i$. If also $\pi_i \circ \psi = \phi_i$, then

$$(\psi b)(i) = \pi_i(\psi b) = (\pi_i \circ \psi)b = \phi_i b = (\phi b)(i),$$

hence $\psi = \phi$.

Conversely, assume that A' and $\pi_i' : A' \to A_i$ satisfy the abstract conditions of Proposition 1. Taking $\phi_i = \pi_i'$ and $B = A'$, we see that there exists $\pi' : A' \to A$ such that $\pi_i \circ \pi' = \pi_i'$. Similarly there exists $\pi : A \to A'$ such that $\pi_i' \circ \pi = \pi_i$. Therefore

$$\pi_i \circ \pi' \circ \pi = \pi_i' \circ \pi = \pi_i = \pi_i \circ 1_A,$$

where 1_A is the identity mapping of A. By the uniqueness property, $\pi' \circ \pi = 1_A$. Similarly $\pi \circ \pi' = 1_{A'}$. Therefore π is an isomorphism.

COROLLARY. *If A is isomorphic to the direct product of modules A_i with canonical mappings $\pi_i : A \to A_i$, then there exist mappings $\kappa_i : A_i \to A$ (also called canonical) such that $\pi_i \circ \kappa_i = 1$ and $\pi_j \circ \kappa_i = 0$ when $i \neq j$.*

Proof. For fixed i consider the mapping $\delta_{ij} : A_i \to A_j$, where $\delta_{ii} = 1$ and $\delta_{ij} = 0$ when $i \neq j$. Then there exists $\kappa_i : A_i \to A$ such that, for all j, $\pi_j \circ \kappa_i = \delta_{ij}$. (Take $\phi_j = \delta_{ij}$ and $\phi = \kappa_i$.)

Dual to the notion of projectivity is that of injectivity. A module M is called *injective* provided it has the following property: Let κ be a monomorphism of some module A into some module B, then any homomorphism $\phi : A \to M$ can be "extended" to a homomorphism $\psi : B \to M$ such that $\psi \circ \kappa = \phi$.

The proof of Proposition 3 in Section 4.1 can be dualized by reversing all mappings and by interchanging the prefixes "epi" and "mono." Thus we have immediately:

PROPOSITION 2. *If M is the direct product of a family of modules $\{M_i \mid i \in I\}$, then M is injective if and only if each M_i is injective.*

A useful criterion for the injectivity of a module is the following:

LEMMA 1 (Baer). *M_R is injective if and only if, for every right ideal K of R and every $\phi \in \text{Hom}_R(K,M)$, there exists an $m \in M$ such that $\phi k = mk$ for all $k \in K$.*

Proof. If M_R is injective then ϕ can be extended to $\psi \in \text{Hom}_R(R,M)$, and the condition follows upon putting $\psi 1 = m$.

Conversely, assume that M_R satisfies the condition. Let B_R be any module, A_R any submodule, and let $\phi \in \text{Hom}_R(A,M)$. We wish to extend ϕ to $\psi \in \text{Hom}_R(B,M)$. Using Zorn's Lemma on the set of partial homomorphisms of B into M, ordered by inclusion of their graphs, we may extend ϕ to $\psi \in \operatorname{Hom}_R(D,M)$, where $A \subset D \subset B$, and ψ cannot be properly extended. It remains to show that $D = B$.

Consider any $b \in B$ and put $K = \{r \in R \mid br \in D\}$, then $bR \cap D = bK$. Now $k \to \psi(bk)$ is a homomorphism of K into M; therefore there exists $m \in M$ such that $\psi(bk) = mk$ for all $k \in K$. Define $\psi' : bR \to M$ by $\psi'(d + br) = \psi d + mr$. This is single-valued, for when $d + br = 0$, then $br = -d \in D$ and so $r \in K$, hence $\psi d + mr = \psi(d + br) = 0$. Clearly ψ' is a homomorphism and extends ψ. Since we assumed that ψ cannot be properly extended, it follows that $b \in D$, and our proof is complete.

An Abelian group $M = M_Z$ is called *divisible* if, for every $m \in M$ and every nonzero integer z, there exists an $m' \in M$ such that $m'z = m$.

PROPOSITION 3.   *An Abelian group is injective if and only if it is divisible.*

Proof. We recall that M_Z is injective if and only if for every ideal K of Z and every $\phi \in \operatorname{Hom}_Z(K,M)$ there exists an $m' \in M$ such that $\phi k = m'k$ for all $k \in K$. Now without loss in generality we may assume that $K \neq 0$, hence that $K = zZ$, where $0 \neq z \in Z$, and that $k = zz'$, where $z' \in Z$. Since ϕ is completely determined by $\phi z = m$, say, it follows that M_Z is injective if and only if, for every $0 \neq z \in Z$ and every $m \in M$, there exists an m' such that, for all $z' \in Z$, $mz' = m'zz'$. This is clearly equivalent to saying that M is divisible.

Let Q be the additive group of rationals, then Q/Z is the group of rationals modulo 1. (This is isomorphic to the multiplicative group of roots of unity.) With any additive group M we associate its *character group*

$$M^* = \operatorname{Hom}_Z(M, Q/Z).$$

If M is a left R-module $_RM$, then M^* is a right R-module M_R^*, where

$$(\chi r)m = \chi(rm) \qquad (\chi \in M^*, r \in R, m \in M).$$

We call M_R^* the *character module* of $_RM$. Similarly, if M is a right R-module, M^* will be a left R-module.

LEMMA 2.   *If $0 \neq m \in M$, then there exists $\chi \in M^*$ such that $\chi m \neq 0$.*

Proof. It suffices to find $\phi \in \operatorname{Hom}_Z(mZ, Q/Z)$ such that $\phi m \neq 0$; for Q/Z is divisible, hence injective, and so ϕ can be extended to $\chi \in \operatorname{Hom}_Z(M, Q/Z)$.

If $mz \neq 0$ for all $0 \neq z \in Z$, then we can define $\phi mz = \pi \frac{1}{2} z$, where $\pi : Q \to Q/Z$ canonically. ($\frac{1}{17}z$ will also do.)

If z_0 is the smallest positive integer such that $mz_0 = 0$, we define $\phi mz = \pi \dfrac{1}{z_0} z$. This is a single-valued mapping, since $mz = 0$ implies $z = z_0 z'$, hence $\phi mz = \pi z' = 0$ in Q/Z.

COROLLARY. *There is a canonical monomorphism of M into* $(M^*)^*$.

Proof. The mapping $\chi \to \chi m$ is a character of M^*, call it $\hat{m}$. Now $\hat{m} = 0$ only when $\chi m = 0$ for all $\chi \in M^*$, that is $m = 0$, by the lemma.

With $\phi : A \to B$ we associate canonically $\phi^* : B^* \to A^*$, defined by $(\chi\phi^*)a = \chi(\phi a)$, when $\chi \in B^*$ and $a \in A$.

LEMMA 3. *If* $\phi : A \to B$ *is epi, then* $\phi^* : B^* \to A^*$ *is mono.*

Proof. Suppose $\chi\phi^* = 0$, then $\chi B = \chi(\phi A) = (\chi\phi^*)A = 0$, hence $\chi = 0$.

PROPOSITION 4. *Every module is isomorphic to a submodule of the character module of a free module.*

Proof. Let M_R be a given module. By the Corollary to Lemma 2, $M \subset (M^*)^*$. Now $_R M^*$ is isomorphic to a factor module of a free module $_R F$, hence we have an epimorphism $\pi : F \to M^*$. By Lemma 3, $\pi^* : (M^*)^* \to F^*$ is a monomorphism.

PROPOSITION 5. *If* $_R F$ *is a free module then* F_R^* *is injective.*

Proof. Let K be a right ideal of R, $\phi \in \text{Hom}_R(K, F^*)$. KF is an additive subgroup of F consisting of all finite sums of terms kf, where $k \in K$ and $f \in F$. If $_R F$ is free with basis $\{f_i \mid i \in I\}$, it is not difficult to show that all elements of KF have the form $\sum_{i \in I} k_i f_i$, where $k_i \in K$ and all but a finite number of the k_i are 0. Introduce $\psi : KF \to Q/Z$ by

$$\psi(\textstyle\sum_{i \in I} k_i f_i) = \sum_{i \in I} (\phi k_i) f_i.$$

This is single-valued, since $\sum_{i \in I} k_i f_i = 0$ implies that all $k_i = 0$, hence that the right-hand side $= 0$. Clearly ψ is a Z-homomorphism, and since Q/Z is divisible and hence injective, ψ may be extended to $\chi \in \text{Hom}_Z(F, Q/Z) = F^*$. Then $(\phi k)f = \psi(kf) = \chi(kf) = (\chi k)f$, for all $f \in F$. Hence $\phi k = \chi k$, for all $k \in K$. Thus F_R^* is injective, by Lemma 1.

COROLLARY. *Every module is isomorphic to a submodule of an injective module.*

Proof. This is an immediate consequence of Propositions 4 and 5.

We call a monomorphism $\kappa : M \to B$ *direct* if there exists a homomorphism $\pi : B \to M$ such that $\pi \circ \kappa = 1$. Note that π is then an epimorphism. As in the case of direct epimorphisms (see Section 4.1), we see that M is then isomorphic to a direct summand of B.

PROPOSITION 6. *M is injective if and only if every monomorphism* $\kappa : M \to B$ *is direct.*

This is sometimes stated loosely thus: M is injective if and only if it is a direct summand of every module of which it is a submodule.

The proof is the precise dual of the proof of Proposition 5 in Section 4.1.

COROLLARY.   *M is injective if and only if it is a direct summand of a character module of a free module.*

PROPOSITION 7.   *Every R-module is injective if and only if R is completely reducible.*

We shall omit the proof, which is similar to that of Proposition 6 of Section 4.1.

Having shown that every module M_R can be extended to an injective module I_R, we shall try and make I as small as possible. A module N extending M will be called an *essential* extension provided every nonzero submodule of N has nonzero intersection with M. In other words, if $M \subset N$, N is an essential extension of M if and only if M is a large submodule of N. The following result shows that all essential extensions of M can be found up to isomorphism in a given injective extension I of M.

LEMMA 4.   *Let N be an essential extension of M and let I be an injective module containing M, then the identity mapping of M can be extended to a monomorphism of N into I.*

Proof.   Since I is injective, the identity mapping of M can be extended to $\phi \in \mathrm{Hom}_R(N,I)$, hence $\phi^{-1}0 \cap M = 0$. Since N is an essential extension, $\phi^{-1}0 = 0$.

PROPOSITION 8.   *M is injective if and only if M has no proper essential extension.*

Proof.   Assume M is injective and N is an essential extension of M. Then M is a direct summand of N, thus $N = M + K$, $M \cap K = 0$, and so $K = 0$. Therefore $N = M$ is not a proper extension.

Conversely, assume M has no proper essential extension. Let I be an injective module containing M, and let M' be a submodule of I which is maximal with respect to the property that $M \cap M' = 0$. We shall see in a minute that I/M' is an essential extension of $(M + M')/M' \cong M$. By assumption, $I/M' \cong M$, hence $I = M + M'$. Thus M is a direct summand of I, hence also injective.

It remains to show that I/M' is an essential extension of $(M + M')/M'$. Indeed, let $M' \subset K \subset I$ and assume that K/M' has zero intersection with $(M + M')/M'$, that is $K \cap (M + M') \subset M'$. Then $K \cap M \subset M' \cap M = 0$, hence $K = M'$, by maximality of M'. Thus $K/M' = 0$ and our proof is complete.

PROPOSITION 9.   *Every module M has a maximal essential extension N. This is unique in the following sense: If N' is another maximal essential extension of M, then the identity mapping of M can be extended to an isomorphism of N' onto N.*

Remark. To say that N is a maximal essential extension of M means that N is an essential extension of M and that no proper extension of N is.

Proof. Let I be an injective module containing M. The union of any simply ordered family of essential extensions of M in I is also an essential extension. Hence, by Zorn's lemma, M has a maximal essential extension N in I.

Now let N' be any essential extension of M containing N, not necessarily in I. Clearly, N' is also an essential extension of N. By Lemma 4, the identity mapping of N can be extended to a monomorphism of N' into I. Its image must still be an essential extension of N, hence $= N$. Therefore N is a maximal essential extension of M, not just in I, but absolutely.

Any essential extension of N is an essential extension of M. Therefore N has no proper essential extension, hence is injective, by Proposition 8. If N' is any essential extension of M, by Lemma 4 we can extend the identity mapping of M to a monomorphism of N' into N. If N' is maximal, this is an isomorphism.

PROPOSITION 10. *Let N be an extension of M. The following statements are equivalent:*

(1) *N is a maximal essential extension of M.*

(2) *N is an essential extension of M and is injective.*

(3) *N is a minimal injective extension of M.*

N is called the *injective hull* of M.

Proof. Assume (1). Then N has no proper essential extension, hence is injective. Thus (1) $\Rightarrow$ (2).

Assume (2) and suppose $M \subset I \subset N$, I injective. Then I is a direct summand of N. But N is an essential extension of I, hence $N = I$. Thus (2) $\Rightarrow$ (3).

Assume (3) and let N' be a maximal essential extension of M in N. Then N' is injective (as above), hence $N' = N$. Thus (3) $\Rightarrow$ (1).

EXERCISES

1. Show that the concept "subdirect product of factor modules" is dual to the concept "sum of submodules."

2. Show that every R-module is injective if and only if R is completely reducible.

3. Show that the character module of a free module is a direct product of copies of R_R^*.

4. Show that M_R is injective if and only if, for every *large* right ideal K of R and every $\phi \in \operatorname{Hom}_R(K,M)$, there exists an $m \in M$ such that $\phi k = mk$ for all $k \in K$.

5. Show that R is right hereditary if and only if every factor module of any injective right R-module is injective.

6. If $M \subset K \subset N$, show that N is an essential extension of M if and only if K is an essential extension of M and N is an essential extension of K.

7. Let I be an injective module containing M, let M' be a submodule of I maximal with respect to the property that $M \cap M' = 0$, and let M'' be a submodule of I containing M maximal with respect to the property that $M'' \cap M' = 0$. Show that M'' is the injective hull of M.

The following exercises are taken from the paper by Bass (1960).

8. A submodule A of M is called *small* if, for any submodule B of M, $A + B = M \Rightarrow B = M$. If A is small in M and $f : M \to M'$, show that fA is small in M'.

9. A *projective cover* of a module M is an epimorphism $P \twoheadrightarrow M$ with small kernel, where P is projective. If $P \twoheadrightarrow M$ and $P' \twoheadrightarrow M'$ are projective covers, show that $P \times P' \to M \times M'$ is a projective cover.

10. Let $P \twoheadrightarrow M$ be a projective cover and $P' \to M$ an epimorphism with kernel K, where P' is also projective. Show that $P' = P_1 + P_2$, $P_1 \cap P_2 = 0$, $P_1 \cong P$, $P_2 \subset K$, $P_1 \cap K$ small in P_1. Deduce that P is unique up to isomorphism.

11. If R is semiprimitive and every irreducible R-module has a projective cover, show that R is completely reducible. (*Hint:* Apply Exercise 10 with $P' = R$ to the projective cover $P \to R/M$, where M is a maximal right ideal of R containing the socle. Use Section 3.2, Exercise 8, to observe that $P_1 \cap M = 0$, and deduce that $M = P_2$, hence $P_1 \subset \operatorname{Soc} R \subset M$.)

12. Let M be an R/K-module, where K is an ideal of R. If $P \to M$ is a projective cover of M as an R-module, show that $P/PK \to M$ is a projective cover of the R/K-module M.

13. If every principal R-module has a projective cover, show that R is semiperfect. [*Hint:* Use Exercise 12 to show that every principal R/N-module has a projective cover, where $N = \operatorname{Rad} R$, then use Exercises 9, 10, and 11 to lift an idempotent πe of $\pi R = R/N$ to one of R, by constructing the projective covers of πeR and $\pi(1 - e)R$ and comparing their direct sum with R_R.]

14 (Nakayama). Let $M = \sum_{i=1}^n m_i A_i$, where the A_i are right ideals of R, $N = \operatorname{Rad} R$. Show that $MN = 0 \Rightarrow M = 0$. [*Hint:* $m_1(1 - a_1) = \sum_{i=2}^n m_i a_i$, $a_i \in A_i \cap N$, hence $m_1 \in \sum_{i=2}^n m_i A_i$.] Deduce that if M_R is finitely generated then MN is small.

15. Let R be semiperfect and M_R finitely generated. Show that M has a projective cover. (*Hint:* Use Section 4.1, Exercise 5, to show that the R/N-module M/MN is isomorphic to a finite direct sum of right ideals of R/N. By lifting idempotents one sees that these summands have the form e_iR/e_iN, $e_i^2 = e_i \in R$. Verify that $\sum_i^* e_iR \to M$ is a projective cover.)

4.3   The complete ring of quotients

Let $I_R = I(R_R)$ be the injective hull of the right module R_R associated with the ring R. Let $H = H(R) = \mathrm{Hom}_R(I,I)$ be the ring of endomorphisms of I_R. As usual, we write these endomorphisms on the left of their arguments and so obtain a bimodule $_HI_R$. Let $Q = Q(R) = \mathrm{Hom}_H(I,I)$ be the ring of endomorphisms of the left H-module $_HI$. We write these new endomorphisms on the right of their arguments and obtain a bimodule $_HI_Q$. The letters R, I, H, and Q will retain their meaning throughout this chapter.

Q is called the *complete ring of right quotients* of R. It will be seen that this concept is equivalent to one introduced by Utumi, and that it reduces to the concept studied in Chapter 2 when R is commutative.

LEMMA 1.   *The obvious canonical mapping of R into Q is a monomorphism. The canonical mapping $h \to h1$ of $_HH$ into $_HI$ is an epimorphism. The canonical mapping $q \to 1q$ of Q_R into I_R is a monomorphism.*

Proof.   The canonical mapping of R into Q associates with each $r \in R$ the mapping $i \to ir$ ($i \in I$). If this is the zero mapping then $r = 1r = 0$. Therefore we have a monomorphism.

For any $i \in I$, the mapping $r \to ir$ is a homomorphism of R_R into I_R and may be extended to some $h \in \mathrm{Hom}_R(I,I)$ by injectivity of I_R. Therefore $h1 = i$, and so $H1 = I$. Thus the mapping $h \to h1$ is an epimorphism.

Finally, we consider the canonical homomorphism $q \to 1q$ of Q_R into I_R. Its kernel is 0; for $1q = 0$ implies, by the above, that $Iq = (H1)q = H(1q) = 0$.

Remark.   We shall henceforth regard R as a subring of Q. However, for clarity, we shall distinguish between Q and its canonical image $1Q$ in I. We observe that, when R_R is injective, then $R = I \cong H \cong Q$ canonically.

PROPOSITION 1.   *The canonical image of Q_R in I_R consists precisely of those elements of I which are annihilated by all elements of H which annihilate R, that is*

$$1Q = \{i \in I \mid \forall_{h \in H}(hR = 0 \Rightarrow hi = 0)\}.$$

Proof.   Let $h \in H$, $hR = 0$, then $h(1Q) = (h1)Q = 0$. Thus $1Q$ is contained in the indicated submodule of I_R. Conversely, assume that

$i \in I$ has the property $\forall_{h \in H}(hR = 0 \Rightarrow hi = 0)$. We shall find $q \in Q$ such that $i = 1q$.

By Lemma 1, any element of I can be written in the form $h1$, $h \in H$. Now consider the mapping $h1 \to hi$ of I into itself. (To see that this is indeed a single-valued mapping, assume $h1 = h'1$, then $(h - h')R = 0$, hence $(h - h')i = 0$ by assumption.) Thus there exists $q \in \mathrm{Hom}_H(I,I)$ such that $(h1)q = hi$. Putting $h = 1$, we obtain $1q = i$, as required.

What happens if we go through the same procedure again, starting with Q_Q in place of R_R?

PROPOSITION 2. *I_Q is the injective hull of the canonical image of Q_Q, and $\mathrm{Hom}_Q(I,I) = H$.*

Proof. Let A_Q be a submodule of B_Q and let $\phi \in \mathrm{Hom}_Q(A,I)$. Since I_R is injective, ϕ can be extended to $\psi \in \mathrm{Hom}_R(B,I)$. It will follow that I_Q is injective if we show that ψ is a Q-homomorphism.

For any $a \in A$ consider $\psi_a q = \psi(aq) - (\psi a)q$. Clearly $\psi_a \in \mathrm{Hom}_R(Q,I)$ and $\psi_a R = 0$. But ψ_a can be extended to an element of H, hence $\psi_a Q = 0$, by Proposition 1. Thus $\psi \in \mathrm{Hom}_Q(B,I)$, as required.

Since I_R is an essential extension of R_R, it is also an essential extension of $(1Q)_R$. Therefore I_Q is an essential extension of $(1Q)_Q$. Being injective, it is the injective hull of the latter.

Obviously, $\mathrm{Hom}_Q(I,I) \subseteq \mathrm{Hom}_R(I,I) = H$. Since $_H I_Q$ is a bimodule, we have equality.

COROLLARY. *Q is its own complete ring of right quotients.*

PROPOSITION 3. *The following conditions are equivalent:*

(1) $_H H \cong {}_H I$ *canonically.*
(2) $I_R \cong Q_R$ *canonically.*
(3) $H \cong Q$ *canonically as rings.*
(4) Q_R *is injective.*
(5) $I_Q \cong Q_Q$ *canonically.*
(6) Q_Q *is injective.*

Proof. Assume (1), then the mapping $h \to h1$ has kernel 0. Thus $hR = 0 \Rightarrow hI = 0$, hence $I = 1Q$ by Proposition 1, that is (2). This argument may be reversed, hence (1) $\Leftrightarrow$ (2).

Assume (1) and (2). Tracing the given isomorphisms $H \to I \leftarrow Q$, we find that $h \in H$ corresponds to $q \in Q$ if and only if $h1 = 1q$. Suppose also $h'1 = 1q'$, then

$$(hh')1 = h(h'1) = h(1q') = (h1)q' = (1q)q' = 1(qq').$$

Thus (1)&(2) $\Rightarrow$ (3).

Assume (3), then the relation $h1 = 1q$ is an isomorphism between H and Q. Now for any $i \in I$ there exists $h \in H$ such that $h1 = i$, by Lemma 1. Hence, by assumption, there exists $q \in Q$ such that $i = 1q$, that is (2). Thus (3) $\Rightarrow$ (2).

Assume (4), then the canonical image of Q_R in I_R is injective. But I_R is an essential extension of this image, hence $I = 1Q$, that is (2). Since clearly (2) $\Rightarrow$ (4), we have (2) $\Leftrightarrow$ (4).

We have established the equivalence of (1), (2), (3), and (4). In view of Proposition 2, we thus also have the equivalence of (1), (5), (3), and (6).

A submodule D of Q_R will be called *dense* if $\forall_{h \in H}(hD = 0 \Rightarrow hR = 0)$. Trivially, R is dense. We shall see presently that, for an ideal of a commutative ring R, this notion coincides with that introduced in Chapter 2.

LEMMA 2. *If D is a dense right ideal of R then, for any $q \in Q$, $q^{-1}D = \{r \in R \mid qr \in D\}$ is also dense.*

Proof. Let $h \in H$, $h(q^{-1}D) = 0$. Consider the mapping $\phi : D + qR \to R$ defined by $\phi(d + qr) = hr$. (If $d + qr = 0$, then $qr \in D$, hence $hr = 0$. Thus we have indeed a single-valued mapping.) Extend ϕ to $h' : I_R \to I_R$, then $h'D = 0$, hence $h'R = 0$. Therefore

$$h1 = \phi q = h'q = (h'1)q = 0.$$

Thus $hR = (h1)R = 0$, as required.

PROPOSITION 4. *If D is a right ideal of R, then D is dense if and only if*

$$\forall_{0 \neq r_1 \in R} \forall_{r_2 \in R} \exists_{r \in R}(r_1 r \neq 0 \quad \& \quad r_2 r \in D).$$

Proof. Assume the above condition and let $hD = 0$. Let $r_1 \in hR \cap R$, then $r_1 = hr_2$, where $r_2 \in R$. If $r_1 \neq 0$, we can pick $r \in R$ so that $r_1 r \neq 0$ and $r_2 r \in D$. But then $r_1 r = hr_2 r \in hD = 0$, a contradiction. Therefore $hR \cap R = 0$. Since I_R is an essential extension of R_R, $hR = 0$. Thus D is dense.

Conversely, assume that D is a dense right ideal of R. Then so is $r_2^{-1}D$, for any $r_2 \in R$, by Lemma 2. Now the mapping $r \to r_1 r$ can be extended to some $h : I_R \to I_R$, hence $r_1(r_2^{-1}D) = 0$ implies $r_1 = 0$. Therefore the condition holds.

COROLLARY. *An ideal D of R is dense as a right R-module if and only if*

$$\forall_{r_1 \in R}(r_1 D = 0 \Rightarrow r_1 = 0).$$

For commutative rings, this was in fact the definition of dense ideals in Chapter 2.

Proof. Assume the condition and let $r_2 \in R$. If $r_1 \neq 0$, we can find $r \in D$ so that $r_1 r \neq 0$. Since D is an ideal, $r_2 r \in D$. By Proposition 4, D is dense.

Conversely, assume that D is dense. The present condition follows upon taking $r_2 = 1$ in the condition of Proposition 4.

PROPOSITION 5. *Let D and G be submodules of Q_R, D dense, then $Hom_R(D,G)$ is canonically isomorphic to the residual quotient $G \cdot D = \{q \in Q \mid qD \subset G\}$.*

Proof. The canonical homomorphism of $G \cdot D$ into $Hom_R(D,G)$ is of course the mapping which associates with each $q \in G \cdot D$ the homomorphism $d \to qd$ of D into G. It is a monomorphism, since $qD = 0$ implies $q = 0$. (Recall that $1q = h1$, for some $h \in H$, and D is dense.) It will follow that it is an isomorphism if to each $f \in Hom_R(D,G)$ we can find $q \in Q$ such that, for all $d \in D$, $fd = qd$.

Indeed, extend f to $h : I \to I$, in the sense that, for any $d \in D$, $h1d = 1fd$. Now consider any $h' \in H$ such that $h'R = 0$. Then $h'h1D \subset h'1Q = 0$, by Proposition 1, and so $h'h1Q = 0$, since D is dense. Therefore $h1Q \subset 1Q$, by Proposition 1. In particular, $h1 = 1q$, for some $q \in Q$. Thus $1fd = h1d = 1qd$, hence $fd = qd$, for all $d \in D$, as required.

COROLLARY 1. *Two dense submodules D and D' of Q_R are isomorphic if and only if there exists a unit q in Q such that $qD = D'$.*

COROLLARY 2. *If D is a dense right ideal of R and $f \in Hom_R(D,R)$, then there exists $q \in Q$ such that $\forall_{d \in D} fd = qd$.*

COROLLARY 3. *Suppose R contains a smallest dense right ideal D_0. Then $Q \cong Hom_R(D_0,D_0)$.*

Proof. For any $q \in Q$, $q^{-1}D_0$ is dense, by Lemma 2. Therefore $D_0 \subset q^{-1}D_0$, that is $qD_0 \subset D_0$. Thus $Q = D_0 \cdot D_0 \cong Hom_R(D_0,D_0)$.

Remark. The assumption of the corollary is satisfied, for example, when R is right Artinian. Incidentally the argument shows that D_0 is an ideal.

LEMMA 3. *If D and D' are dense right ideals of R then so is $D \cap D'$.*

Proof. We use the condition of Proposition 4. Let $0 \neq r_1 \in R$ and $r_2 \in R$. Since D is dense, we can find $r \in R$ such that $r_1 r \neq 0$ and $r_2 r \in D$. Since D' is dense, we can find $r' \in R$ such that $r_1 rr' \neq 0$ and $r_2 rr' \in D'$. But then $r_2 rr' \in D \cap D'$; thus $D \cap D'$ is dense.

PROPOSITION 6. *Let D range over all dense right ideals of R, and consider the set*

$$\bigcup_D Hom_R(D,R)/\theta,$$

*where θ is the equivalence relation that holds between two homomorphisms
that agree on the intersection of their domains. This set may be made
into a ring isomorphic to Q with operations defined as follows. Let
$f_i \in \mathrm{Hom}_R(D_i, R)$, $i = 1, 2$, and let*

$$f_1 + f_2 \in \mathrm{Hom}_R(D_1 \cap D_2, R), \qquad f_1 f_2 \in \mathrm{Hom}\,(f_2^{-1}D_1, R)$$

be defined by

$$(f_1 + f_2)d = f_1 d + f_2 d, \qquad (f_1 f_2)d = f_1(f_2 d).$$

Then

$$\theta f_1 + \theta f_2 = \theta(f_1 + f_2), \qquad \theta f_1 \theta f_2 = \theta(f_1 f_2).$$

If we ignore the multiplication, this is an example of a direct limit of
Abelian groups, an important concept not studied here.

Proof. For any $q \in Q$, let $D = q^{-1}R = \{d \in R \mid qd \in R\}$. This is a
dense right ideal, by Lemma 2, and $q \in R \mathbin{.^{\cdot}} D$. Therefore $Q = \bigcup_D (R \mathbin{.^{\cdot}} D)$.
Proposition 5 gives an isomorphism $R \mathbin{.^{\cdot}} D \cong \mathrm{Hom}_R(D, R)$, where
$q \in R \mathbin{.^{\cdot}} D$ corresponds to $f \in \mathrm{Hom}_R(D, R)$ such that $fd = qd$ for all $d \in D$.

Let $q_i \in R \mathbin{.^{\cdot}} D_i$ thus correspond to $f_i \in \mathrm{Hom}_R(D_i, R)$. Then $q_1 = q_2$
if and only if $f_1 \,\theta\, f_2$, as we shall now see.

Indeed, assume $f_1 d = f_2 d$ for all $d \in D_1 \cap D_2$. Then $q_1 d = q_2 d$, hence
$(q_1 - q_2)(D_1 \cap D_2) = 0$. Since $D_1 \cap D_2$ is dense, and $1(q_1 - q_2) = h1$
for some $h \in H$, therefore $1(q_1 - q_2) = 0$, hence $q_1 = q_2$. The converse is
trivial.

Finally, we leave it as an exercise to verify that $q_1 + q_2$ and $q_1 q_2$ correspond to $\theta(f_1 + f_2)$ and $\theta(f_1 f_2)$.

In view of the Corollary of Proposition 4, this shows that, for commutative R, Q coincides with the complete ring of quotients defined in
Chapter 2. In particular, Q is then also commutative. In general, this is how
the complete ring of right quotients was first defined by Utumi (he called
it "maximal" rather than "complete"), following a construction by R. E.
Johnson that we shall meet in the next section.

COROLLARY. *$Q = R$ if and only if, for every dense right ideal D, and every
$f \in \mathrm{Hom}_R(D, R)$, there exists an element $r \in R$ such that $\forall_{d \in D} fd = rd$.*

Another consequence of Proposition 5 is the following interesting result:

PROPOSITION 7 (Utumi). *Let R be a prime ring with nonzero socle. Then Q
is the ring of all linear transformations of a vector space.*

Proof. The socle S is an ideal. (See Sections 3.3 and 3.4.) Since R is
prime, $rS = 0$ implies $r = 0$, for all $r \in R$. Therefore S is dense, by the
Corollary to Proposition 4. On the other hand, S is contained in every
large right ideal; for every large right ideal contains every minimal right

ideal. Since every dense right ideal is large (an immediate consequence of Proposition 4), S is the smallest dense right ideal of R. Therefore $Q \cong \operatorname{Hom}_R(S,S) \cong \operatorname{Hom}_{eRe}(Re,Re)$, by Corollary 3 of Proposition 5, and by Section 3.4, Lemma 2.

Let R be a subring of S. Then S is called a *ring of right quotients* of R if, for every $0 \neq s \in S$, $s^{-1}R = \{r \in R \mid sr \in R\}$ is a dense right ideal of R and $s(s^{-1}R) \neq 0$.

PROPOSITION 8.   *Q is a ring of right quotients of R. If S is any ring of right quotients of R, the identity mapping of R can be extended to a unique homomorphism of S_R into Q_R, and this is a ring monomorphism.*

Proof.   Since trivially R_R is dense, $q^{-1}R$ is dense by Lemma 2. Moreover, when $q \neq 0$, $q(q^{-1}R) = qR \cap R \neq 0$, since Q_R is an essential extension of R_R.

Now let S be any ring of right quotients of R. Whenever $0 \neq s \in S$, $sR \cap R = s(s^{-1}R) \neq 0$, hence S_R is an essential extension of R_R. Thus S_R may be regarded as a submodule of I_R. Now suppose $h \in H$ and $hR = 0$. Then, for any $s \in S$, $hs(s^{-1}R) = 0$, and so $hsR = 0$, since $s^{-1}R$ is dense. Thus $hS = 0$, and consequently $S \subset 1Q$, by Proposition 1.

Suppose ϕ is any homomorphism of S_R into $1Q_R$ which extends the identity mapping of R. Extend the mapping $s \to \phi s - s$ to some $h \in H$, then $hR = 0$, hence $hS = 0$, by Proposition 1. Thus $\phi s = 1s$, and so there is only one such homomorphism of S_R into $1Q_R$, hence into Q_R. Furthermore this is a monomorphism.

Thus we may regard S_R as a submodule of Q_R. Is S a subring of Q? Let us temporarily denote multiplication in S by $*$. Consider $s, s' \in S$ and compare $s' * s$ with $s's$, the product in Q. Let $d \in s^{-1}R$, then

$$(s' * s)d = s'(sd) = (s's)d,$$

hence $(s' * s - s's)(s^{-1}R) = 0$. Since $s^{-1}R$ is dense, $s' * s = s's$. Thus S may be regarded as a subring of Q.

COROLLARY.   *Let R be a subring of S. Then the identity mapping of R can be extended to an isomorphism of S onto Q if and only if the following two conditions hold:*

(1) *S is a ring of right quotients of R.*
(2) *For every dense right ideal D of R and every $f \in \operatorname{Hom}_R(D,R)$,*

$$\exists_{s \in S} \forall_{d \in D} fd = sd.$$

We are now in a position to prove the following result, which has already been stated in the commutative case:

PROPOSITION 9 (Utumi).

$$Q(\textstyle\prod_{j\in J}R_j) \cong \textstyle\prod_{j\in J}Q(R_j)$$

Proof. We may regard $R = \prod_{j\in J}R_j$ as a subring of $Q' = \prod_{j\in J}Q(R_j)$. Let $0 \neq q \in Q'$ and put $D' = \prod_{j\in J}q(j)^{-1}R_j$. Then $qD' \subset R$, hence $D' \subset q^{-1}R$. A straightforward computation shows that D' is dense, using Proposition 4, and that $qD' \neq 0$. We omit the tedious details. Therefore Q' is a ring of right quotients of R.

Next, let D be any dense right ideal of R, D_j its canonical image in R_j. Again, using Proposition 4, one may easily show that D_j is a dense right ideal of R_j. Now let $f \in \mathrm{Hom}_R(D,R)$, we shall find $q \in Q'$ such that $\forall_{d\in D}qd = fd$.

Indeed, let $\kappa_j : D_j \to D$ and $\pi_j : R \to R_j$ canonically. Then $\pi_j \circ f \circ \kappa_j \in \mathrm{Hom}_R(D_j,R_j)$, hence there exist $q_j \in Q(R_j)$ such that

$$\forall_{d_j\in D_j}q_jd_j = \pi_j(f(\kappa_jd_j)).$$

Now let $d \in D$, and observe that $\kappa_jd(j) = de_j$, where e_j is the idempotent of R associated with R_j. Define $q \in Q'$ by $q(j) = q_j$. A simple computation then shows that $(qd)(j) = (fd)(j)$, for all j, and so $qd = fd$, as required.

The result now follows from the above corollary. The reader may have to do a little work to fill in the details of the proof.

EXERCISES

1. Show that $Q \cong P/K$, where $K = \{h \in H \mid h1 = 0\}$ and $P = \{h \in H \mid Kh \subset K\}$.

2. Show that Q_R is injective if and only if $KI \cap R = 0$.

3. If R is commutative, show that Q is isomorphic to the center of H.

4 (Utumi). Let F be any field, $S = F[x]/(x^4)$, the ring of polynomials in x over F modulo x^4, $R = F + F\bar{x}^2 + F\bar{x}^3$ the subring of S generated by 1, $\bar{x}^2$, and $\bar{x}^3$, where $\bar{x}$ is the image of x in S. Show that Q_R is not injective and that H is not commutative.

5. Show that every dense right ideal is large.

6 (Utumi). Let R be a subring of S. Show that S is a ring of right quotients of R if and only if

$$\forall_{0\neq s\in S}\forall_{s'\in S}\exists_{r\in R}(sr \neq 0 \quad \& \quad s'r \in R).$$

7. If S is a ring of right quotients of R and T is a ring of right quotients of S, show that T is a ring of right quotients of R.

8 (Utumi). If $R = A_n$, the ring of all $n \times n$ matrices over A, show that $Q = B_n$, where B is the complete ring of right quotients of A.

9 (Gabriel). If D is a dense right ideal of R and A is any right ideal of R such that $d^{-1}A$ is dense for all $d \in D$, then A is also dense.

10 (Tewari). A mapping $d : R \rightarrow R$ is called a *derivation* of R if $d(r_1 + r_2) = dr_1 + dr_2$, $d(r_1r_2) = (dr_1)r_2 + r_1dr_2$ for all r_1, $r_2 \in R$. Show that every derivation d of R can be extended to a unique derivation d' of Q.

11. With every element a of R there is associated the derivation d_a of R such that

$$d_a r = ar - ra$$

for all $r \in R$. Using the preceding exercise, show that Q will be commutative if R is.

12. Let R be the ring of all 2×2 matrices

$$\begin{pmatrix} a & b \\ c & d \end{pmatrix}$$

over a field F such that $a + c = b + d$. Show that Q is the ring of all 2×2 matrices.

13 (Findlay). An ideal A in a commutative ring R is called *invertible* in a ring S containing R as a subring if there is a submodule B of S_R such that $AB = R$. Show that the following statements are equivalent:

(a) A is invertible in some S.
(b) A is invertible in Q.
(c) A is dense, finitely generated and projective.

14. Show that the sum of all

$$R \cdot A = \{q \in Q \,|\, qA \subset R\},$$

where A is invertible in Q, is a subring of Q.

4.4 Rings of endomorphisms of injective modules

Recall that a submodule L of a module M_R is *large* if it has nonzero intersection with every nonzero submodule of M_R.

LEMMA 1.   *Let $F = Hom_R(M,M)$.*

(1) *The intersection of a finite number of large submodules of M_R is large.*

(2) *If L is a large submodule of M_R and $f \in F$, then $f^{-1}L = \{m \in M \,|\, fm \in L\}$ is large.*

(3) *The set of all g in F which annihilate large submodules of M_R is an ideal.*

Proof.

(1) Let L and L' be large submodules, K any nonzero submodule of M_R. Then $L' \cap K \neq 0$, since L' is large. Hence $L \cap L' \cap K \neq 0$, since L is large.

(2) Assume $f^{-1}L \cap K = 0$, then $L \cap fK = 0$, hence $fK = 0 \subset L$. Therefore $K \subset f^{-1}L \cap K = 0$.

(3) If g annihilates L and g' annihilates L', then $g + g'$ annihilates $L \cap L'$. If f is any element of F then fg annihilates L and gf annihilates $f^{-1}L$.

We need another lemma, concerning the Jacobson radical of a module.

LEMMA 2. *Let K be a submodule of A_R and $\pi : A \to A/K$ canonically. Then $\pi \operatorname{Rad} A \subset \operatorname{Rad} \pi A$. If $K \subset \operatorname{Rad} A$, then $\pi \operatorname{Rad} A = \operatorname{Rad} \pi A$.*

Proof. Every maximal submodule of πA has the form πM, where M is a maximal submodule of A containing K, and $\operatorname{Rad} \pi A$ is the intersection of these.

PROPOSITION 1. *Let I_R be an injective module, $H = \operatorname{Hom}_R(I,I)$ and N the ideal of all h in H which annihilate a large submodule of I_R. Then*

(1) *H/N is regular in the sense of von Neumann,*

(2) *N is the Jacobson radical of H,*

(3) *idempotents modulo N can be lifted in H.*

Comment. (1) is due to Johnson, (2) is due to Utumi, and (3) seems to have been discovered independently by several people.

Proof.

(1) Let $h \in H$ and consider a submodule K of I_R which is maximal such that $h^{-1}0 \cap K = 0$, where $h^{-1}0 = \{i \in I \mid hi = 0\}$. Then $h^{-1}0 + K$ will be a large submodule of I_R, by Section 3.3, Lemma 1. Since the restriction of h to K is a monomorphism, there exists $\phi \in \operatorname{Hom}_R(hK,I)$ such that $\phi hk = k$, for all $k \in K$. Since I_R is injective, we may extend ϕ to $h' \in H$. For any $i \in h^{-1}0 + K$, we then have $hh'hi = hi$, thus $hh'h - h \in N$. Hence H/N is a regular ring.

(2) Let $\pi : H \to H/N$ be the canonical epimorphism. By the above, $\operatorname{Rad} \pi H = 0$. Hence, by Lemma 2, $\pi \operatorname{Rad} H = 0$, that is $\operatorname{Rad} H \subset N$.

Conversely, let $h \in N$, then $h^{-1}0$ is a large submodule of I_R. But $h^{-1}0 \cap (1 - h)^{-1}0 = 0$, hence $(1 - h)^{-1}0 = 0$. Therefore $(1 - h)I_R$ is isomorphic to I_R, hence also injective, and so a direct summand of I_R. But, for any $i \in h^{-1}0$, one has $(1 - h)i = i$, hence $(1 - h)I$ contains $h^{-1}0$ and thus is a large submodule of I_R. It follows that $(1 - h)I = I$, and so $1 - h$ is an automorphism of I_R. Thus $1 - h$ is a unit, for every element h of the ideal N, and so $N \subset \operatorname{Rad} H$.

(3) Let $u \in H$ and assume that $u^2 - u \in N$. Then there exists a large submodule L of I_R such that $(u^2 - u)L = 0$. The injective hull of uL, being its minimal injective extension, can be embedded in the injective module I_R, hence may be assumed to have the form eI, where $e^2 = e \in H$. Now e induces the identity mapping on uL, hence $(eu - u)L = 0$, and so $eu \equiv u$ modulo N. Unfortunately we cannot show $e \equiv u$, or we should be finished. Put $f = e + eu(1 - e)$, then $ef = f$, $fe = e$, and $f^2 = f$. Let $L' = (1 - e)I + uL$, then a routine verification (left as an exercise) shows that L' is large and that $(f - eu)L' = 0$. Therefore $f \equiv eu \equiv u$ modulo N, and our proof is complete.

Following Goldie, the module M_R is called *finite dimensional* if there do not exist infinitely many nonzero submodules whose sum is direct. Clearly, all Noetherian and all Artinian modules are finite dimensional.

PROPOSITION 2.   *Let M_R be finite dimensional. Then*

  (1) *its injective hull I_R is the direct sum of a finite number of indecomposable injective modules,*

  (2) *the ring H of endomorphisms of I_R is semiperfect.*

We recall that the second statement means H/N is completely reducible and idempotents can be lifted modulo $N = \text{Rad } H$.

Proof.

(1) Consider any orthogonal set E of nonzero idempotents of H. Then $\sum_{e \in E} eI \cap M$ is a direct sum of nonzero submodules of M_R. By assumption, E must be finite. We shall apply this principle twice.

First we show that, for any nonzero idempotent e of H, eHe contains a primitive idempotent. Indeed, if e is not already primitive, eHe will contain a nonzero idempotent $f_1 \neq e$. If f_1 is not primitive, $f_1 H f_1$ contains a nonzero idempotent $f_2 \neq f_1$, and so on. The idempotents $e - f_1$, $f_1 - f_2, \ldots$ form an orthogonal set, which must be finite.

Secondly we deduce that there exists a maximal orthogonal set e_1, $e_2, \ldots, e_n$ of primitive idempotents. Let e be their sum and suppose that $e \neq 1$. Then $(1 - e)H(1 - e)$ would contain a primitive idempotent orthogonal to e, hence to all e_i, contradicting maximality. Therefore $1 = \sum_{i=1}^{n} e_i$, hence $I = \sum_{i=1}^{n} e_i I$, each component being indecomposable.

(2) Since any primitive idempotent of H remains primitive modulo N (see Section 3.6, Exercise 3), it is also true in H/N that 1 is a finite sum of primitive idempotents. Therefore H/N is the direct sum of a finite number of indecomposable right ideals. Since H/N is regular, these are minimal right ideals. Thus H/N is completely reducible. By Proposition 1, idempotents modulo N can be lifted, hence H is semiperfect.

COROLLARY 1. *Let M_R be finite dimensional and assume that all indecomposable components of its injective hull are isomorphic. Then $H/\mathrm{Rad}\, H$ and H are isomorphic to the rings of all endomorphisms of finitely generated free modules over a division ring and over a local ring respectively.*

Proof. The statement concerning $H/\mathrm{Rad}\, H$ follows from the classical Wedderburn-Artin Theorem (Section 3.4, Proposition 6), and the statement concerning H follows from Section 3.7, Proposition 4.

COROLLARY 2. *Assume that every nonzero submodule of M_R is large. Then I_R is indecomposable and H is a local ring.*

A closer examination of the results of this chapter shows that most of them hold under more general circumstances than have been stated. Johnson and Wong have called a module M_R *quasi-injective* if every partial endomorphism of M_R can be extended to a full endomorphism, that is to say if, for every submodule K_R of M_R and every $f \in \mathrm{Hom}_R(K,M)$ there exists a $g \in \mathrm{Hom}_R(M,M)$ such that $gk = fk$ for all $k \in K$. Thus Proposition 1 remains valid if "injective" is replaced by "quasi-injective," as will be brought out in one of the exercises below.

EXERCISES

1. In the proof of Proposition 1, show that L' is large.

2. Prove that every nonzero submodule of M_R is large if and only if the injective hull of M_R is indecomposable.

3. If I_R is injective and indecomposable, show that $\mathrm{Hom}_R(I,I)$ is a local ring.

4 (Johnson). If I_R is injective, $H = \mathrm{Hom}_R(I,I)$ and $\mathrm{Rad}\, H = 0$, show that H_H is injective. (*Hint:* The easiest way to do this is to use Section 5.4, Exercise 7.)

5. The *rational completion* $\bar{M}_R$ of the module M_R has been defined as the set of all elements of the injective hull I_R of M_R which are annihilated by all endomorphisms of I_R which annihilate M_R. Show that $\bar{M}_R$ is also the set of all elements of I_R which are invariant under all automorphisms of I_R which leave all elements of M_R invariant.

6 (Johnson and Wong). Let I_R be the injective hull of M_R and $H = \mathrm{Hom}_R(I,I)$. Show that M_R is quasi-injective if and only if $HM \subset M$. Deduce that, in general, HM_R is the smallest quasi-injective essential extension of M_R.

7 (Faith and Utumi). Let M_R be quasi-injective and suppose the submodule K_R of M_R has no essential extension in M. Show that K_R is a direct summand of M_R. Deduce that K_R is also quasi-injective.

8. Use the above exercise to extend Proposition 1 to quasi-injective modules.

The following exercises are based on Matlis (1958) and the book by Lesieur-Croisot (1963).

9. A submodule X of a module M_R is called *meet-irreducible* if $X = Y \cap Z$ implies $X = Y$ or $X = Z$, for all submodules Y and Z of M_R. Show that this is equivalent to saying that the injective hull $I(M/X)$ of M/X is indecomposable. (See Exercise 2 above.)

10. Let $X = X_1 \cap X_2 \cap \cdots X_n$ be written as the intersection of meet-irreducible submodules X_i of M_R, none of which is redundant, that is $X_i \not\subseteq \bigcap_{j \neq i} X_j$. Show that $I(M/X) = \sum_{i=1}^n I(M/X_i)$ as a direct sum.

11. Let the injective module I_R be expressed in two different ways as a direct sum of indecomposable injective modules,

$$I = \sum_{i=1}^m I_i = \sum_{j=1}^n I'_j .$$

Then $m = n$, and there exists a permutation p of the numbers 1 to m such that

$$I_i \cong I'_{p(i)}.$$

(*Hint:* Use Exercise 3 above and Azumaya's Theorem; see Section 3.7, Corollary to Proposition 3.)

12. Let M_R be Noetherian. Call M_R *homogeneous of type* T if $I(M_R)$ is a direct sum of indecomposable injective modules all isomorphic to a given module T. Show that, if M/X and M/Y are homogeneous of type T, so is $M/(X \cap Y)$. Deduce that any Noetherian module is a subdirect product of a finite number of homogeneous modules of distinct types (*Hint:* First express 0 as the intersection of a finite number of meet-irreducible submodules of M_R.)

13. Let M_R be expressed as the subdirect product of nonredundant homogeneous modules of distinct types in two different ways,

$$0 = X_1 \cap X_2 \cap \cdots X_m = Y_1 \cap Y_2 \cap \cdots Y_n.$$

Then $m = n$, and there exists a permutation p of the numbers 1 to m such that M/X_i has the same type as $M/Y_{p(i)}$.

14. The *tertiary radical* of a module M_R consists of all elements of R which annihilate a large submodule of M_R. Show that it is an ideal of R. Also show that it is the same for any essential extension of M_R.

15. Let R be right Noetherian. Show that the tertiary radical of M_R is the right annihilator of a single large submodule of M_R.

16. If R is right Noetherian or commutative, show that the tertiary radical of an indecomposable injective R-module is a prime ideal.

17. If M_R is a homogeneous and finite dimensional module, show that its tertiary radical is the same as that of any indecomposable component of $I(M_R)$.

18. If R is commutative and M_R is finite dimensional, show that all indecomposable components of $I(M_R)$ have the same tertiary radical if and only if M_R is homogeneous.

4.5 Regular rings of quotients

We aim to extract some information about rings of quotients from Section 4.4. First we shall collect a few results concerning Johnson's so-called "singular submodule."

PROPOSITION 1. *For any module M_R let $J(M_R)$ be the set of all elements of M which annihilate large right ideals of R.*

(1) $J(M_R)$ *is an F-R-submodule of $_F M_R$, where $F = Hom_R(M,M)$.*

(2) $J(R_R)$ *is an ideal of R.*

(3) *If I_R is the injective hull of R_R then $J(I_R) = Rad\,(_H I)$.* (Recall that $H = Hom_R(I,I)$.)

(4) $I/J(I_R)$ *is isomorphic to the additive group of the regular ring H/N, $N = Rad\,H$.*

$J(M_R)$ is called the *singular* submodule of M_R and $J(R_R)$ the *right singular* ideal of R.

Proof. (1) is shown exactly like Lemma 1 (3) of Section 4.4, and (2) is a special case of (1).

To show (3) and (4), let $\pi \in Hom_H\,(H,I)$ be the epimorphism $\pi h = h1$ $(h \in H)$, which has already been discussed in Section 4.3, Lemma 1, and let K be its kernel. The inverse image $\pi^{-1}J(I_R)$ in H is clearly the same as the ideal N of Proposition 1 of Section 4.4, where it was shown that $N = Rad\,H$, hence $I/J(I_R) \cong H/N$. Since $K \subset N$, Lemma 2 of Section 4.4 yields $J(I_R) = \pi\,Rad\,H = Rad\,\pi H = Rad\,(_H I)$.

PROPOSITION 2 (Johnson). *Let I_R be the injective hull of R_R, $J(I_R)$ its singular submodule, $H = Hom_R(I,I)$, $Q = Hom_H(I,I)$. Then the following conditions are equivalent.*

(1) $J(R_R) = 0$.

(2) $J(I_R) = 0$.

(3) *Rad H = 0.*

(4) *Rad $(_H I) = 0$.*

(5) *Q is regular.*

Proof. We have $(1) \Leftrightarrow (2)$, since $J(R_R) = J(I_R) \cap R$ and I_R is an essential extension of R_R. $(2) \Leftrightarrow (4)$ is an immediate consequence of Proposition 1 above, and $(3) \Rightarrow (2)$ since $J(I_R) = \pi \operatorname{Rad} H$.

We shall now prove $(5) \Rightarrow (1)$. Let L be a large right ideal of R, hence a large submodule of Q_R, and assume $rL = 0$ for $0 \neq r \in R$. If Q is a regular ring, there exists $q \in Q$ such that $rqr = r$. Therefore $qr \neq 0$ and so $qrR \cap L \neq 0$. Hence we can find $s \in R$ such that $0 \neq qrs \in L$. But then $rs = rqrs \in rL = 0$, a contradiction.

Finally we complete the proof by showing that (2) implies (3) and (5). We assume that $J(I_R) = 0$, then

$$N = \{ h \in H \mid h1 \in J(I_R) \} = \{ h \in H \mid hR = 0 \}.$$

Now N is an ideal of H, hence

$$NI = NH1 \subset N1 = 0.$$

By Section 4.3, Proposition 1, we therefore have $I = 1Q$. Thus the equivalent conditions of Section 4.3, Proposition 3 are satisfied. In particular N, which now turns out to be the kernel of the canonical epimorphism $h \to h1$ of $_H H$ onto $_H I$, must be zero. Therefore $Q \cong H = H/N$, which is a regular ring by Proposition 1 of Section 4.4.

COROLLARY. *If the right singular ideal of R is zero, Q_Q is injective.*

Proof. We have just seen, in the last part of the above proof, that $I = 1Q$. By Section 4.3, Proposition 3, Q_Q is injective.

PROPOSITION 3 (Goldie). *If R is right Noetherian then $J(R_R)$ is nilpotent.*

Proof. Let $a \in J(R_R)$ and let n be any positive integer. Consider the right "annihilator" ideal

$$(a^n)^r = \{ x \in R \mid a^n x = 0 \},$$

and note that $(a^n)^r \subset (a^{2n})^r$. Choose m so that $(a^m)^r$ is maximal, then $(a^m)^r = (a^{2m})^r$. Since $a^m \in J(R_R)$, $(a^m)^r$ is large.

Now suppose $a^m \neq 0$. Then $a^m R \cap (a^m)^r \neq 0$, hence there exists $y \in R$ such that $a^m y \neq 0$ and $a^{2m} y = 0$. But this contradicts the equation $(a^m)^r = (a^{2m})^r$. Therefore $a^m = 0$.

Thus $J(R_R)$ is nil, hence nilpotent, by Levitzki's Theorem—see Section 3.5, Corollary to Proposition 5.

COROLLARY. *If R is right Noetherian and semiprime, then Q is completely reducible.*

Proof. By Proposition 3, $J(R_R) = 0$. Hence, by Proposition 2, $\operatorname{Rad} H = 0$. It follows from the proof of Proposition 2 that the equivalent conditions of Section 4.3, Proposition 3 are satisfied. In particular,

$Q \cong H$. Now, by Proposition 2 of Section 4.4, $H/\mathrm{Rad}\ H$ is completely reducible.

This last result is also due to Goldie, with one difference: In place of Q he had the "classical" ring of right quotients of R. We shall consider this concept in the next chapter.

EXERCISES

1. Show that $J(R_R) = 0$ if and only if every large right ideal is dense (see Section 4.3). When R is commutative, deduce that $J(R_R) = 0$ if and only if R is semiprime.

2. Show that the compound mapping

$$R \to I_R \to I/J(I_R) \to H/\mathrm{Rad}\ H$$

is a ring homomorphism.

3 (Johnson). If I_R is the injective hull of R_R, show that

$$I/J(R_R) \cong \bigcup_L \mathrm{Hom}_R(L,R)/\theta,$$

where L ranges over all large right ideals of R, and θ is the equivalence relation that holds between $f \in \mathrm{Hom}_R(L,R)$ and $f' \in \mathrm{Hom}_R(L',R)$ if and only if they agree on some large right ideal contained in $L \cap L'$.

4. If R_R is finite dimensional, show that Q is a direct sum of a finite number of indecomposable right ideals.

5 (Goldie). Show that the Corollary to Proposition 3 can be strengthened thus: If R is semiprime, R_R is finite dimensional and every set of right annihilators has a maximal element, then Q is completely reducible.

6. Show that the tertiary radical of M_R (see Section 4.4, Exercise 14) contains all nilpotent ideals of R. If R is commutative Noetherian, show that its tertiary radical, singular ideal and prime radical all coincide.

4.6 Classical rings of quotients

An element r of the ring R is called a *non-zero-divisor* if $sr \neq 0$ and $rs \neq 0$ for any $0 \neq s \in R$. (We avoid the common term "regular element," because of possible confusion with other uses of the word "regular.")

Let R be a subring of S. Then S is called a *classical ring of right quotients* of R if and only if two conditions hold:

(1) *All non-zero-divisors of R are units in S (that is, have inverses in S).*

(2) *All elements of S have the form ab^{-1}, where a, $b \in R$ and b is a non-zero-divisor of R.*

Not every ring has a classical ring of right quotients. In fact, assume that S is a classical ring of right quotients of R, and let a, $b \in S$, such that b is a non-zero-divisor. By (2), $b^{-1}a = cd^{-1}$, where c, $d \in R$ and d is a non-zero-divisor. Thus we have shown the necessity of the following, putting $c = a'$, $d = b'$:

CONDITION (Ore). For all a, $b \in R$, b being a non-zero-divisor, there exist a', $b' \in R$, b' being a non-zero-divisor, such that $ab' = ba'$.

It is known that this condition is also sufficient. The following proof of this fact makes use of Q, the complete ring of right quotients of R.

Assume the Ore condition, and let b be a non-zero-divisor of R. We claim that bR is a dense right ideal.

Indeed, let $0 \neq r_1 \in R$ and $r_2 \in R$. By the Ore condition, using $r_2 = a$, there exist a', $b' \in R$, b' being a non-zero-divisor, such that $r_2b' = ba'$, thus $r_2b' \in bR$. Since b' is a non-zero-divisor, we also have $r_1b' \neq 0$. Therefore bR is dense, by Section 4.3, Proposition 4.

Next, define $f \in \operatorname{Hom}_R(bR,R)$ by $fbr = r$, noting that $br = br' \Rightarrow r = r'$. Therefore there exists $q \in Q$ such that $qb = fb = 1$, by Section 4.3, Corollary 2 to Proposition 5. Thus $(bq - 1)bR = 0$, and bR is dense, hence also $bq = 1$. (Recall that a nonzero element of Q cannot annihilate a dense right ideal of R.) Therefore b is a unit in Q.

Let $Q_{cl} = Q_{cl}(R)$ consist of all elements of $Q = Q(R)$ of the form ab^{-1}, where a, $b \in R$ and b is a non-zero-divisor. It is not difficult to see that Q_{cl} is a subring of Q. Thus

$$ab^{-1} + cd^{-1} = (ad' + cb')(bd')^{-1},$$

where $bd' = db'$ and d' is a non-zero-divisor. Also

$$(ab^{-1})(cd^{-1}) = (ac')(db')^{-1},$$

where $cb' = bc'$ and b' is a non-zero-divisor.

It is clear from the above that Q_{cl} is a classical ring of right quotients. We shall see that, in a certain sense, it is the only one. Suppose S is any classical ring of right quotients of R. Let the element ab^{-1} of S correspond to the element ab^{-1} of Q_{cl}. That this correspondence is an isomorphism follows from the fact that $ab^{-1} = 0$ in S or in Q_{cl} if and only if $a = 0$.

The following sums up what we have proved:

PROPOSITION 1. *A ring R possesses a classical ring of right quotients S if and only if it satisfies the Ore condition. Moreover, there is an isomorphism between S and*

$$Q_{cl} = \{ab^{-1} \in Q \mid a,\ b \in R\ \ \&\ \ b \text{ is a non-zero-divisor}\}$$

which induces the identity mapping on R.

Let us call attention to the fact that the Ore condition is automatically satisfied when R is commutative, hence every commutative ring possesses a classical ring of quotients. (See Chapter 2.)

PROPOSITION 2.   *If every large right ideal of R contains a non-zero-divisor, then $Q = Q_{cl}$.*

Proof.   We show that Q satisfies the two conditions in the definition of "classical ring of right quotients."

First, we observe that $J(R_R) = 0$, since it consists of annihilators of large right ideals, hence of non-zero-divisors. By Proposition 2 of the last section, Q is a regular ring. Therefore every non-zero-divisor of Q is a unit. (For assume q is a non-zero-divisor of Q, then from $q(q'q - 1) = 0$ we infer $q'q = 1$, etc.) Moreover, every non-zero-divisor r of R is a non-zero-divisor in Q. (For $rq = 0$ implies $rq(q^{-1}R) = 0$, hence $qR \cap R = q(q^{-1}R) = 0$, hence $q = 0$.) Thus every non-zero-divisor of R is a unit in Q. This is the first condition.

Finally, let q be any element of Q. Then $q^{-1}R$ is dense, hence large, hence contains a non-zero-divisor b of R. Therefore $qb = a \in R$. But b is a unit in Q, hence $q = ab^{-1}$. This is the second condition.

LEMMA 1.   *If R is the ring of all linear transformations of a finite dimensional vector space, then an element $r \in R$ is a unit if either $rr' = 1$ or $r'r = 1$ for some $r' \in R$.*

Proof.   Let V_D be a finite dimensional vector space over the division ring D, and assume $R = \mathrm{Hom}_D(V,V)$.

Suppose $rr' = 1$, then for any $v \in V$ we have $r(r'v) = v$, hence r is epi. By Section 1.4, Proposition 8, r is an automorphism of V_D, hence a unit in R.

Suppose $r'r = 1$, then for any $0 \neq v \in V$ we have $0 \neq v = r'(rv)$, hence $rv \neq 0$, and so r is mono. By the proposition quoted above, r is an automorphism of V_D, hence a unit in R.

PROPOSITION 3 (Goldie).   *If R is prime and Q is completely reducidle, then every large right ideal of R contains a unit of Q.*

Proof.   Let L be a large right ideal of R and let Q be completely reducible. Recall (Section 3.5, Proposition 2) that Q is left Noetherian and regular. Thus we can find $a \in L$ so that Qa is maximal and $a' \in Q$ so that $aa'a = a$. Then $e = aa'$ and $f = a'a$ are idempotents; we shall see that they are both 1.

Consider any $b \in (1 - e)Q \cap L$, then $e(a + b) = a$, hence $Qa \subset Q(a + b)$, with $a + b \in L$. Since Qa was maximal with $a \in L$, it follows that $b \in Qa$. Thus $(1 - e)Q \cap L \subset Qa$. Now $a(1 - f) = 0$, hence

$$((1 - e)Q \cap L)((1 - f)Q \cap L) = 0.$$

Since R is prime, one of the factors is 0. Since L is large, either $e = 1$ or $f = 1$.

The result will now follow from Lemma 1, if we show that Q is the ring of all linear transformations of a finite dimensional vector space, that is to say that Q is simple (in addition to being completely reducible). See the Wedderburn-Artin Theorem (Section 3.4, Proposition 6).

Since R is a prime ring, so is its complete ring of quotients Q. For if q, $q' \in Q$ and $qQq' = 0$, then $(qR \cap R)(q'R \cap R) = 0$, whence $qR \cap R = 0$ or $q'R \cap R = 0$, from which it follows that $q = 0$ or $q' = 0$, Q_R being an essential extension of R_R. Now Q is a direct sum of simple rings and prime, hence itself simple. This completes our proof.

COROLLARY 1. *If R is prime and Q is completely reducible, then $Q = Q_{cl}$.*

This is an immediate consequence of Propositions 3 and 2.

COROLLARY 2. *If R is right Noetherian and prime, then Q_{cl} is completely reducible and simple.*

This is an immediate consequence of the above and the Corollary to Proposition 3 of Section 4.5.

Having shown that the complete ring of quotients of a right Noetherian prime ring is classical, we aim to extend this result to semiprime rings. First we need some elementary facts about "annihilator ideals," which have already been discussed in the commutative case (see Section 2.4).

With any two-sided ideal A of the ring R one may associate its left annihilator $\{r \in R \mid rA = 0\}$ and its right annihilator $\{r \in R \mid Ar = 0\}$. Clearly both of these are ideals. Now if R is semiprime, 0 is the intersection of all prime ideals, hence the left annihilator of the ideal A consists of those $r \in R$ which belong to all prime ideals of R not containing A. By symmetry, the same is true for the right annihilator of A, hence the two are equal, and we shall merely speak of the *annihilator* ideal A^* of A. If B is an annihilator ideal, then $(B^*)^* = B$.

PROPOSITION 4. *If R is semiprime, the annihilator ideals of R form a complete Boolean algebra, with intersection as inf and * as complementation. If, moreover, R_R is Noetherian, then this Boolean algebra is finite. Any maximal proper annihilator ideal is prime.*

Proof. The first statement has already been established in the commutative case (Section 2.4, Proposition 2). The proof in the noncommutative case is the same, and will not be repeated. At any rate, the crux of the matter is to verify that, for two annihilator ideals A and B,

$$A \cap B^* = 0 \Leftrightarrow A \subset B.$$

If R_R is Noetherian, then this Boolean algebra is finite. Indeed, if each set of elements of a Boolean algebra contains a maximal element, the Boolean algebra is readily seen to be finite. This will be left as an exercise.

Finally, let P be any maximal element in the set of all proper annihilator ideals of R, and suppose that $AB \subset P$, where A and B are any two ideals. Then

$$A \subset P \mathrel{.\vphantom{.}^{\cdot}} B = \{r \in R \mid rB \subset P\}.$$

Now $P \subset P \mathrel{.^{\cdot}} B$, and the latter is an annihilator ideal if P is, as $(P^*)^* \mathrel{.^{\cdot}} B = (0 \mathrel{.^{\cdot}} P^*) \mathrel{.^{\cdot}} B = 0 \mathrel{.^{\cdot}} (BP^*) = (BP^*)^*$ (see Section 1.2, Proposition 9). Therefore $P \mathrel{.^{\cdot}} B = P$ or $P \mathrel{.^{\cdot}} B = R$. In the first case $A \subset P$, and in the second case $B = RB = (P \mathrel{.^{\cdot}} B)B \subset P$. Thus P is prime, as was to be shown.

PROPOSITION 5 (Goldie). *Let R be a semiprime right Noetherian ring with maximal proper annihilator ideals P_1, P_2, \ldots, P_n. Then the complete ring of right quotients $Q(R)$ is isomorphic to the direct product of the rings $Q(R/P_i)$, these are total matrix rings, and $Q(R)$ is the classical ring of right quotients of R.*

Proof.   First let us observe that P_1^*, \ldots, P_n^* are the atoms (that is minimal nonzero elements) of the finite Boolean algebra B of annihilator ideals, hence that their sum is the identity element of B, to wit R. Therefore the intersection of the P_i is $R^* = 0$.

Thus the canonical mapping

$$\kappa : R \to \textstyle\prod_{i=1}^{n} R/P_i$$

is a monomorphism. Now R/P_i is a Noetherian prime ring (see Section 3.5, Exercise 1), hence it has for its complete and classical ring of right quotients a total matrix ring S_i (see Corollary 2 of Proposition 3). We claim that $S = \prod_{i=1}^{n} S_i$ is the complete and classical ring of right quotients of κR.

Indeed, S is its own complete ring of right quotients (by Section 4.3, Proposition 9). Moreover, it is easily seen that every non-zero-divisor of κR is a unit in S, by looking at each S_i. It remains to show that, for any $s \in S$, there exists a non-zero-divisor c of κR such that $sc \in \kappa R$.

Put $s = (s_1, \ldots, s_n)$, with $s_i \in S_i$. For each i, there is a non-zero-divisor a_i of R/P_i such that $s_i a_i \in R/P_i$.

Next consider the ideal $L_i = (P_i + P_i^*)/P_i$ in R/P_i. This is nonzero, since otherwise $P_i^* \subset P_i \cap P_i^* = 0$ and so $P_i = 0^* = R$. Now in a prime ring every nonzero two-sided ideal L is large as a right ideal (since

$L \cap rR = 0$ would imply that $rL \subset L \cap rR = 0$, hence $r = 0$). In particular, L_i is a large right ideal, hence contains a non-zero-divisor b_i of R/P_i, by Proposition 3.

Put $c = (a_1 b_1, \ldots, a_n b_n)$. This is a unit in S. (For $a_i b_i$ is a unit in S_i.) Finally c and $sc = (s_1 a_1 b_1, \ldots, s_n a_n b_n) \in \kappa R$, since $a_i b_i$ and $s_i a_i b_i \in L_i$ and

$$\prod_{i=1}^{n} L_i \subset \kappa R,$$

as we shall now verify.

Indeed, any element of L_i has the form $\pi_i r_i$, where $r_i \in P_i{}^*$ and $\pi_i : R \to R/P_i$ canonically. Now, for all $j \neq i$, $P_i{}^* \subset P_j$, hence $\pi_j r_i = 0$. Putting $r = r_1 + \cdots + r_n$, we thus have

$$(\pi_1 r_1, \ldots, \pi_n r_n) = (\pi_1 r, \ldots, \pi_n r) = \kappa r,$$

and our proof is complete.

EXERCISES

1. Generalize Proposition 1, using in place of the set of all non-zero-divisors any set of non-zero-divisors closed under finite products.

2. Let B be a Boolean algebra every nonempty subset of which contains a maximal element. Show that B is finite. Also show that the sum of the atoms is 1.

3. Suppose the ring R contains a field A in its center and every element r of R satisfies a polynomial equation

$$r^n + a_{n-1} r^{n-1} + \cdots + a_0 = 0$$

with coefficients in A. Show that $Q_{cl}(R) = R$.

4 (Faith). Show that there exist finite rings for which $Q \neq Q_{cl}$. (*Hint:* Use Section 4.3, Exercise 12.)

5 (Small). Let R be a commutative ring in which every set of annihilator ideals has a maximal element. Show the following:
   (a) Every maximal proper annihilator ideal is prime.
   (b) Every set of annihilator ideals has a minimal element.
   (c) The number of maximal proper annihilator ideals is finite. (*Hint:* Observe that the sequence $P_1 \supset P_1 \cap P_2 \supset \ldots$. becomes stationary.)
   (d) Every zero-divisor belongs to some maximal proper annihilator ideal.
   (e) An ideal consisting entirely of zero-divisors is contained in a maximal proper annihilator ideal. (*Hint:* Use Section 2.1, Exercise 9.)

(f) Every dense ideal contains a regular element.

(g) $Q(R) = Q_{cl}(R)$.

4.7 The Faith-Utumi Theorem

We have been dealing above with a completely reducible prime ring Q. By the Wedderburn-Artin Theorem, Q is isomorphic to the ring of all $n \times n$ matrices over a division ring D. The reader will have no difficulty in verifying that Q then contains elements e_{ij} $(i, j = 1, \ldots, n)$ such that

$$e_{ij}e_{kl} = \begin{cases} e_{il} & \text{if } j = k \\ 0 & \text{if } j \neq k. \end{cases}$$

The e_{ij} are called *matrix units*, although they are not units in the sense of "invertible elements." Moreover one can assume that D consists of all elements of Q which commute with the e_{ij} and that

$$Q = \sum_{i,j} e_{ij}D.$$

It is not difficult to show that

$$D \cong e_{11}Qe_{11},$$

the isomorphism being given by the inverse mappings

$$d \to de_{11} = e_{11}de_{11},$$

$$e_{11}qe_{11} \to \sum_i e_{i1}(e_{11}qe_{11})e_{1i} = \sum_i e_{i1}qe_{1i}.$$

By a *right order* S of Q we understand an additive subgroup of Q, closed under multiplication, in which, for every element q of Q, there exists a unit s of Q in S such that $qs \in S$. We do not insist that S contain the element 1. Thus, in our terminology, S need not be a subring of Q, in fact, it need not be a ring at all. It is an easy exercise to show that, for any finite set of elements $q_1, q_2, \ldots, q_n$ of Q, there exists a unit s of Q in S such that $q_i s \in S$ for $i = 1, 2, \ldots, n$.

It is easy to manufacture right orders of Q from given right orders of D. Thus let C be any right order of D, and let S be any additive subgroup of Q which is closed under multiplication and contains $\sum_{i,j} e_{ij}C$. Then S is a right order of Q. Indeed, let $q = \sum e_{ij}d_{ij}$, $d_{ij} \in D$. Pick a unit c of D in C such that all $d_{ij}c \in C$. Then $qc = \sum e_{ij}(d_{ij}c) \in S$.

As a matter of fact, there are no other right orders in Q. This is the content of the following remarkable theorem by Faith and Utumi.

PROPOSITION. *Let S be a right order in the completely reducible prime ring Q. Then*

$$\sum e_{ij}C \subset S \subset Q = \sum e_{ij}D,$$

where the e_{ij} are a complete set of matrix units in Q, D consists of all elements of Q which commute with the e_{ij}, and C is a right order in D.

Proof. To start with, we may write

$$Q = \sum e'_{ij} D'$$

where the e'_{ij} form a complete set of matrix units and D' is the associated division ring. Let a be a unit of Q in S such that $e'_{ij}a \in S$. Then the elements $e_{ij} = a^{-1}e'_{ij}a$ form another set of matrix units, $D = a^{-1}D'a$ is the associated division ring, and $ae_{ij} \in S$.

Consider

$$A = \{s \in S \mid \forall_{i,j} se_{ij} \in S\}, \qquad B = \{s \in S \mid \forall_{i,j} e_{ij}s \in S\}.$$

Clearly A and B are additive subgroups of S and

$$SA \subset A, \qquad Ae_{kl} \subset A, \qquad BS \subset B, \qquad e_{kl}B \subset B.$$

A contains the above-mentioned unit a, and B contains some unit b of Q.

Now put

$$C = \{\sum_k e_{k1}qe_{1k} \mid q \in BA\}.$$

Then $C \subset D$ and

$$\sum_{i,j} Ce_{ij} = \sum_{i,j} e_{i1}Ce_{1j} \subset \sum_{i,j} e_{i1}BAe_{1j} \subset S,$$

since $e_{i1}B \subset S$ and $Ae_{1j} \subset S$. Clearly C is an additive subgroup of D closed under multiplication, in fact $C \cong e_{11}BAe_{11}$ (additively and multiplicatively) under the isomorphism $D \cong e_{11}Qe_{11}$ mentioned at the beginning of this section. It remains to show that C is a right order in D, or equivalently that $e_{11}BAe_{11}$ is a right order in $e_{11}Qe_{11}$.

Let us abbreviate $e_{11} = e$. Given any $q \in eQe$, we are invited to find a nonzero element x of $eBAe$ such that $qx \in eBAe$. Let a and b be as above, and pick a unit t of Q in S such that $b^{-1}qbt \in S$. Now consider any $x \in ebtAse$. Then surely $x \in eBAe$ and

$$qx \in eqebtSae \subset ebSae \subset eBAe.$$

It remains to make sure that we can pick $x \neq 0$, so we must prove that $ebtSae \neq 0$. Since a, b, and t are units, $ebt \neq 0$ and $ae \neq 0$. The result now follows from the following:

Remark. If S is a right order in the simple ring Q, and if p and p' are nonzero elements of Q, then $pSp' \neq 0$.

Indeed, suppose $pSp' = 0$ and $p \neq 0$. Then $1 \in Q = QpQ$, since Q is simple, and so $1 = \sum_{i=1}^n q_i pq_i'$, q_i and q_i' in Q. Pick a unit s of Q in S

such that all $q_i's \in S$, then

$$s = \sum_{i=1}^n q_i p q_i's \in QpS.$$

Hence $sp' \in QpSp' = 0$, and so $p' = 0$.

EXERCISES

1. Establish the isomorphism $D \cong e_{11}Qe_{11}$ mentioned at the beginning of this section. (See also Section 3.5, Exercise 6.)

2. Given a right order S of Q and a finite set $q_1, q_2, \ldots, q_n \in Q$, show that there exists a unit s of Q in S such that $q_1s, q_2s, \ldots, q_ns \in S$.

3. Extend the Faith-Utumi Theorem to right orders in completely reducible rings which are not necessarily prime.

4. Give a simpler proof of the Faith-Utumi Theorem in the special case when S is not only a right order but also a left order in Q. (Any e_{ij} will then do.)

5 (Burgess). Show that a unit in the ring of all $n \times n$ matrices over a local ring L contains a unit of L in each row and each column. Deduce that the Faith-Utumi Theorem remains valid if Q is the ring of all $n \times n$ matrices over a local ring.

CHAPTER FIVE

Introduction to Homological Algebra

5.1 Tensor product of modules

Let A_R, $_RB$ be given right and left R-modules. We shall construct their *tensor product* $A \otimes_R B$.

We begin by considering all "formal" sums $\sum_{i=1}^n (a_i, b_i)$ of pairs of elements $a_i \in A$ and $b_i \in B$. It is tacitly assumed that formal sums are subject to the commutative and associative laws of addition. They then form a commutative semigroup $S(A,B)$ under addition. Now let θ be the smallest congruence relation on $S(A,B)$ for which

$$(a + a', b) \quad \theta \quad (a,b) + (a',b), \tag{1}$$

$$(a, b + b') \quad \theta \quad (a,b) + (a,b'), \tag{2}$$

$$(ar,b) \quad \theta \quad (a,rb), \tag{3}$$

for all a, $a' \in A$, b, $b' \in B$, and $r \in R$. Thus θ is the intersection of all congruence relations on $S(A,B)$ which satisfy (1) to (3).

It is customary to write the equivalence class

$$\theta((a,b)) = a \otimes b,$$

hence

$$\theta(\sum_{i=1}^n (a_i, b_i)) = \sum_{i=1}^n a_i \otimes b_i,$$

and we write

$$S(A,B)/\theta = A \otimes_R B.$$

PROPOSITION 1. *$A \otimes_R B$ is an Abelian group under addition.*

Proof. Since θ is a congruence relation on the semigroup $S(A,B)$, $A \otimes_R B$ is also a semigroup. It remains to define

$$0 = 0 \otimes 0$$

and

$$-\sum_{i=1}^n a_i \otimes b_i = \sum_{i=1}^n (-a_i) \otimes b_i,$$

which incidentally is

$$= \sum_{i=1}^n a_i \otimes (-b_i)$$

by (3), and to verify the usual rules. Thus

$$\left(\sum_{i=1}^n a_i \otimes b_i\right) + (0 \otimes 0) = \sum_{i=1}^n a_i \otimes b_i,$$

since

$$(a_n \otimes b_n) + (0 \otimes 0) = (a_n \otimes b_n) + (0 \otimes b_n)$$
$$= a_n \otimes b_n,$$

using the fact that

$$0 \otimes b = 00 \otimes b = 0 \otimes 0b = 0 \otimes 0,$$

according to (3). Moreover

$$\sum a_i \otimes b_i + -\sum a_i \otimes b_i$$
$$= \sum (a_i \otimes b_i + (-a_i) \otimes b_i)$$
$$= \sum 0 \otimes b_i$$
$$= \sum 0 \otimes 0 = 0 \otimes 0 = 0.$$

We shall now discuss the main property of the additive Abelian group $A \otimes_R B$.

Let C be any additive Abelian group. A mapping $\Phi : A \times B \to C$ is called *bilinear* from $(A_R, {}_RB)$ to C provided

$$\Phi(a + a', b) = \Phi(a,b) + \Phi(a',b),$$
$$\Phi(a, b + b') = \Phi(a,b) + \Phi(a,b'),$$
$$\Phi(ar,b) = \Phi(a,rb),$$

for all a, $a' \in A$, b, $b' \in B$, and $r \in R$. Here $A \times B$ denotes the Cartesian product of the sets A and B, not their direct product as groups.

Clearly the canonical mapping $\pi : A \times B \to A \otimes_R B$ defined by

$$\pi(a,b) = a \otimes b$$

is bilinear.

PROPOSITION 2. *Let Φ be any bilinear mapping from $(A_R, {}_RB)$ to C, then there exists a unique homomorphism $\phi : A \otimes_R B \to C$ such that $\phi \circ \pi = \Phi$.*

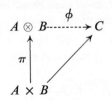

Proof. We put

$$\phi(\sum_{i=1}^{n} a_i \otimes b_i) = \sum_{i=1}^{n} \Phi(a_i, b_i)$$

and shall verify that ϕ is a mapping. Define a congruence relation θ' on $S(A,B)$ by stipulating that

$$\sum (a_i, b_i) \quad \theta' \quad \sum (a_j', b_j')$$

if and only if

$$\sum \Phi(a_i, b_i) = \sum \Phi(a_j', b_j').$$

Since Φ is bilinear, θ' also satisfies (1) to (3). For example,

$$\Phi(ar, b) = \Phi(a, rb)$$

implies

$$(ar, b) \quad \theta' \quad (a, rb).$$

Now θ was the smallest congruence relation on $S(A,B)$ satisfying (1) to (3). Therefore $\theta \le \theta'$ in the lattice of congruence relations on $S(A,B)$. Thus we may infer from

$$\sum a_i \otimes b_i = \sum a_j' \otimes b_j',$$

which means

$$\sum (a_i, b_i) \quad \theta \quad \sum (a_j', b_j'),$$

that

$$\sum (a_i, b_i) \quad \theta' \quad \sum (a_j', b_j'),$$

which is the same as

$$\sum \Phi(a_i, b_i) = \sum \Phi(a_j', b_j').$$

This shows that ϕ is indeed a single-valued mapping.

It is easily verified that ϕ is a homomorphism. Finally

$$(\phi \circ \pi)(a, b) = \phi(a \otimes b) = \Phi(a, b),$$

and this completes the proof, if we observe that clearly ϕ is uniquely determined.

We recall that an *R-S-bimodule* $_R A_S$ consists of a left module $_R A$ which is also a right module A_S such that

$$(ra)s = r(as)$$

for all $r \in R$, $a \in A$ and $s \in S$.

PROPOSITION 3. *Let $_R A_S$, $_T B_S$, and $_T C_R$ be bimodules. There is a canonical way of turning $F = Hom_S(A,B)$, $G = Hom_T(B,C)$, and $H = C \otimes {_R A}$*

into bimodules $_TF_R$, $_SG_R$, and $_TH_S$ such that

$$(fr)a = f(ra), \qquad (tf)a = t(fa), \tag{1}$$

$$b(gr) = (bg)r, \qquad b(sg) = (bs)g, \tag{2}$$

$$\left(\sum c_i \otimes a_i\right)s = \sum c_i \otimes a_i s, \qquad t \sum c_i \otimes a_i = \sum tc_i \otimes a_i, \tag{3}$$

for all a, $a_i \in A$, $b \in B$, $c_i \in C$, $r \in R$, $s \in S$, $t \in T$, $f \in F$ and $g \in G$.

Note that (1) to (3) all take the form of associative and distributive laws. In the case of (2) this was achieved by the notational trick of writing the function symbol g on the right of its argument.

Proof. (1) and (2) may indeed be taken as definitions of fr and $tf \in F$, and gr and $sg \in G$, the last two being subject to the just mentioned notational convention governing elements of G.

It is not so obvious that (3) determines hs and $th \in H$ for $h = \sum c_i \otimes a_i$. To show this, consider the mapping $\Phi : C \times A \to H$ defined by

$$\Phi(c,a) = c \otimes as.$$

It is readily verified that Φ is a bilinear mapping from $(C_R, {}_RA)$ to H. For example, let $r \in R$, then

$$\Phi(cr,a) = cr \otimes as = c \otimes ras = \Phi(c,ra).$$

By Proposition 2, there is a unique homomorphism $\phi : H \to H$ such that

$$\phi h = \phi \sum c_i \otimes a_i = \sum \Phi(c_i, a_i) = \sum c_i \otimes a_i s.$$

Writing $\phi h = hs$, we see that hs is in fact determined by (3). A similar process yields th.

Finally, a routine verification shows that $_TF_R$, $_SG_R$, and $_TH_S$ are bimodules.

In order to remember Proposition 3 more easily, we shall frequently write

$$_TF_R = {}_TB_S \oslash {}_RA_S \qquad \text{(read } B \text{ over } A\text{)},$$

$$_SG_R = {}_TB_S \obackslash {}_TC_R \qquad \text{(read } B \text{ under } C\text{)},$$

$$_TH_S = {}_TC_R \otimes {}_RA_S,$$

or more concisely,

$$F = B \oslash_S A, \qquad G = B \obackslash_T C, \qquad H = C \otimes_R A,$$

only the last notation being standard. Sometimes we shall omit the subscripts S, T, and R altogether.

The notations $\varnothing$ and $\diagdown$ are useful in more than one connection. Let us only point out now that in the situation $_RM_R$ and $_RN_R$, the generally distinct modules $N \varnothing M$ and $M \diagdown N$ are not distinguished by the usual notation $\mathrm{Hom}_R(M,N)$.

EXERCISES

For the purpose of these exercises only, let us say that the ring R *extends* the ring A if there is given a ring homomorphism of A into R. (This need not be a monomorphism.) The ring R then gives rise in a natural way to a bimodule $_AR_A$.

1. If R and S are rings extending the commutative ring A, show that the module $R \otimes_A S$ may be turned into a ring extending A such that $(r \otimes s)(r' \otimes s') = rr' \otimes ss'$, for all $r, r' \in R$, and $s, s' \in S$.

2. Let $_RM_S$ be any R-S-bimodule, where R and S extend the commutative ring A, and assume that $am = ma$, for all $a \in A$ and $m \in M$. Show that $_RM_S$ may be "considered" as a right module $M_{S \otimes R^o}$, where R^o is the ring obtained from R by inverting the order of multiplication.

3. If R is a simple ring with center F, show that $T = R \otimes_F R^o$ has an irreducible module R_T. What can be deduced from the Density Theorem?

5.2   Hom and ⊗ as functors

Let $_RA_S$ and $_RA'_S$ be bimodules with matching rings of operators. A mapping $\alpha : A \to A'$ is called a (bimodule) *homomorphism* of $_RA_S$ into $_RA'_S$ provided it is a homomorphism of $_RA$ into $_RA'$ and of A_S into A'_S, thus if it is a group homomorphism and if

$$\alpha(as) = (\alpha a)s, \qquad r(\alpha a) = \alpha(ra),$$

for all $a \in A$, $s \in S$, and $r \in R$. Unfortunately no notational device will allow us to present both these equations in the form of associative laws simultaneously. For the sake of symmetry we sometimes write $\alpha a = a\alpha$.

PROPOSITION 1.   *Given bimodule homomorphisms*

$$\alpha : {}_RA_S \to {}_RA'_S, \qquad \beta : {}_TB_S \to {}_TB'_S, \qquad \gamma : {}_TC_R \to {}_TC'_R,$$

there exist canonical homomorphisms

$$\beta \varnothing \alpha : {}_TB_S \varnothing {}_RA'_S \to {}_TB'_S \varnothing {}_RA_S,$$
$$\beta \diagdown \gamma : {}_TB'_S \diagdown {}_TC_R \to {}_TB_S \diagdown {}_TC'_R,$$
$$\gamma \otimes \alpha : {}_TC_R \otimes {}_RA_S \to {}_TC'_R \otimes {}_RA'_S,$$

such that

$$(\beta \oslash \alpha)f = \beta \circ f \circ \alpha,$$

$$(\beta \boxtimes \gamma)g = \beta * g * \gamma,$$

$$(\gamma \otimes \alpha) \sum c_i \otimes a_i = \sum \gamma c_i \otimes \alpha a_i,$$

for all $f \in B \oslash_S A'$, $g \in B' \boxtimes_T A$, $c_i \in C$, *and* $a_i \in A$.

We recall that $*$ does for function symbols written on the right what $\circ$ does for function symbols on the left. Thus, for any $b \in B$,

$$b(\beta * g * \gamma) = ((b\beta)g)\gamma = \gamma((\beta b)g).$$

(See the remark at the beginning of this section.) The usual notations for $\beta \oslash \alpha$ and $\beta \boxtimes \gamma$ are $\mathrm{Hom}(\alpha,\beta)$ and $\mathrm{Hom}(\beta,\gamma)$, respectively.

Proof. We shall omit the routine verifications that $f \to \beta \circ f \circ \alpha$ defines a homomorphism of $B \oslash A'$ into $B' \oslash A$. Similarly $\beta \boxtimes \gamma$ causes no difficulty, except perhaps notationally. It remains to show that $\sum c_i \otimes a_i \to \sum \gamma c_i \otimes \alpha a_i$ is a homomorphism of $C \otimes A$ into $C' \otimes A'$.

The crux of the proof is to show that it is a mapping, and this follows from the fact that $(c,a) \to \gamma c \otimes \alpha a$ is a bilinear mapping from $(C_R, {}_R A)$ to $C' \otimes {}_R A'$.

In stating the next result we shall omit all subscripts, which are assumed to be as in the last proposition.

PROPOSITION 2. *Let there be given bimodule homomorphisms*

$$\alpha : A \to A', \qquad \beta : B \to B', \qquad \gamma : C \to C'$$

and

$$\alpha' : A' \to A'', \qquad \beta' : B' \to B'', \qquad \gamma' : C' \to C'',$$

then

$$(\beta' \oslash \alpha) \circ (\beta \oslash \alpha') = (\beta' \circ \beta) \oslash (\alpha' \circ \alpha),$$

$$(\beta \boxtimes \gamma') \circ (\beta' \boxtimes \gamma) = (\beta' \circ \beta) \boxtimes (\gamma' \circ \gamma),$$

$$(\gamma' \otimes \alpha') \circ (\gamma \otimes \alpha) = (\gamma' \circ \gamma) \otimes (\alpha' \circ \alpha).$$

Proof. For example, to show the first equation, apply the left side to $f \in B \oslash_S A''$, and obtain

$$\beta' \circ (\beta \circ f \circ \alpha') \circ \alpha = (\beta' \circ \beta) \circ f \circ (\alpha' \circ \alpha),$$

which also results from applying the right side to f. The other two equations are proved similarly.

The above results are often stated more concisely by saying that $\oslash$, $\boxtimes$ and $\otimes$ are *functors* in two variables, and that $\beta \oslash \alpha$ is *covariant* in β and *contravariant* in α, $\beta \boxtimes \gamma$ is contravariant in β and covariant in

γ, and $\gamma \otimes \alpha$ is covariant in both variables. We shall refrain from spelling out a rigorous definition of the words "functor," "covariant," and "contravariant."

COROLLARY. *If* 1 *denotes the identity mapping of A, B, or C, we have*

$$(1 \oslash \alpha) \circ (\beta \oslash 1) = \beta \oslash \alpha = (\beta \oslash 1) \circ (1 \oslash \alpha),$$
$$(1 \between \gamma) \circ (\beta \between 1) = \beta \between \gamma = (\beta \between 1) \circ (1 \oslash \gamma),$$
$$(1 \otimes \alpha) \circ (\gamma \otimes 1) = \gamma \otimes \alpha = (\gamma \otimes 1) \circ (1 \otimes \alpha).$$

This is often rendered by the assertion that $\oslash$, $\between$, and $\otimes$ are *bifunctors*.

PROPOSITION 3. *Given modules* $_R A_S$, $_T B_S$, $_U C_R$, *and* $_T D_U$, *there are canonical isomorphisms*

$$\sigma_1 : (D \otimes C) \otimes A \simeq D \otimes (C \otimes A),$$
$$\sigma_2 : (B \oslash A) \oslash C \simeq B \oslash (C \otimes A),$$
$$\sigma_3 : D \between (B \oslash A) \simeq (D \between B) \oslash A,$$
$$\sigma_4 : C \between (D \between B) \simeq (D \otimes C) \between B,$$
$$\sigma_5 : R \otimes A \simeq A(\simeq A \otimes S),$$
$$\sigma_6 : R \between A \simeq A(\simeq A \oslash S),$$

such that

$$\sigma_1((d \otimes c) \otimes a) = d \otimes (c \otimes a),$$
$$(\sigma_2 f_2)(c \otimes a) = (f_2 c)a,$$
$$d((\sigma_3 f_3)a) = (df_3)a,$$
$$(d \otimes c)(\sigma_4 f_4) = d(cf_4),$$
$$\sigma_5(r \otimes a) = ra,$$
$$\sigma_6 f_6 = 1f_6,$$

where $d \in D$, $c \in C$, $a \in A$, *and* f_i *belongs to the domain of* σ_i.

Proof. It is easily verified that these mappings exist and are in fact isomorphisms. As examples, we shall consider σ_2 and σ_5 in some detail.

Clearly $(c,a) \to (f_2 c)a$ is a bilinear mapping of $(C_R, {}_R A)$ into B. By Proposition 2 of Section 5.1, there is a mapping $f_2' : C \otimes A \to B$ such that $f_2'(c \otimes a) = (f_2 c)a$. Thus we have a mapping $f_2 \to f_2'$, which is evidently a homomorphism of T-U-bimodules, and may be denoted by σ_2.

On the other hand, let $f_2' \in B \oslash (C \otimes A)$ be given, then we may define $f_2 \in (B \oslash A) \oslash C$ by $(f_2 c)a = f_2'(c \otimes a)$, and it is clear that the mapping $f_2' \to f_2$ thus defined is inverse to the mapping $\sigma_2 : f_2 \to f_2'$, which is therefore an isomorphism.

Again, $(r,a) \to ra$ is a bilinear mapping of $(R_R, {}_R A)$ into A. By Proposition 2 of Section 5.1, there exists a mapping $\sigma_5 : R \otimes A \to A$ such that $\sigma_5(r \otimes a) = ra$, and this is easily seen to be an R-S-homomorphism. Moreover, σ_5 is clearly the inverse of the mapping $a \to 1 \otimes a$, hence an isomorphism.

The canonical isomorphisms of Proposition 3 have an important property which is illustrated by the following commutative diagram concerning σ_2. It is assumed that $\alpha : A \to A'$, $\beta : B \to B'$ and $\gamma : C \to C'$.

$$
\begin{array}{ccc}
(B \oslash A') \oslash C' & \xrightarrow{\ \sigma_2\ } & B \oslash (C' \otimes A') \\
\Big\downarrow {\scriptstyle (\beta \oslash \alpha) \oslash \gamma} & & \Big\downarrow {\scriptstyle \beta \oslash (\gamma \otimes \alpha)} \\
(B' \oslash A) \oslash C & \xrightarrow[\ \sigma_2\ ]{} & B' \oslash (C \otimes A)
\end{array}
$$

To see that this diagram does in fact commute, let $f \in (B \oslash A') \oslash C'$ and apply $((\beta \oslash (\gamma \otimes \alpha)) \circ \sigma_2) f$ to $\sum_{i=1}^{n} c_i \otimes a_i$, where $c_i \in C$ and $a_i \in A$. A straightforward calculation yields $\sum_{i=1}^{n} \beta((f(\gamma c_i))(\alpha a_i))$, and this is also what we get when we apply $\sigma_2 \circ ((\beta \oslash \alpha) \oslash \gamma)$ to $\sum_{i=1}^{n} c_i \otimes a_i$.

This result is usually stated more concisely by saying that the isomorphism σ_2 between the functors $(\beta \oslash \alpha) \oslash \gamma$ and $\beta \oslash (\gamma \otimes \alpha)$ is *natural*. What it means in practice is that there is no harm in identifying $(B \oslash A) \oslash C$ with $B \oslash (C \otimes A)$.

We shall not give a rigorous definition of "natural" isomorphisms between functors (we did not even define "functors"), but we hope that the above discussion will make the concept clear. We then state without proof:

PROPOSITION 4. *The canonical isomorphisms of Proposition 3 are all natural.*

We recall that $\sum^*$ denotes the direct sum of modules.

PROPOSITION 5. *Let there be given a family of bimodules* $\{ {}_R A^i {}_S \mid i \in I \}$ *and bimodules* ${}_T B_S$ *and* ${}_U C_R$. *Then there exist canonical isomorphisms*

$$\prod_{i \in I} (B \oslash A^i) \cong B \oslash \textstyle\sum_{i \in I}^{*} A^i, \tag{1}$$

$$\prod_{i \in I} (A^i \oslash B) \cong (\textstyle\prod_{i \in I} A^i) \oslash B, \tag{2}$$

$$\textstyle\sum_{i \in I}^{*} (C \otimes A^i) \cong C \otimes \textstyle\sum_{i \in I}^{*} A^i. \tag{3}$$

The "mirror duals" of these isomorphisms are of course also valid.

Proof. To exhibit (1), let us recall (Section 4.1, Proposition 1) that for any family of homomorphisms $f_i \in \text{Hom}_S(A^i, B)$ there exists a unique homomorphism $f : A \to B$ such that $f \circ \kappa_i = f_i$, where $A = \sum_{i \in I}^* A^i$ and $\kappa_i : A^i \to A$ canonically. Thus we have a one-to-one correspondence between families $\{f_i : A^i \to B \mid i \in I\}$ and homomorphisms $\{f : A \to B\}$. This correspondence is easily seen to be a T-R-isomorphism between $\prod_{i \in I}(B \oslash A^i)$ and $B \oslash A$. We have thus established (1), and (2) is proved similarly.

We shall now consider (3), using the same notation as above. Thus we have

$$1_C \otimes \kappa_i : C \otimes A^i \to C \otimes A,$$

and there exists a unique homomorphism $f : B \to C \otimes A$ such that $f \circ \lambda_i = 1_C \otimes \kappa_i$, where $B = \sum_{i \in I}^* (C \otimes A^i)$ and $\lambda_i : C \otimes A^i \to B$ canonically. To prove that f is an isomorphism we shall exhibit its inverse.

If $a = \sum_{i \in I} \kappa_i a_i$ ($a_i \in A^i$) is any element of A, we have a bilinear mapping $(c, a) \to \sum_{i \in I} \lambda_i(c \otimes a_i)$ of $(C_R, {}_R A)$ into B, hence a homomorphism $g : C \otimes A \to B$ such that

$$g(c \otimes a) = \sum_{i \in I} \lambda_i(c \otimes a_i).$$

We omit the routine verification that g is indeed the inverse of f. Note that the two sums appearing in this paragraph are finite sums, since all but a finite number of the a_i are zero.

To illustrate some of the foregoing, let us consider the character module of a right module M_R. Put $K = Q/Z$, the rationals modulo 1, and consider the bimodules ${}_Z M_R$ and ${}_Z K_Z$. We define $M^* = M \oslash_Z K$ (see also Section 4.2). By Proposition 3 of the last section, this is a bimodule ${}_R M^*_Z$, hence a left module ${}_R M^*$. Similarly, of course, the character module of a left module will be a right module.

Let $\alpha : A_R \to B_R$ be an R-homomorphism, and put $\alpha^* = \alpha \oslash 1_K$. By Proposition 1, $\alpha^* : {}_R B^* \to {}_R A^*$. By Proposition 2, * is a contravariant functor. Thus if $\beta : B_R \to C_R$, one has $(\beta \circ \alpha)^* = \alpha^* \circ \beta^*$.

Given modules ${}_R C$ and D_R, Proposition 3 yields the isomorphism

$$\sigma : C \oslash D^* \cong (D \otimes C)^*,$$

where, for $d \in D$, $c \in C$, and $g \in C \oslash D^*$,

$$(d \otimes c)\sigma g = d(cg).$$

(We have put $B = K$ in σ_4.) By Proposition 4, this isomorphism is natural, hence the following diagram commutes, assuming that $\gamma : C \to C'$ and

$\delta : D \to D'$ are given homomorphisms.

$$
\begin{array}{ccc}
C' \otimes D'^* & \xrightarrow{\ \ \sigma\ \ } & (D' \otimes C')^* \\[2mm]
{\scriptstyle \gamma \otimes \delta^*}\Big\downarrow & & \Big\downarrow{\scriptstyle (\delta \otimes \gamma)^*} \\[2mm]
C \otimes D^* & \xrightarrow[\ \ \sigma\ \ ]{} & (D \otimes C)^*
\end{array}
$$

Finally, Proposition 5 yields the isomorphism

$$\prod_{i \in I} A_i^* \cong \left(\sum_{i \in I}^* A_i\right)^*,$$

for any family $\{A_i \mid i \in I\}$ of right modules. Of course, the same is true for left modules, or even for bimodules.

EXERCISES

1. Show the existence of a canonical homomorphism: $A \to (B \varnothing A) \otimes B$.

2. Carry out the suggested calculation to show that σ_2 of Proposition 3 is natural.

3. Prove that σ_5 of Proposition 3 is natural.

4. Are the isomorphisms of Proposition 5 natural?

5. Exhibit the natural isomorphism

$$A^* \varnothing\ C \cong (C \otimes A)^*.$$

6. Show that A^* is a direct summand of A^{***}.

7 (Tewari). If either M_R or N_R is projective and finitely generated, show that the canonical homomorphism

$$\sigma : N \otimes (R \varnothing M) \to N \varnothing M$$

is an isomorphism, where

$$\sigma(n \otimes f)m = n(fm),$$

for $n \in N, f \in R \varnothing\ M, m \in M$.

5.3 Exact sequences

For the time being A, B, and C will denote additive Abelian groups, modules or bimodules, and the word "homomorphism" is to be understood correspondingly. Let $f : A \to B$ be such a homomorphism, one calls A the *domain* of f, B the *range* of f,

$$\text{Im } f = fA = \{ fa \mid a \in A \}$$

the *image* of f and

$$\text{Ker } f = f^{-1}0 = \{ a \in A \mid fa = 0 \}$$

the *kernel* of f.

Now consider a pair (f,g) of homomorphisms so that the range of f is the same as the domain of g. We may illustrate this situation by the diagram

$$A \xrightarrow{\; f \;} B \xrightarrow{\; g \;} C.$$

Such a pair is called *exact* if $\text{Im } f = \text{Ker } g$, that is to say

$$\forall_{b \in B} (\exists_{a \in A} b = fa \Leftrightarrow gb = 0).$$

More generally, a "sequence" of homomorphisms

$$\cdots \xrightarrow{\; f_{n-1} \;} A_n \xrightarrow{\; f_n \;} A_{n+1} \xrightarrow{\; f_{n+1} \;} \cdots$$

is called exact if each adjacent pair is exact, that is if $\text{Im } f_n = \text{Ker } f_{n+1}$ for all admissible n. Such a sequence may be finite, or infinite in one or both directions.

Given right modules A_R, B_R, and C_R, let $_RA^*$, $_RB^*$, and $_RC^*$ be their character modules. We recall that $A^* = \text{Hom}_Z(A,Q/Z)$, and that for any $f \in \text{Hom}_R(A,B)$ there is canonically associated $f^* \in \text{Hom}_R(B^*, A^*)$ such that

$$(b^*f^*)a = b^*(fa) \qquad (a \in A, b^* \in B^*).$$

PROPOSITION 1. *The pair*

$$A \xrightarrow{\; f \;} B \xrightarrow{\; g \;} C$$

is exact if and only if the pair

$$C^* \xrightarrow{\; g^* \;} B^* \xrightarrow{\; f^* \;} A^*$$

is exact.

Proof. Let $b^* \in B^*$, then $b^* \in \text{Ker } f^*$ if and only if

$$b^*(\text{Im } f) = b^*(fA) = (b^*f^*)A = 0.$$

On the other hand, $b^* \in \text{Im } g^*$ if and only if there exists a character c^* of C such that $b^* = c^*g^*$, that is

$$b^*b = (c^*g^*)b = c^*(gb)$$

for all $b \in B$. This is the same as saying that $b^*(\mathrm{Ker}\ g) = 0$; for if so, then $gb \to b^*b$ is a homomorphism of Im g into Q/Z, and this can be extended to a homomorphism $c^* : C \to Q/Z$, in view of the fact that Q/Z is divisible, hence injective.

Thus Im $f = \mathrm{Ker}\ g$ clearly implies that $\mathrm{Ker} f^* = \mathrm{Im}\ g^*$. Conversely, let us assume the latter. Then by the above

$$b^*(\mathrm{Im} f) = 0 \Leftrightarrow b^*(\mathrm{Ker}\ g) = 0.$$

This being so for all $b^* \in B^*$, can we deduce that Im $f = \mathrm{Ker}\ g$? Yes, in view of the following general observation.

LEMMA.   *Let D_R be any submodule of B_R, b any element of B not in D. Then there exists a character b^* of B which annihilates D but not b.*
   Proof.   Apply Section 4.2, Lemma 2 to B/D.

COROLLARY.   *A sequence of modules is exact if and only if the corresponding sequence of character modules (directed the opposite way) is exact.*

The *zero homomorphism* of A into B sends each element of A onto the zero element of B. Let 0 denote the group or module consisting only of one element, then for any group or module A there exists exactly one homomorphism $A \to 0$ and one homomorphism $0 \to A$, in each case the zero homomorphism.

What does it mean to say that the following sequences are exact?

$$0 \longrightarrow A \xrightarrow{f} B,$$

$$A \xrightarrow{f} B \longrightarrow 0,$$

$$0 \longrightarrow A \xrightarrow{f} B \longrightarrow 0,$$

$$0 \longrightarrow A \xrightarrow{f} B \xrightarrow{g} C \longrightarrow 0.$$

Clearly the exactness of the first three sequences asserts that f is a monomorphism, epimorphism, or isomorphism, respectively. The last sequence, often called a *short exact sequence*, asserts that $f : A \to B$ is mono, that $B/fA \cong C$, and that g is the epimorphism of B onto C induced by this isomorphism. In particular, if $A \subset B$, we have a short exact sequence

$$0 \longrightarrow A \xrightarrow{\kappa} B \xrightarrow{\pi} B/A \longrightarrow 0,$$

where κ and π are the canonical monomorphism and epimorphism, respectively.

We shall now investigate what the functors $\otimes$ and Hom do to short exact sequences.

PROPOSITION 2.   *Given a short exact sequence*

$$0 \longrightarrow {}_RA_S \xrightarrow{f} {}_RB_S \xrightarrow{g} {}_RC_S \longrightarrow 0,$$

the following sequences are exact, for each ${}_TE_S$ *and* ${}_TD_R$:

$$0 \longrightarrow A \oslash E \xrightarrow{f \oslash 1} B \oslash E \xrightarrow{g \oslash 1} C \oslash E, \qquad (1)$$

$$0 \longrightarrow E \oslash C \xrightarrow{1 \oslash g} E \oslash B \xrightarrow{1 \oslash f} E \oslash A, \qquad (2)$$

$$D \otimes A \xrightarrow{1 \otimes f} D \otimes B \xrightarrow{1 \otimes g} D \otimes C \longrightarrow 0. \qquad (3)$$

Moreover

$g \oslash 1$ *is epi for every epimorphism g if and only if* E_S *is*   (1')
projective,

$1 \oslash f$ *is epi for every monomorphism f if and only if* E_S *is*   (2')
injective,

$1 \otimes f$ *is mono for every monomorphism f if and only if* ${}_RD^*$ *is*   (3')
injective.

In stating this theorem, subscripts have been liberally suppressed. (1) and (2) are often condensed by saying that Hom is *left exact*, while (3) is rendered by saying that $\otimes$ is a *right exact* functor. ${}_RD^*$ is of course the character module of D_R. It goes without saying that the above remain valid if $A \oslash E$, $D \otimes A$, etc. are replaced by their "mirror duals" $E \otimes A$, $A \otimes D$, etc. (However, arrows must not be reversed.)

Proof. (1) The kernel of $f \oslash 1$ consists of all $p : E \to A$ such that $f \circ p = 0$. Since f is mono, this kernel is 0 as required.

The image of $f \oslash 1$ consists of all $f \circ p$, where $p : E \to A$. The kernel of $g \oslash 1$ consists of all $q : E \to B$ such that $g \circ q = 0$. Clearly, the former is contained in the latter. To prove equality, we must show the converse. Thus assume $g \circ q = 0$, then $\mathrm{Im}\, q \subset \mathrm{Ker}\, g = \mathrm{Im}\, f$. For any $e \in E$ we may therefore define pe as the a for which $fa = qe$, the uniqueness of a being due to the fact that f is mono.

Finally, the image of $g \oslash 1$ consists of all $g \circ q$, where $q : E \to B$, that is all those elements r of $C \oslash E$ which can be "lifted" to B:

This is all of $C \oslash E$, for an arbitrary epimorphism g, if and only if E is projective.

(2) The kernel of $1 \oslash g$ consists of all $p : C \to E$ such that $p \circ g = 0$. Since g is epi, this kernel is 0 as required.

The image of $1 \oslash g$ consists of all $p \circ g$, where $p : C \to E$. The kernel of $1 \oslash f$ consists of all $q : B \to E$ such that $q \circ f = 0$. Clearly, the former is contained in the latter. To prove equality, we must show the converse. Thus assume $q \circ f = 0$, then $\operatorname{Ker} g = \operatorname{Im} f \subset \operatorname{Ker} q$. For any $b \in B$ we may therefore define $p(gb) = qb$, and it follows that $q = p \circ g$.

Finally, the image of $1 \oslash f$ consists of all $q \circ f$, where $q : B \to E$, that is all those elements r of $E \oslash A$ which can be "extended" to B:

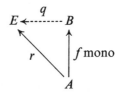

This is all of $E \oslash A$, for an arbitrary monomorphism f, if and only if E is injective.

(3) We recall from the last section that the canonical isomorphism

$$\sigma : D^* \oslash A \to (D \otimes A)^*$$

is natural. Therefore the squares in the following diagram are commutative:

$$
\begin{array}{ccccccc}
0 \to & D^* \oslash C & \to & D^* \oslash B & \to & D^* \oslash A \\
& \downarrow & & \downarrow & & \downarrow \\
0 \to & (D \otimes C)^* & \to & (D \otimes B)^* & \to & (D \otimes A)^*
\end{array}
$$

Now by (2), the top row is exact. Since the vertical mappings are all isomorphisms, it readily follows that also the bottom row is exact. Hence (3) is exact by Proposition 1.

Finally, in view of Proposition 1, the sequence

$$0 \longrightarrow D \otimes A \xrightarrow{1 \otimes f} D \otimes B$$

is exact if and only if the bottom row of the following diagram is exact:

$$
\begin{array}{ccccc}
D^* \oslash B & \to & D^* \oslash A & \to 0 \\
\downarrow & & \downarrow & & \downarrow \\
(D \otimes B)^* & \to & (D \otimes A)^* & \to 0
\end{array}
$$

Again, this means that the top row is exact, and by (2′) this is the case for all monomorphisms f if and only if D^* is injective.

The module D_R is called *flat* if for any monomorphism $f: {}_R A \to {}_R B$ the induced homomorphism $1 \otimes f: D \otimes_R A \to D \otimes_R B$ is also mono. Roughly speaking, this means that from $A \subset B$ we can infer $D \otimes A \subset D \otimes B$. (3') of the last Proposition may thus be rephrased as follows.

COROLLARY. *The module D_R is flat if and only if its character module ${}_R D^*$ is injective.*

The same holds for left modules.

PROPOSITION 3. *Let ${}_R A_S$, ${}_T B_S$, and ${}_T C_R$ be given bimodules. Then*

$$C_R \text{ projective} \quad \& \quad A_S \text{ projective} \Rightarrow (C \otimes A)_S \text{ projective}, \qquad (1)$$

$$_T B \text{ injective} \quad \& \quad A_S \text{ projective} \Rightarrow {}_T(B \oslash A) \text{ injective}, \qquad (2)$$

$$B_S \text{ injective} \quad \& \quad {}_R A \text{ flat} \qquad \Rightarrow (B \oslash A)_R \text{ injective}, \qquad (3)$$

$$C_R \text{ flat} \quad \& \quad A_S \text{ flat} \qquad \Rightarrow (C \otimes A)_S \text{ flat}. \qquad (4)$$

The "mirror duals" of these statements are of course also valid.

Proof. This is shown with the help of the criteria for projectivity, injectivity, and flatness contained in Proposition 2, using the natural associativity relations of the last section. Here, for example, is a proof of (3).

Let $0 \to X_R \to Y_R$ be exact. Then $0 \to X \otimes A \to Y \otimes A$ is also exact, since ${}_R A$ is flat. Since B_S is injective, we deduce the exactness of

$$B \oslash (Y \otimes A) \to B \oslash (X \otimes A) \to 0.$$

Using the natural isomorphism σ_2 of Propositions 3 and 4 of Section 5.2, we readily conclude that

$$(B \oslash A) \oslash Y \to (B \oslash A) \oslash X \to 0$$

is exact. Now, by (1') of the present Proposition 2, $B \oslash A$ is injective.

EXERCISES

1. If A is a submodule of B, show that $(B/A)^*$ is isomorphic with the submodule of B^* consisting of all characters which annihilate A.

2. Deduce Section 4.2, Lemma 3 from the present Proposition 1.

3. Give a direct proof of the right exactness of $\otimes$.

4. (a) If $\kappa: A \to B$ is mono and $\phi: C \to B$ then there exists $\psi: C \to A$ such that $\kappa \circ \psi = \phi$ if and only if Im $\phi \subset$ Im κ.

(b) If $\pi: B \to A$ is epi and $\phi: B \to C$ then there exists $\psi: A \to C$ such that $\psi \circ \pi = \phi$ if and only if Ker $\pi \subset$ Ker ϕ.

5. In the diagram

it is assumed that both squares are commutative and that the vertical mappings are isomorphisms. Show that the top row is exact if and only if the bottom row is exact.

5.4   Flat modules

In the preceding section we introduced the concept of flatness. A left module $_RM$ was called flat provided, whenever $\kappa : A_R \to B_R$ is mono, then $\kappa \otimes 1 : A \otimes_R M \to B \otimes_R M$ is also mono. We had proved that always, if $\pi : B_R \to C_R$ is epi, then $\pi \otimes 1 : B \otimes_R M \to C \otimes_R M$ is epi.

To put matters into more down-to-earth terms, assume $A \subset B$ and let the image of $\kappa \otimes 1$ be denoted by $[A \otimes M]$. Then $[A \otimes M]$ consists of all elements of $B \otimes M$ of the form $\sum_{i=1}^n a_i \otimes m_i$, where $a_i \in A$. $[A \otimes M]$ must be distinguished from $A \otimes M$, in fact, the canonical mapping $A \otimes M \to [A \otimes M]$ is an isomorphism if and only if M is flat. On the other hand, we always have

$$(B \otimes M)/[A \otimes M] \cong B/A \otimes M.$$

Let us look at an example to see why the isomorphism between $A \otimes M$ and $[A \otimes M]$ should not be taken for granted.

Example.   Let $R = Z$ be the ring of integers, B the additive group of integers, A the additive group of even integers. Put $M = Z/2Z$, the additive group of integers modulo 2. Then $[A \otimes M]$ consists of all

$$\sum_{i=1}^n 2b_i \otimes m_i = \sum_{i=1}^n b_i \otimes 2m_i = 0,$$

where $b_i \in B = Z$, hence $[A \otimes M] \cong 0$. On the other hand $A \cong Z$, hence $A \otimes M \cong Z \otimes M \cong M$.

PROPOSITION 1.   *The module $_RM$ is flat if and only if, for any right ideal A of R, $A \otimes_R M \cong AM$ canonically. The same is true if A is any finitely generated right ideal.*

Proof.   We recall that the mapping $(r,m) \to rm$ gives the canonical isomorphism $R \otimes M \cong M$. Now when $_RM$ is flat the canonical mapping $A \otimes M \to R \otimes M$ is mono, hence so is the compound mapping $A \otimes M \to M$. Since the image of this mapping is clearly AM, flatness of M implies that $A \otimes M \to AM$ is an isomorphism.

Conversely, let us assume that $A \otimes M \simeq AM$, hence that $A \otimes M \to M$ is mono. Then $M^* \to (A \otimes M)^*$ is epi, by Proposition 1 of the last section. Since $(A \otimes M)^*$ is canonically isomorphic with $\text{Hom}\,(A,M^*)$ (see Proposition 3 of Section 5.2), the condition for injectivity (Section 4.2, Lemma 1) allows us to conclude that M_R^* is injective, hence that $_RM$ is flat (see the Corollary to Proposition 2 of Section 5.3).

Suppose now we only assume that $A \otimes M \simeq AM$ for finitely generated right ideals A. Then let B be any right ideal, we claim that $B \otimes M \to M$ is still mono. Thus assume that $\sum_{i=1}^{n} b_i m_i = 0$, then $\sum_{i=1}^{n} b_i \otimes m_i = 0$ in $A \otimes M$, where $A = \sum_{i=1}^{n} b_i R$ is a finitely generated right ideal. In view of the canonical homomorphism $A \otimes M \to B \otimes M$, we may deduce that also $\sum_{i=1}^{n} b_i \otimes m_i = 0$ in $B \otimes M$. The proof is now complete.

The time has come to consider examples of flat modules. Clearly $_RR$ is flat, for if A_R is a submodule of B_R then the canonical isomorphism $B \otimes_R R \simeq B$ induces the canonical isomorphism $A \otimes_R R \simeq A$.

PROPOSITION 2. *The direct sum of a family of left R-modules $\{M_i \mid i \in I\}$ is flat if and only if each M_i is flat.*

Proof. The direct sum is flat if and only if its character module is injective (see Section 5.3, Corollary to Proposition 2), that is if and only if $\prod_{i \in I} M_i^*$ is injective [Section 5.2, Proposition 5 (1)]. But this means that each M_i^* is injective (by Section 4.2, Proposition 2), that is each M_i is flat.

COROLLARY. *Every free module and every projective module is flat.*

Proof. A free left R-module is a direct sum of copies of $_RR$ and a projective left R-module is a direct summand of a free one.

Since every module is isomorphic to a factor module of a free module, the following criterion for flatness is of interest.

PROPOSITION 3. *Let $_RM \simeq F/K$ where $_RF$ is flat, for example free. Then $_RM$ is flat if and only if $AF \cap K = AK$ for every right ideal A. The same is true if A is any finitely generated right ideal.*

Remark. Since $AK \subset AF \cap K$ in any case, the condition for flatness is $AF \cap K \subset AK$.

Proof. By the right exactness of $\otimes$, we have an exact sequence

$$A \otimes K \to A \otimes F \to A \otimes M \to 0.$$

Since F is flat, $A \otimes F \simeq AF$ canonically, and the image of $A \otimes K$ in $A \otimes F$ corresponds to AK under this canonical isomorphism. Therefore $A \otimes M \simeq AF/AK$. Hence, by Proposition 1, M is flat if and only if $AM \simeq AF/AK$ for all right ideals A or for all finitely generated right ideals A.

Now, in any case, AM consists of all

$$\sum_{i=1}^{n} a_i(f_i \pi) = \sum_{i=1}^{n} (a_i f_i)\pi,$$

where

$$\pi : {}_RF \to {}_RM, \qquad f_i \in F, \qquad a_i \in A.$$

Thus

$$AM = (AF)\pi \cong AF/(AF \cap K).$$

Therefore, M is flat if and only if

$$AF/(AF \cap K) \cong AF/AK$$

for all A or all finitely generated A. Since $AK \subset AF \cap K$, this can happen if and only if $AF \cap K = AK$.

COROLLARY. *Let R be a ring in which every finitely generated ideal is principal. Let ${}_RM \cong F/K$, where ${}_RF$ is free. Then ${}_RM$ is flat if and only if $rF \cap K \subset rK$ for all elements r of R.*

Proof. The finitely generated right ideal A of Proposition 3 may be taken to be of the form $A = rR$.

For what rings are all modules flat? We recall that a ring is called *regular* if for every element r there exists an element r' such that $rr'r = r$.

PROPOSITION 4. *Every left R-module is flat if and only if R is regular.*

Remark. Since regularity is a symmetric concept, we may replace "left" by "right" in this proposition.

Proof. (1) Let $r \in R$ and assume that R/Rr is flat. Then, by Proposition 3, $A \cap Rr = Ar$ for any right ideal A. In particular, take $A = rR$, then $r \in rR \cap Rr = rRr$, and so $r = rr'r$ for some $r' \in R$.

(2) Assume that R is regular and let ${}_RM \cong F/K$, ${}_RF$ free. Recall that any finitely generated right ideal is principal (see von Neumann's Lemma in Section 3.5). Thus we may use the corollary to Proposition 3 and need only show that $rF \cap K \subset rK$. Let $k \in K \cap rF$; then, for some $f \in F$, $k = rf = rr'rf = rr'k \in rK$, and this completes the proof.

The Corollary to Proposition 3 may also be used to show that a module over the ring of integers is flat if and only if it is torsion-free. The latter concept may be defined for arbitrary integral domains, which term we may as well extend to noncommutative rings. Thus we call the ring R an *integral domain* if the product of two nonzero elements of R is nonzero. The left module ${}_RM$ is then called *torsion-free* if $0 \neq r \in R$ and $0 \neq m \in M$ implies $0 \neq rm$.

LEMMA. *If R is an integral domain, every free R-module is torsion-free.*

Proof. Let ${}_RF$ be free with basis $\{f_i \mid i \in I\}$. Let $0 \neq r \in R$ and suppose

$rf = 0$, where $f = \sum_{i \in I} r_i f_i$, all but a finite number of the r_i being zero. Then, for all $i \in I$, $rr_i = 0$, hence $r_i = 0$. Thus $f = 0$ as required.

PROPOSITION 5. *Let R be an integral domain in which every finitely generated right ideal is principal. Then a left R-module is flat if and only if it is torsion-free.*

Proof. Let $_R M \simeq F/K$, where $_R F$ is free. By the corollary to Proposition 3, $_R M$ is flat if and only if

$$\forall_{0 \neq r \in R} \forall_{f \in F} (rf \in K \Rightarrow rf \in rK).$$

(We are clearly allowed to restrict r to be $\neq 0$.) Since F is torsion-free, $rf \in rK$ if and only if $f \in K$. The condition therefore becomes

$$\forall_{0 \neq r \in R} \forall_{f \in F} (rf \in K \Rightarrow f \in K).$$

Replacing F/K by M, we may write this

$$\forall_{0 \neq r \in R} \forall_{m \in M} (rm = 0 \Rightarrow m = 0),$$

which asserts that $_R M$ is torsion-free.

It is also possible to deduce this result directly from Proposition 1.

EXERCISES

1. Show that $_R M$ is flat if and only if, for any large right ideal L of R, $L \otimes M \simeq LM$ canonically.

2. Suppose that $_R M \simeq F/K$, $_R F$ free. Show that $_R M$ is flat if and only if $LF \cap K = LK$ for every large right ideal L.

3. If B is any left ideal of R, show that R/B is flat if and only if $rR \cap B = rB$ for all $r \in R$.

4. Give another proof of Proposition 5, deducing it directly from Proposition 1.

5. Let $\{K_i \mid i \in I\}$ be a family of submodules of M, simply ordered under inclusion, such that M/K_i is flat for each $i \in I$. If $K = \bigcup_{i \in I} K_i$, show that M/K is also flat.

6 (Tewari). If S is the sum of all $R : A$, A any ideal of the commutative ring R invertible in Q (see Section 4.3, Exercise 14), show that S_R is flat.

7 (Utumi). If R is a regular ring, B_S is injective, and $_R A_S$ is any R-S-bimodule, show that $\text{Hom}_S (A,B)$ is injective as a right R-module. [*Hint:* Use Section 5.3, Proposition 3 (3).]

The following exercises are taken from Bass (1960).

8. Let N be an ideal of R, $0 \to K_R \to P_R \to M_R \to 0$ exact, P_R flat. Show that $M \otimes N = PN/KN$.

9. Let R be semiperfect, $N = \text{Rad } R$, $P \to M$ a projective cover of the finitely generated module M_R with kernel K. Show that $K \subset PN$ and $MN \cong PN/K$. (*Hint:* Use the construction of P in Section 4.2, Exercise 15.)

10. Let R be semiperfect and M_R finitely generated. Show that the following statements are equivalent:

(a) M is projective.

(b) M is flat.

(c) $M \otimes N \cong MN$ canonically.

[*Hint:* In order to show that (c) $\Rightarrow$ (a), use Exercises 8 and 9 to establish $KN = K$, then use Section 4.2, Exercise 14, to deduce $K = 0$.]

5.5   Torsion and extension products

If $\lambda \in \text{Hom}_R(A,B)$ we may write $A \to B$ for λ if there is no other homomorphism around to compete for this designation. Thus, in the diagram below, $A \to E$ is allowed to stand for $\beta \circ \lambda$ only because this is equal to $\lambda' \circ \alpha$.

PROPOSITION 1.   *In the diagram*

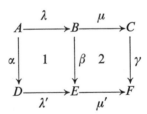

both squares are assumed to be commutative and both top and bottom rows are assumed to be exact. Then

$$\frac{\text{Im}\,(B \to E) \cap \text{Im}\,(D \to E)}{\text{Im}\,(A \to E)} \cong \frac{\text{Ker}\,(B \to F)}{\text{Ker}\,(B \to C) + \text{Ker}\,(B \to E)}.$$

Proof.

$$\text{Im }\beta \cap \text{Im }\lambda' = \text{Im }\beta \cap \text{Ker }\mu' = \{\beta b \mid \mu'\beta b = 0\}$$

$$= \{\beta b \mid \gamma\mu b = 0\} = \beta \,\text{Ker}\,(\gamma \circ \mu),$$

$$\text{Im }(\beta \circ \lambda) = \beta \,\text{Im }\lambda = \beta \,\text{Ker }\mu = \beta(\text{Ker }\mu + \text{Ker }\beta).$$

The result now follows from one of the classical isomorphism theorems of group theory (Section 1.4, Proposition 2), since clearly

$$\frac{\beta \, \text{Ker} \, (\gamma \circ \mu)}{\beta(\text{Ker} \, \mu + \text{Ker} \, \beta)} \simeq \frac{\text{Ker} \, (\gamma \circ \mu)/\text{Ker} \, \beta}{(\text{Ker} \, \mu + \text{Ker} \, \beta)/\text{Ker} \, \beta} \, .$$

As will be seen, Proposition 1 is extremely useful in the popular pastime called "diagram chasing." Instead of chasing elements, as is customary, we prefer to chase squares. To this purpose we shall write the result more concisely

$$\text{Im} \, 1 \simeq \text{Ker} \, 2,$$

where 1 and 2 denote the two commutative squares of the diagram.

To prepare for our first chase, let A_R and $_RA'$ be given R-modules. We can find flat modules F_R and $_RF'$ and epimorphisms $\pi : F \to A$ and $\pi' : F' \to A'$, for example by taking F and F' to be free. Letting K and K' be the kernels of π and π', respectively, we obtain exact sequences

$$0 \longrightarrow K \xrightarrow{\kappa} F \xrightarrow{\pi} A \longrightarrow 0, \qquad 0 \longrightarrow K' \xrightarrow{\kappa'} F' \xrightarrow{\pi'} A' \longrightarrow 0,$$

where κ and κ' are the inclusion mappings. Now put

$$X = \text{Ker} \, (K \otimes A' \to F \otimes A'), \qquad X' = \text{Ker} \, (A \otimes K' \to A \otimes F')$$

and consider the following diagram:

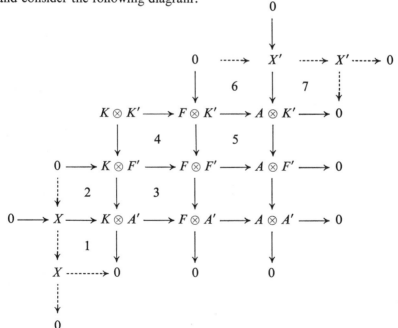

It follows from the right exactness of $\otimes$, the defining property of flat modules, and the above definitions of X and X' that all rows and all columns in this diagram are exact. For example, the second undotted column is exact because F is flat. Moreover, one readily sees that all squares in the diagram are commutative. For example, the compound mapping of $K \otimes K'$ into $F \otimes F'$ is

$$(1 \otimes \kappa') \circ (\kappa \otimes 1) = \kappa \otimes \kappa'$$

one way, and

$$(\kappa \otimes 1) \circ (1 \otimes \kappa') = \kappa \otimes \kappa'$$

the other way. (The general fact illustrated by this example is usually stated by saying that $\otimes$ is a *bifunctor*.) The dotted portion of the diagram may be added with impunity.

We now apply Proposition 1 to the above diagram and obtain

$$X = \text{Ker } 1 \cong \text{Im } 2 \cong \text{Ker } 3 \cong \text{Im } 4 \cong \text{Ker } 5 \cong \text{Im } 6 \cong \text{Ker } 7 = X'.$$

In the following result only X and X' have been retained.

PROPOSITION 2. *Let* $0 \to K \to F \to A \to 0$ *be an exact sequence of right R-modules with* F_R *flat, and let* $0 \to K' \to F' \to A' \to 0$ *be an exact sequence of left R-modules with* $_R F'$ *flat, then*

$$\text{Ker } (K \otimes A' \to F \otimes A') \cong \text{Ker } (A \otimes K' \to A \otimes F').$$

Of the two expressions whose isomorphism is asserted, the first does not depend on the sequence $0 \to K' \to F' \to A' \to 0$ and the second does not depend on the sequence $0 \to K \to F \to A \to 0$, hence both can depend only on A and A'. One writes $\text{Tor } (A, A')$ for this common value (up to isomorphism) and calls it the *torsion product* of A and A'.

If in the proof of Proposition 2 we also retain $\text{Im } 4$, we obtain the following corollary to the proof, which expresses the torsion product symmetrically.

COROLLARY.

$$\text{Tor } (A, A') \cong \frac{\text{Im } (K \otimes F' \to F \otimes F') \cap \text{Im } (F \otimes K' \to F \otimes F')}{\text{Im } (K \otimes K' \to F \otimes F')}.$$

The proof of the following is quite analogous to that of Proposition 2 and will be omitted.

PROPOSITION 3. *Let* $0 \to K \to P \to A \to 0$ *and* $0 \to B \to I \to I/B \to 0$ *be exact sequences of right R-modules with* P_R *projective and* I_R *injective, then*

$$\frac{Hom \, (K, B)}{Im \, (Hom \, (P, B) \to Hom \, (K, B))} \cong \frac{Hom \, (A, I/B)}{Im \, (Hom \, (A, I) \to Hom \, (A, I/B))}.$$

Since the expression on the left does not depend on the sequence $0 \to B \to I \to I/B \to 0$ and since the expression on the right does not depend on the sequence $0 \to K \to P \to A \to 0$, both sides can depend only on A and B. One writes Ext (A,B) for this common value (up to isomorphism) and calls it the *extension product* of A and B. The analog of the above corollary will be relegated to the exercises.

LEMMA 1. *Given a commutative square*

$$
\begin{array}{ccc}
A & \overset{\lambda}{\longrightarrow} & B \\
\alpha \downarrow & & \downarrow \beta \\
A' & \underset{\lambda'}{\longrightarrow} & B'
\end{array}
$$

there exist canonical homomorphisms $\phi : Ker\ \alpha \to Ker\ \beta$, $\phi' : A'/Im\ \alpha \to B'/Im\ \beta$ *so that the following two additional squares commute:*

$$
\begin{array}{ccc}
Ker\ \alpha & \overset{\phi}{\longrightarrow} & Ker\ \beta \\
\downarrow & & \downarrow \\
A & \underset{\lambda}{\longrightarrow} & B
\end{array}
\qquad
\begin{array}{ccc}
A' & \overset{\lambda'}{\longrightarrow} & B' \\
\downarrow & & \downarrow \\
A'/Im\ \alpha & \underset{\phi'}{\longrightarrow} & B'/Im\ \beta
\end{array}
$$

If moreover

$$
\begin{array}{ccc}
B & \overset{\mu}{\longrightarrow} & C \\
\beta \downarrow & & \downarrow \gamma \\
B' & \underset{\mu'}{\longrightarrow} & C'
\end{array}
$$

is another commutative square such that

$$0 \to A \to B \to C \to 0, \qquad 0 \to A' \to B' \to C' \to 0$$

are exact, then the following are exact:

$$Ker\ \alpha \to Ker\ \beta \to Ker\ \gamma, \qquad A'/Im\ \alpha \to B'/Im\ \beta \to C'/Im\ \gamma.$$

Proof. For any $a \in Ker\ \alpha$ define $\phi a = \lambda a$, the point being that this is an element of Ker β, since

$$\beta(\lambda a) = \lambda'(\alpha a) = 0.$$

Next, let $\pi : A' \to A'/\text{Im } \alpha$ and $\pi' : B' \to B'/\text{Im } \beta$ be the canonical epimorphisms. For any $a' \in A'$ define $\phi'(\pi a') = \pi'(\lambda' a')$. Of course one must verify that this is a single-valued mapping. Thus suppose $\pi a' = 0$, then $a' = \alpha a$ for some $a \in A$, hence

$$\pi'(\lambda' a') = (\pi' \circ \lambda' \circ \alpha)a = (\pi' \circ \beta \circ \lambda)a = 0.$$

Finally, we shall prove the exactness of the kernel sequence, leaving the remaining sequence for the exercises. Consider the following diagram, in which all squares are commutative and all but the dotted row are exact. We aim to prove the exactness of the dotted row.

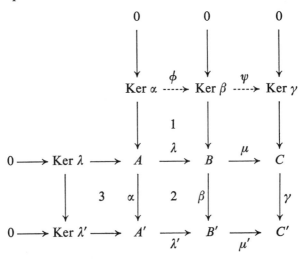

We now perform our second diagram chase:

$$\text{Im } 1 \cong \text{Ker } 2 \cong \text{Im } 3.$$

Clearly

$$\text{Im } 1 = \frac{\text{Ker } \beta \cap \text{Im } \lambda}{\lambda \text{ Ker } \alpha}$$

and

$$\text{Im } 3 = \frac{\text{Im } \alpha \cap \text{Ker } \lambda'}{\alpha \text{ Ker } \lambda}.$$

But we are given that $\text{Ker } \lambda' = 0$. (We are also given that $\text{Ker } \lambda = 0$, but this fact will not be used.) Hence $\text{Im } 1 \cong \text{Im } 3 = 0$, and so

$$\text{Ker } \beta \cap \text{Im } \lambda = \lambda \text{ Ker } \alpha.$$

Now we see that

$$\text{Im } \phi = \lambda \text{ Ker } \alpha,$$

and

$$\text{Ker } \psi = \{b \in \text{Ker } \beta \mid \mu b = 0\} = \text{Ker } \beta \cap \text{Ker } \mu = \text{Ker } \beta \cap \text{Im } \lambda.$$

Therefore $\text{Im } \phi = \text{Ker } \psi$, and our proof is complete.

Let

$$_RC \to {}_RC' \quad \text{and} \quad B_R \to B_R'$$

be given module homomorphisms. Apply the first part of the above lemma to the following three situations:

$$
\begin{array}{ccc}
K \otimes C & \longrightarrow & K \otimes C' \\
\downarrow & & \downarrow \\
F \otimes C & \longrightarrow & F \otimes C'
\end{array}
\qquad (F_R \text{ flat, } F/K \cong A_R), \qquad (1)
$$

$$
\begin{array}{ccc}
\text{Hom } (P,B) & \longrightarrow & \text{Hom } (P,B') \\
\downarrow & & \downarrow \\
\text{Hom } (K,B) & \longrightarrow & \text{Hom } (K,B')
\end{array}
\qquad (P_R \text{ projective, } P/K \cong A_R), \qquad (2)
$$

$$
\begin{array}{ccc}
\text{Hom } (B',I) & \longrightarrow & \text{Hom } (B,I) \\
\downarrow & & \downarrow \\
\text{Hom } (B',I/A) & \longrightarrow & \text{Hom } (B,I/A)
\end{array}
\qquad (I_R \text{ injective, } A_R \subset I_R). \qquad (3)
$$

There result canonical homomorphisms

$$\text{Tor } (A,C) \to \text{Tor } (A,C'), \qquad (1)$$

$$\text{Ext } (A,B) \to \text{Ext } (A,B'), \qquad (2)$$

$$\text{Ext } (B',A) \to \text{Ext } (B,A). \qquad (3)$$

The second part of the lemma now yields:

PROPOSITION 4.   *Let* $0 \to C \to C' \to C'' \to 0$ *and* $0 \to B \to B' \to B'' \to 0$ *be exact sequences of left and right modules, respectively. Then the following are exact:*

$$\textit{Tor } (A,C) \to \textit{Tor } (A,C') \to \textit{Tor } (A,C''),$$

$$\textit{Ext } (A,B) \to \textit{Ext } (A,B') \to \textit{Ext } (A,B''),$$

$$\textit{Ext } (B'',A) \to \textit{Ext } (B',A) \to \textit{Ext } (B,A).$$

While this is what one might have expected, the next result is more surprising to the beginner.

PROPOSITION 5. *Under the above assumptions there are "connecting homomorphisms"* ---➤ *which render the following sequences exact:*

$$Tor\ (A,C') \longrightarrow Tor\ (A,C'') \dashrightarrow A \otimes C \longrightarrow A \otimes C',$$

$$Hom\ (A,B') \longrightarrow Hom\ (A,B'') \dashrightarrow Ext\ (A,B) \longrightarrow Ext\ (A,B'),$$

$$Hom\ (B',A) \longrightarrow Hom\ (B,A) \dashrightarrow Ext\ (B'',A) \longrightarrow Ext\ (B',A).$$

Proof. This is an immediate consequence of the following.

LEMMA 2. *Given the diagram*

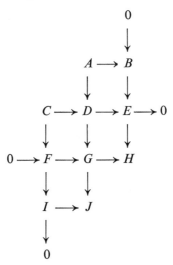

in which all rows and columns are exact and all squares commute. Then there exists a "connecting homomorphism" ---➤ *so that* $A \to B$ ---➤ $I \to J$ *is exact.*
Proof. Putting

$$X = B/\text{Im}\ (A \to B), \qquad Y = \text{Ker}\ (I \to J),$$

we obtain exact sequences

$$A \to B \to X \to 0, \qquad 0 \to Y \to I \to J.$$

Our problem then is to prove that $X \cong Y$. Part of the above diagram may be enlarged, preserving exactness and commutativity, thus:

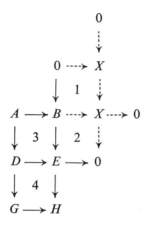

In our third diagram chase we now compute

$$X = \text{Im } 1 \cong \text{Ker } 2 \cong \text{Im } 3 \cong \text{Ker } 4.$$

Since the square labeled 4 was symmetrically situated in the original diagram, we also have $Y \cong \text{Ker } 4$, hence $X \cong Y$, as was to be shown.

COROLLARY.

$$Tor\ (A,C) = 0 \quad \textit{for all C,} \quad \Leftrightarrow \quad \textit{A is flat,}$$

$$Ext\ (A,B) = 0 \quad \textit{for all B,} \quad \Leftrightarrow \quad \textit{A is projective,}$$

$$Ext\ (B,A) = 0 \quad \textit{for all B,} \quad \Leftrightarrow \quad \textit{A is injective.}$$

The proof of this is left as an exercise.

EXERCISES

1. In the notation of Proposition 3, show that Ext (A,B) is isomorphic to

$$\frac{\text{Ker (Hom } (P,I) \to \text{Hom } (K,I/B))}{\text{Ker (Hom } (P,I) \to \text{Hom } (P,I/B)) + \text{Ker (Hom } (P,I) \to \text{Hom } (K,I))}.$$

2. If $B^* = \text{Hom}_Z(B,Q/Z)$ is the character module of B, show that

$$(Tor\ (A,B))^* \cong Ext\ (A,B^*).$$

3. Complete the proof of Lemma 1.

4. Prove the Corollary to Proposition 5.

5. In the following diagram all rows and columns are exact and all squares are commutative. Prove that $X \cong Y$.

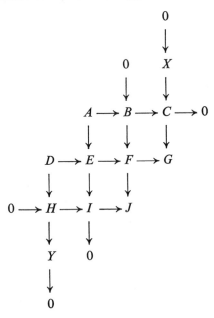

Appendixes

FUNCTIONAL REPRESENTATIONS

Let Π be a set of prime ideals of the commutative ring R. With each element $r \in R$ there is associated a function

$$\hat{r} : \Pi \to \bigcup_{P \in \Pi} R/P$$

of Π into a disjoint union of integral domains R/P, where $\hat{r}(P)$ is the canonical image of r in R/P. Thus we have a representation of R as a ring of functions, and this representation will be faithful if and only if its kernel

$$\Delta\Pi = \bigcap_{P \in \Pi} P = 0.$$

This is of course the situation in which R is a subdirect product of the integral domains R/P. One can also introduce a topology into the set $\bigcup_{P \in \Pi} R/P$ which will render all the functions $\hat{r}$ continuous, but we shall desist from doing so here.

We note that $\hat{r}(P) = 0$ if and only if $r \in P$. When will it happen that $\hat{r}$ vanishes not only at P but on some open set containing P? It suffices to consider a basic open set Γs, $s \in R$, and this will contain P if and only if $s \notin P$. We are thus looking for the set of all r for which there exists an $s \notin P$ such that $r \in P'$ whenever $s \notin P'$, that is to say such that $rs \in P'$ for all $P' \in \Pi$, that is $rs \in \Delta\Pi$. We shall denote the set in question by $(\Delta\Pi)_P$; in fact, for any ideal A, we shall write

$$A_P = \{r \in R \mid \exists_{s \notin P} rs \in A\} = \{r \in R \mid r^{-1}A \not\subseteq P\},$$

where $r^{-1}A = \{s \in R \mid rs \in A\}$. This is known in the literature as the *P-component* of A.

PROPOSITION 1. *If P is any subset of R whose complement is closed under finite products, A_P is an ideal of R containing A. Moreover $A \subseteq P$ implies $A_P \subseteq P$.*

Proof. The condition asserts that $1 \notin P$ and $s_1, s_2 \notin P \Rightarrow s_1 s_2 \notin P$.

Assume $r_1, r_2 \in A_P$, then there exists $s_1, s_2 \notin P$ such that $r_1 s_1 \in A$ and $r_2 s_2 \in A$. Therefore $(r_1 + r_2) s_1 s_2 \in A$ and $s_1 s_2 \notin P$, hence $r_1 + r_2 \in A_P$.

Assume $r_1 \in A_P$, $r_2 \in R$, then there exists s_1 as above. Therefore $(r_1 r_2) s_1 \in A$ and $s_1 \notin P$, hence $r_1 r_2 \in A_P$.

Assume $a \in A$. Since $1 \notin P$ and $a1 \in A$, therefore $a \in A_P$.

Assume $A \subset P$ and $r \in A_P$. Then $rs \in A \subset P$, for some $s \notin P$, hence $r \in P$.

Note that $R_P = R$, and, when P is a prime ideal, $P_P = P$.

PROPOSITION 2. *If Π contains all maximal ideals of the commutative ring R, then*
$$\bigcap_{P \in \Pi} A_P = A.$$

Proof. Let $r \in R$. Then $r \in \bigcap_{P \in \Pi} A_P$ if and only if, for all $P \in \Pi$, $r \in A_P$, that is $r^{-1}A \not\subset P$. Now, if $r^{-1}A$ is a proper ideal, it will be contained in some maximal ideal. Thus the above means that $1 \in r^{-1}A$, that is, $r \in A$.

COROLLARY. *If Π contains all maximal ideals of the commutative ring R, then R is a subdirect product of the rings $R/0_P$ where $P \in \Pi$.*

Proof. Let $\hat{r}(P)$ be the canonical image of r in $R/0_P$. The kernel of the representation $r \to \hat{r}$ is $\bigcap_{P \in \Pi} 0_P = 0$.

NOTE. The condition that Π contain all maximal ideals of R may be relaxed a little. Thus for the corollary it suffices that, for every element $r \neq 0$ of R, there exists a prime ideal $P \in \Pi$ such that $r^* = r^{-1}0 \subset P$.

PROPOSITION 3. *If $\hat{r} : \Pi \to \bigcup_{P \in \Pi} R/0_P$ is the canonical representation of $r \in R$, then $\hat{r}$ vanishes at P only if it vanishes on some open set containing P.*

Proof. Let $\hat{r}(P) = 0$, that is $r \in 0_P$. Thus there is an $s \notin P$ such that $rs = 0$. Now let $P' \in \Gamma s$, then $s \notin P'$, hence $r \in 0_{P'}$. Thus $\hat{r}(P') = 0$ for all P' in the basic open set Γs containing P.

We shall now take a closer look at the rings $R/0_P$. We recall from Proposition 1 that $0_P \subset P$.

PROPOSITION 4. *If P is a prime ideal of the commutative ring R, then $P/0_P$ is a prime ideal of $R/0_P$, and it contains all zero-divisors of $R/0_P$.*

Proof. Let $\pi : R \to R/0_P$ canonically. Assume $\pi r_1 \pi r_2 \in \pi P$, then $r_1 r_2 \in P$, hence r_1 or $r_2 \in P$, hence πr_1 or $\pi r_2 \in \pi P$. Moreover $\pi 1 \notin \pi P$, since $1 \notin P$, hence πP is a prime ideal.

Now assume $\pi r_1 \pi r_2 = 0$, $\pi r_2 \neq 0$. This means that $r_1 r_2 \in 0_P$, $r_2 \notin 0_P$. Thus $r_2(r_1 s) = (r_1 r_2)s = 0$ for some $s \notin P$. Since $r_2 \notin 0_P$, $r_1 s \in P$, hence $r_1 \in P$, and so $\pi r_1 \in \pi P$.

Further algebraic properties of the ring $R/0_P$ may be deduced from topological properties of the point P in Π. Two points of a topological space are said to be *separated* if they are contained in disjoint open sets. If any two distinct points are separated, the space is called a *Hausdorff* space.

PROPOSITION 5. *Let Π be a prime ideal space of the commutative ring R such that $\Delta\Pi = 0$. Then the point P of Π is separated from all other points if and only if P is the only member of Π containing 0_P.*

When Π is the set of all maximal ideals, this means that $R/0_P$ is a local ring. When Π is the set of all prime ideals it means that $R/0_P$ is fully primary.

Proof. P will be separated from $P' \in \Pi$ if and only if there exist $r \notin P$ and $s \notin P'$ such that $\Gamma rs = \Gamma r \cap \Gamma s = \varnothing$, that is, $rs \in \Delta\Pi = 0$. We can write this condition thus: $\exists_{s \notin P'} s \in 0_P$, that is to say $0_P \not\subset P'$. Thus P will be separated from all $P' \neq P$ if and only if $0_P \subset P' \Rightarrow P' = P$.

COROLLARY. *The maximal (prime) ideal space of a commutative semi-primitive (semiprime) ring is Hausdorff if and only if $R/0_P$ is a local (fully primary) ring, for every maximal (prime) ideal P of R.*

As we shall see, even when $R/0_P$ is not a local ring, there is a local ring closely associated with it. As usual, let $Q(R)$ be the complete ring of quotients of R. For any ideal A of R, we write

$$A^P = \{q \in Q(R) \mid \exists_{s \in R}\ s \notin P\ \ \&\ \ qs \in A\}$$
$$= \{q \in Q(R) \mid q^{-1}A \not\subset P\}.$$

Here $q^{-1}A = \{s \in R \mid qs \in A\}$, and P may be as in Proposition 1.

PROPOSITION 6. *R^P is a subring of $Q(R)$ containing R, and A^P is an ideal of R^P containing A.*

Thus R^P is a ring of quotients of R. In particular, if D is the set of zero-divisors of R, R^D is the classical ring of quotients of R. Note that $A^P \cap R = A_P$.

Proof. If $q_1, q_2 \in A^P$ then $q_1 + q_2 \in A^P$, as in the proof of Proposition 1. Assume $q_1 \in A^P$, $q_2 \in R^P$, then $q_1 s_1 \in A$ and $q_2 s_2 \in R$, for some $s_1, s_2 \notin P$. Hence $(q_1 q_2)(s_1 s_2) \in A$ and $s_1 s_2 \notin P$. Therefore $q_1 q_2 \in A^P$. Taking $A = R$, we see that R^P is a ring. In general, A^P is an ideal in R^P. Finally $A^P \supset A^P \cap R = A_P \supset A$.

PROPOSITION 7. *If Π contains all maximal ideals of the commutative ring R, then*
$$\bigcap_{P \in \Pi} A^P = A.$$

This is proved like Proposition 2.

PROPOSITION 8. *If all zero-divisors of the commutative ring R are contained in the prime ideal P, then R^P is a local ring with maximal ideal P^P. Moreover $R^P \subset R^D$, the classical ring of quotients of R.*

Proof. Let $q \in R^P$ be a nonunit. Then either q is a zero-divisor, or q^{-1} exists in $Q(R)$ but fails to lie in R^P. Now $qs \in R$ for some $s \notin P$. In the first case, qs is a zero-divisor and so lies in P, thus $q \in P^P$. In the second case, $q^{-1}t \in R$ implies $t \in P$, for any $t \in R$. In particular, taking $t = qs$, we see that $qs \in P$, $s \notin P$, hence again $q \in P^P$. Finally, $D \subset P$ implies $R^P \subset R^D$.

COROLLARY. *If P is any prime ideal of the commutative ring R, then $(R/0_P)^{P/0_P}$ is a local ring. It is contained in the classical ring of quotients of $R/0_P$.*

Proof. This is an immediate consequence of Propositions 8 and 4.

PROPOSITION 9. *If P is any subset of the commutative ring R whose complement is closed under finite products, then*

$$R/0_P \subset R^P/0^P \subset (R/0_P)^{P/0_P},$$

up to isomorphism.

Proof. Since $R \cap 0^P = 0_P$, we have

$$R/0_P = R/(R \cap 0^P) \cong (R + 0^P)/0^P \subset R^P/0^P.$$

Consider an element $\pi q \in R^P/0^P$, where $q \in R^P$ and π is the canonical epimorphism. Then $qs \in R$, $s \notin R$, thus $\pi q \pi s \in R/0_P$, $\pi s \notin P/0_P$. In view of Proposition 4, πs is not a zero-divisor. Hence πq lies in the classical ring of quotients of $R/0_P$. Thus $R^P/0^P$ may be regarded as a subring of $Q_{cl}(R/0^P)$, as is $(R/0_P)^{P/0_P}$, by the above corollary. As such, $R^P/0^P$ is contained in the latter, since $\pi s \notin P/0_P$ in the above argument.

With any $q \in Q(R)$ one may also wish to associate a function $\hat{q}$ into $\bigcup_{P \in \Pi} R^P/P^P$ or $\bigcup_{P \in \Pi} R^P/0^P$, by letting $\hat{q}(P)$ be the canonical image of q in R^P/P^P or $R^P/0^P$. Now this makes sense only when $q \in R^P$ in the first place. Thus $\hat{q}$ is not defined on the whole space Π but only on the open subset

$$V(q) = \{P \in \Pi \mid q \in R^P\} = \{P \in \Pi \mid q^{-1}R \nsubseteq P\} = \Gamma(q^{-1}R).$$

It is not difficult to turn the disjoint union

$$S = \bigcup_{P \in \Pi} R/0_P$$

into a topological space by taking as basic open sets the sets

$$\hat{r}(V) = \{\hat{r}(P) \mid P \in V\},$$

where $r \in R$ and V is any open subset of Π. It then follows that each point $\hat{r}(P_0)$ of S is contained in an open set which is homeomorphic to its image in Π under the canonical projection $\hat{r}(P) \to P$. For this reason, S is called a *sheaf*, but this term need not concern us here. A continuous function $f : \Pi \to S$ is called a *section* if $f(P) \in R/0_P$ for each $P \in \Pi$. Crucial to what follows is the observation that if two sections agree at a point P_0 of Π, then they agree on an open set containing P_0. Indeed, suppose $f(P_0) = g(P_0)$, then this point of S is contained in an open set U which is homeomorphic to its canonical image U' in Π, and on the open set $U' \cap f^{-1}U \cap g^{-1}U$ both f and g agree with the inverse of the canonical mapping $S \to \Pi$. It is easily verified that $\hat{r}$ is a section for each $r \in R$, and this was in fact the reason for defining the topology of S in the way we did. Not so obvious is the converse statement:

PROPOSITION 10 (Grothendieck). *If Π is the set of all prime ideals, every section of S has the form $\hat{r}$, for some $r \in R$.*

Actually Grothendieck and Dieudonné (1960) proved this for the sheaf of local rings

$$\bigcup (R/0_P)^{P/0_P},$$

but the proof in our case is a little simpler. We shall base it on the following:

LEMMA. *Let Π be the set of all prime ideals of R, $r \in R$. Then $r \in 0_P$ for all $P \in \Gamma s$ if and only if $rs^n = 0$ for some natural number n.*

Proof of Lemma. $r \in 0_P$ for all $P \in \Gamma s$ if and only if $r^{-1}0 \not\subseteq P$ whenever $s \notin P$, that is $s \in \bigcup_{r^{-1}0 \subset P} P$. In view of Section 2.1, Proposition 8, this is the same as saying $s^n \in r^{-1}0$, that is $rs^n = 0$, for some n.

Proof of Proposition. Let $f : \Pi \to S$ be any section. For each $P \in \Pi$,

$$f(P) = \hat{r}_P(P),$$

and so $f - \hat{r}_P$ vanishes on some basic open set Γs_P containing P. By compactness, there exist points $P_1, P_2, \ldots, P_m$ such that

$$\bigcup_{i=1}^m \Gamma s_{P_i} = \Pi.$$

We shall write s_i for s_{P_i} and r_i for r_{P_i}. Thus $\hat{r}_i(P) = \hat{r}_j(P)$ for all $i, j = 1, 2, \ldots, m$ and $P \in \Gamma s_i \cap \Gamma s_j = \Gamma s_i s_j$. By the lemma, there exist natural numbers $n(i,j)$ such that

$$(s_i s_j)^{n(i,j)}(r_i - r_j) = 0.$$

Putting n for the maximum of all $n(i,j)$ ($i, j = 1, 2, \ldots, m$), we have

$$s_j^n s_i^n r_i = s_i^n s_j^n r_j.$$

Now

$$\Pi = \bigcup_{i=1}^{m} \Gamma s_i = \bigcup_{i=1}^{m} \Gamma s_i^{\,n} = \Gamma \sum_{i=1}^{m} s_i^{\,n} R.$$

Hence there exist $t_i \in R$ such that

$$\sum_{i=1}^{m} s_i^{\,n} t_i = 1.$$

Put

$$r = \sum_{i=1}^{m} s_i^{\,n} r_i t_i,$$

then a simple calculation shows

$$s_j^{\,n} r = s_j^{\,n} r_j.$$

Now $s_j \notin P_j$, hence $s_j^{\,n} \notin P_j$, hence $r - r_j \in 0_{P_j}$, and so $\hat{r} = \hat{r}_j$ for all $j = 1, 2, \ldots, m$. Therefore $\hat{r} = f$, and the proof is complete.

A similar result holds for

$$\bigcup_{P \in \Pi} R^P / 0^P.$$

EXERCISES

R will be a commutative ring in Exercises 1 to 9.

1. Show that the classical ring of quotients of R is local if and only if the zero-divisors of R form an ideal.

2. If P is a minimal prime ideal of R, show that $R/0_P$ is primary.

3. If P is a prime ideal of R, show that P^P is a prime ideal of R^P and that $P^P/0^P$ is a prime ideal of $R^P/0^P$ containing all its zero-divisors.

4. If R is regular, show that $0_P = P$, $0^P = P^P$.

5. Show that either $\Delta\Pi$ is a dense ideal or $Q(R)$ is the union of all R^P, $P \in \Pi$.

6. Give an example of a ring in which $\Delta\Pi$ is a dense ideal.

7. If A and B are ideals of R, write

$$A^B = \{ q \in Q(R) \mid \forall_{r \notin B} \exists_{s \in R} rs \notin B \quad \& \quad qs \in A \}.$$

Show that R^B is a ring and that A^B is an ideal in it. If B is a prime ideal P, A^B coincides with the ideal A^B defined earlier. Moreover $R^0 = Q(R)$.

8. A subset of a topological space is called *dense* if it meets every nonempty open set. Show that a subset V of Π is dense if and only if $\Delta V = \Delta\Pi$.

9. Show that $V(q)$ is dense if and only if $q \in R^{\Delta\Pi}$ and that $\hat{q}$ vanishes on a dense set if and only if $q \in 0^{\Delta\Pi}$. Deduce that the ring $R^{\Delta\Pi}/0^{\Delta\Pi}$ may be faithfully represented by a ring of functions defined on dense open subsets of Π modulo an obvious equivalence relation.

In the following exercises R is no longer assumed commutative.

10. Show that the results of this appendix, in particular Proposition 10, remain valid for any associative ring R, provided Π is taken as the set of all prime ideals of the center of R.

11. With any maximal right ideal M of R associate the ideal $0_M = \{r \in R \mid \forall_{x \in R} \exists_{t \in M} rxt = 0\}$. Show that 0_M is the right annihilator of the injective hull of the right R-module R/M.

12. Thierrin has called a ring R *metaprimitive* if there exists a faithful subdirectly irreducible right R-module. Show that R is metaprimitive if and only if it has a maximal right ideal M such that $0_M = 0$. Deduce that always $R/0_M$ is metaprimitive.

13 (Thierrin). Show that every ring is a subdirect product of metaprimitive rings, and that each metaprimitive ring is a ring of endomorphisms of a module $_L I$, where L is local. [*Hint:* Let I_R be the injective hull of R/M, $L = \mathrm{Hom}_R(I, I)$.]

14. For R metaprimitive and $_L I$ as above, show the following: Given any finitely generated submodule G of $_L I$ and any e in $\mathrm{Hom}_L(G, R/M)$, there is an element r in R such that $G(e - r) = 0$. [A similar result was proved by Thierrin (1960).]

THE GROUP RING

The following discussion of group rings is taken almost entirely from the papers by I. Connell (1963) and D. S. Passman (1962). A similar account may be found in the lecture notes by P. Ribenboim (1965).

We shall require no ring theory beyond Chapter 3 and Sections 4.1 and 4.2 of this book. On the other hand, we shall abandon the pretense that the reader of this book is unfamiliar with the fundamentals of group theory. We shall in fact presume the most elementary statements concerning the order of a finite group, cosets, and normal subgroups. We begin with three group theoretical prerequisites that will not be presumed.

LEMMA A (Poincaré). *The intersection of a finite number of subgroups of finite index has finite index.*

Proof. Let H and K be subgroups of G of finite index. Elements a and b of G lie in the same right coset of $H \cap K$ if and only if $ab^{-1} \in H \cap K$, that is $ab^{-1} \in H$ and $ab^{-1} \in K$. Thus we obtain all right cosets of $H \cap K$ by taking all nonempty intersections of right cosets of H with right cosets of K.

LEMMA B (Passman). *If a group G is covered by a finite number of right cosets of subgroups $H_1, \ldots, H_n$, then at least one of the H_i has finite index.*

Proof. We use induction on n. If all cosets of H_n are among the covering cosets, then surely H_n has finite index. Suppose $H_n g$ is missing, while $H_n g_1, \ldots, H_n g_k$ are present. Since $H_n g \cap H_n g_j$ is empty, $H_n g$ can be covered by cosets of $H_1, \ldots, H_{n-1}$ alone. Therefore H_n can be covered by a finite number of cosets of $H_1, \ldots, H_{n-1}$ not necessarily in the original collection. Thus G can be covered by a finite number of cosets of $n - 1$ subgroups, and the inductional assumption applies.

LEMMA C (Dietzmann). *Let M be a finite subset of the group G such that $g^{-1}Mg \subset M$ for all $g \in G$. Assume that all elements of M have finite order. Then the subgroup generated by M is finite.*

Proof. Let k be the number of elements of M, m the least common multiple of the orders of the elements of M, and A the subgroup of G generated by M. It suffices to prove that every element a of A can be expressed as a product of not more than $k(m - 1)$ factors.

Suppose $a = a_1 a_2 \cdots, a_t$, $a_i \in M$, $t > k(m - 1)$. Then one of the elements of M, say a_0, occurs at least m times. Let a_i be the first term of the product such that $a_i = a_0$, and put $a_0^{-1} a_j a_0 = a_j{}'$ for all $j < i$. Then $a_j{}' \in M$ and

$$a = a_0 a_1{}' \cdots a_{i-1}{}' a_{i+1} \cdots a_t.$$

Applying the same device to the first among the remaining factors $a_{i+1}, \ldots, a_t$ which equals a_0, and continuing in this manner, we ultimately obtain an expression

$$a = a_0{}^m a_1{}^* \cdots a_{t-m}{}^* = a_1{}^* \cdots a_{t-m}{}^*$$

having fewer than t factors.

Having gotten the preliminaries out of the way, we shall now define the group ring. Given a group G and a ring A, the *group ring* $R = AG$ consists of all functions $r : G \to A$ with finite support. The *support* of r is $\{g \in G \mid r(g) \neq 0\}$. R is endowed with ring operations by defining

$$0(g) = 0,$$
$$1(g) = 1 \quad \text{if} \quad g = 1, = 0 \quad \text{if} \quad g \neq 1,$$
$$(-r)(g) = -r(g),$$
$$(r + r')(g) = r(g) + r'(g),$$
$$(rr')(g) = \sum_{g = hh'} r(h)r'(h').$$

We leave it as an exercise to verify that $R(0,1,-,+,\cdot)$ is in fact a ring.

(As usual, we have written rr' for $r \cdot r'$.)

With any $a \in A$ and $g \in G$ we associate elements a^* and g^+ of $R = AG$ as follows. For any $h \in G$, put

$$a^*(h) = a \quad \text{if} \quad h = 1, \ = 0 \quad \text{if} \quad h \neq 1,$$

$$g^+(h) = 1 \quad \text{if} \quad h = g, \ = 0 \quad \text{if} \quad h \neq g.$$

It is easily verified that $a \to a^*$ is a ring monomorphism of A into R, that $g \to g^+$ is a semigroup monomorphism of G into R, and that, for any $r \in R$,

$$r = \sum_{g \in G} r(g)^* g^+ = \sum_{g \in G} g^+ r(g)^*.$$

If we write $ra = ra^*$, R becomes a free A-module R_A with basis $\{g^+ \mid g \in G\}$.

Henceforth we shall omit the symbols $*$ and $+$, so that

$$r = \sum_{g \in G} r(g)g = \sum_{g \in G} gr(g),$$

for any $r \in R$. Note the formulas

$$(rg)(h) = r(hg^{-1}),$$

$$(gr)(h) = r(g^{-1}h),$$

$$ga = ag,$$

for all $r \in R$, $g, h \in G$, $a \in A$.

We shall investigate under what conditions on G and A the group ring $R = AG$ is right Noetherian, right Artinian, regular, completely reducible, and semiprime. In some of these cases a complete answer will be given.

LEMMA 1. *With any subgroup H of G associate the right ideal ωH of $R = AG$ generated by all $1 - h$, $h \in H$. The mapping ω from the lattice of subgroups of G to the lattice of right ideals of AG is faithful and preserves joins. Moreover, if H is normal, ωH is an ideal, in fact the kernel of the canonical epimorphism $AG \to A(G/H)$. If the set $\{g_i\}$ generates the subgroup H then the right ideal generated by $\{1 - g_i\}$ is ωH.*

If $\pi : G \to G/H$ canonically, the canonical epimorphism $AG \to A(G/H)$ sends $\sum_{g \in G} r(g)g$ onto $\sum_{g \in G} r(g)\pi g$.

The proof of this lemma will be left as an exercise.

PROPOSITION 1.

(a) *AG is right Noetherian if A is right Noetherian and G is finite.*

(b) *If AG is right Noetherian, then A is right Noetherian and every ascending sequence of subgroups of G becomes ultimately stationary.*

(c) *If G is Abelian, then AG is right Noetherian if and only if A is right Noetherian and G is finitely generated.*

Proof.

(a) AG is a finitely generated free A-module, hence a Noetherian A-module, hence a right Noetherian ring.

(b) $A \cong AG/\omega G$ is right Noetherian. Moreover, any ascending sequence of subgroups $H_1 \subset H_2 \subset \cdots$ gives rise to an ascending sequence $\omega H_1 \subset \omega H_2 \subset \cdots$ of right ideals of AG. By assumption, there exists an n such that $\omega H_n = \omega H_{n+1} = \cdots$, hence also $H_n = H_{n+1} = \cdots$, by Lemma 1.

(c) Assume G Abelian and finitely generated and A right Noetherian. Let $G \cong F/N$, where F is a finitely generated free Abelian group. Then $AG \cong AF/\omega N$ will be right Noetherian if AF is. If F has generators $x_1, \ldots, x_n$, we regard $x_1, x_1^{-1}, \ldots, x_n, x_n^{-1}$ as $2n$ indeterminates, hence AF is a homomorphic image of $A[x_1, x_1^{-1}, \ldots, x_n, x_n^{-1}]$, the polynomial ring in $2n$ indeterminates over A. The result now follows from Hilbert's Basis Theorem (Section 3.5, Proposition 6).

We gather some statements concerning the left annihilator $(\omega H)^l$ of the right ideal ωH of $R = AG$, where H is a subgroup of G. In particular H may be the subgroup generated by a single element g of G.

LEMMA 2.

    (a) *If H is an infinite subgroup of G, $(\omega H)^l = 0$.*

    (b) *If H is a finite subgroup of G, $(\omega H)^l = R(\sum_{h \in H} h)$.*

    (c) *If G is finite, $(\omega G)^l = (\sum_{g \in G} g)A$.*

    (d) *If $g \in G$ has infinite order, $(1 - g)^l = 0$.*

    (e) *If $g \in G$ has finite order n, $(1 - g)^l = R(1 + g + \cdots + g^{n-1})$.*

The proof of this will be left as an exercise.

Our next result essentially goes back to Maschke.

LEMMA 3. *Let $R = AG$, where G has finite order n, and n is a unit in A. Then any right R-module is projective if it is projective as an A-module.*

Proof. Let there be given a right R-module P_R. Since $A \subset R$, this is automatically an A-module P_A. We assume that P_A is projective and wish to show that P_R is projective.

Let $\pi : N_R \twoheadrightarrow M_R$ be an epimorphism and let $\phi : P_R \to M_R$. We want to lift ϕ to $\phi' : P_R \to N_R$. By assumption, we have $\psi : P_A \to N_A$ such that $\pi \circ \psi = \phi$. For any element $p \in P$, we put

$$\phi' p = n^{-1} \sum_{g \in G} \psi(pg)g^{-1}.$$

An easy computation shows that, for any $h \in G$, $\phi'(ph) = (\phi' p)h$. From this it follows that ϕ' is an R-homomorphism. Moreover, it is readily verified that $\pi(\phi'p) = \phi p$, and this completes the proof.

COROLLARY. *Let $R = AG$, where G has finite order n, and n is a unit in A. Then R is regular if A is.*

Proof. R_A is a finitely generated free A-module. Take any $r \in R$, then rR is a direct summand of R_A, by Section 4.1, Proposition 8 and Exercise 6. Thus rR is a projective A-module, hence a projective R-module, by Lemma 3. Being a factor module of R_R, it is therefore a direct summand of R_R. Thus R is regular.

This result will be absorbed in the next theorem, due to Auslander, McLaughlin, and Connell.

PROPOSITION 2. *The group ring $R = AG$ is regular if and only if*

(1) *A is regular,*
(2) *every finitely generated subgroup of G is finite,*
(3) *the order of any finite subgroup of G is a unit in A.*

Proof. First assume R regular. Then so is $A \simeq R/\omega G$. If H is a finitely generated subgroup of G, then ωH is a finitely generated right ideal, by Lemma 1, hence a direct summand of R_R. (See Section 3.5, Lemma.) It follows that the left annihilator of ωH is not zero, hence H is finite by Lemma 2. Finally, let g be an element of order n. Since R is regular, we can find $r \in R$ such that $(1 - g)r(1 - g) = 1 - g$, that is,

$$(1 - (1 - g)r)(1 - g) = 0.$$

(See Section 2.2, Exercise 3.) It follows from Lemma 2 that

$$1 - (1 - g)r = r'(1 + g + \cdots + g^{n-1}),$$

for some $r' \in R$. Now let $\pi : R \to A$ be the canonical epimorphism

$$\pi r = \sum_{g \in G} r(g),$$

Applying π to the above equation, we obtain

$$1 = \pi r' n,$$

and therefore n is a unit.

Conversely, we assume the three conditions and want to show that R is regular. Given any $r \in R$, we seek $r' \in R$ such that $rr'r = r$. Now the support of r is finite. It generates a finite subgroup H of G. Applying the above corollary to the group ring AH, we find r' in $AH \subset AG$ such that $rr'r = r$.

The next theorem is the completion by Connell of a classical result by Maschke.

PROPOSITION 3. *The group ring $R = AG$ is completely reducible if and only if*

(1) *A is completely reducible,*
(2) *G is finite,*
(3) *the order of G is a unit in A.*

Proof. First assume R completely reducible, hence right Noetherian and regular. (See Section 3.5, Proposition 2.) By Proposition 1, A is right Noetherian and G is finitely generated. By Proposition 2, A is regular and every finitely generated subgroup of G is finite. Therefore A is completely reducible and G is finite. Finally, (3) follows from Proposition 2.

Conversely, assume the conditions. By Propositions 1 and 2, R is right Noetherian and regular, hence completely reducible. The proof is now complete.

We record some elementary facts about the prime radical of a group ring.

LEMMA 4. *If B is a subring of A, then*

$$BG \cap rad\ AG \subset rad\ BG,$$

with equality if B is contained in the center of A. If H is a subgroup of G, then

$$AH \cap rad\ AG \subset rad\ AH,$$

with equality if H is contained in the center of G. In particular,

$$A \cap rad\ AG = rad\ A.$$

The proof will be left as an exercise.

The first part of the following theorem is classical, the proof being due to Pascual Jordan. The second part was obtained independently by Passman and Connell.

PROPOSITION 4. *The group ring AG over a field A contains no nonzero nil ideals in either of two cases:*
(a) *A is algebraically closed of characteristic 0.*
(b) *The characteristic of A is a prime p, and no element of G has order p.*

Proof. (a) A is obtained from a real closed field P by adjunction of i, $i^2 = -1$. (See, for example, Van der Waerden I, § 71.) With any element $a = p + ip'$ of A one associates its conjugate $a^* = p - ip'$. Now let $r = \sum_{g \in G} r(g)g$ be any nonzero element of the ideal K of R. Define

$$r^* = \sum_{g \in G} r(g)^* g^{-1},$$

and verify that $(r_1 r_2)^* = r_2^* r_1^*$. Then $s = rr^* \in K$ and $s^* = s$. Moreover,

$$s(1) = \sum_{g \in G} r(g) r^*(g^{-1}) = \sum_{g \in G} r(g) r(g)^* > 0 \quad \text{in} \quad P,$$

being a sum of squares. Again $(s^2)^* = s^2$ and

$$s^2(1) = \sum_{g \in G} s(g) s(g^{-1}) = \sum_{g \in G} s(g) s(g)^* > 0 \quad \text{in} \quad P.$$

Repeating the argument, we have $s^{2^n} \neq 0$ for all n. Therefore K is not nil.

(b) If K is any nonzero ideal of AG, then K contains at least one element r such that $r(1) = 1$. (Indeed, if $0 \neq r' \in K$, there exists $g \in G$ such that $0 \neq r'(g) = a$. Put $r = a^{-1} r' g^{-1}$.) We shall prove presently that this implies $r^p(1) = 1$. Since for the same reason, $r^{p^2}(1) = 1$, etc., we obtain arbitrarily high nonvanishing powers of r, so again K is not nil.

Indeed,

$$r^p(1) = \sum r(g_1) r(g_2) \cdots r(g_p),$$

the sum extending over all p-tuples $(g_1, g_2, \ldots, g_p)$ such that $g_1 g_2 \cdots g_p = 1$. Now from $g_1 g_2 \cdots g_p = 1$ one obtains $g_{k+1} g_{k+2} \cdots g_{k+p} = 1$, subscripts being taken modulo p. If the p cyclic permutations of the p-tuple $(g_1, g_2, \ldots, g_p)$ are all distinct, their combined contribution to the sum is a multiple of p, hence 0 in A. Can $(g_1, g_2, \ldots, g_p) = (g_{k+1}, g_{k+2}, \ldots, g_{k+p})$ with $k \neq 0$? Only if $g_1 = g_{1+k} = g_{1+2k} = \cdots$. But the subscripts range over all nonzero residues modulo p, hence all g_i would be equal, hence $g_1^p = 1$, hence $g_1 = 1$. Therefore

$$r^p(1) = r(1)^p = 1,$$

and the proof is complete.

COROLLARY. *If B is any field of characteristic* 0, *then the group ring BG is semiprime.*

Proof. Let A be the algebraic closure of B. By Lemma 4 and Proposition 4(a), we compute

$$\text{rad } BG = BG \cap \text{rad } AG = 0.$$

With any element g of the group G one associates its *centralizer* $C(g) = \{h \in G \mid hg = gh\}$. Clearly, $C(g)$ is a subgroup of G. It is not difficult to show that $C(g)$ has finite index if and only if the total number of distinct conjugates of g in G is finite. We shall put

$$G^* = \{g \in G \mid C(g) \quad \text{has finite index}\}.$$

It is then easily verified that G^* is a normal subgroup of G.

PROPOSITION 5 (Passman). *If A is any ring and G^* is the normal subgroup of G consisting of all elements with finitely many conjugates, then the group ring AG is semiprime if AG^* is semiprime.*

Proof. Assume that AG is not semiprime. Then it contains a nonzero ideal whose square is zero. In particular, we can find $0 \neq r \in AG$ such that $rAGr = 0$. We may even assume that $r(1) \neq 0$. (Indeed, if $r(g) \neq 0$, replace r by $g^{-1}r$.) Write $r = r^* + r'$, where $r^* \in AG^*$ and $r'(G^*) = 0$. Then $r^*(1) \neq 0$.

Put

$$C(r^*) = \bigcap_{r^*(g) \neq 0} C(g).$$

Since r^* has finite support, and since each $C(g)$ has finite index, therefore $C(r^*)$ has finite index, by Poincaré's Lemma (Lemma A).

Assume AG^* semiprime. Then we can find elements g^* and h^* in G^* and a in A such that

$$(r^*ag^*r^*)(h^*) \neq 0.$$

Now take any $g \in C(r^*)$, then

$$(r^* + g^{-1}r'g)ag^*(r^* + r') = 0.$$

Working this out at h^*, we get

$$(r^*ag^*r^*)(h^*) + (g^{-1}r'gag^*r')(h^*) = 0.$$

The other terms vanish, since G^* is a normal subgroup of G and $r'(G^*) = 0$. Therefore

$$(g^{-1}r'gag^*r')(h^*) \neq 0.$$

Hence there exist group elements x and y in the support of r' such that

$$h^* = g^{-1}xgg^*y,$$

that is,

$$g^{-1}xg = h^*y^{-1}g^{*-1}.$$

Thus g lies in a right coset of $C(x)$ depending on y. Allowing x and y to vary over the support of r', we obtain a finite set of right cosets in G covering $C(r^*)$. Since $C(r^*)$ has finite index and each of its right cosets can be covered similarly, we get a finite covering of G by cosets of $C(x)$, x in the support of r'. By Lemma B, at least one of the $C(x)$ has finite index, contradicting $r'(G^*) = 0$. This completes a most remarkable proof!

COROLLARY. *If A is a field of characteristic p, and if p does not divide the order of any finite normal subgroup of G, then the group ring AG is semiprime.*

Proof. Suppose AG is not semiprime, then neither is AG^*, by the above. By Proposition 4(b), some element g of G^* has order p. The set of all conjugates of g in G is a finite set. By Dietzmann's Lemma (Lemma C), the (normal) subgroup generated by this set is still finite. As it contains g, its order is divisible by p.

We shall defer the investigation of semiprime group rings to determine all right Artinian group rings, which may conveniently be done at this stage.

PROPOSITION 6 (Connell). *The group ring $R = AG$ is right Artinian if and only if A is right Artinian and G is finite.*

Proof. If A_A is Artinian and G is finite, then R_A is a finite direct sum of copies of A, hence R_A is Artinian, and a fortiori R_R is Artinian.

Conversely, assume R right Artinian. Then so is $A \cong R/\omega G$. But R is also right Noetherian (see Section 3.5, Corollary to Proposition 3). Therefore, by Proposition 1, every ascending sequence of subgroups of G becomes ultimately stationary. The same is true for every descending sequence of subgroups (by the same argument), and it is an unsolved problem whether these two chain conditions imply that G is finite. Without solving this problem, we shall prove that G is finite, using Proposition 5.

Since AG is right Artinian, so is its factor ring $(A/\text{rad } A)G$. We may therefore assume without loss in generality, that A is semiprime. Since A is also right Artinian, it is therefore completely reducible. We may put $A = A^{(1)} \times \cdots \times A^{(n)}$, where the $A^{(i)}$ are simple Artinian. Then also $AG = A^{(1)}G \times \cdots \times A^{(n)}G$, and $A^{(1)}G$ is right Artinian, $A^{(1)}$ simple. Write $B = A^{(1)}$ and let C be the center of B. We claim that BG right Artinian implies CG right Artinian.

Indeed, let $K_1 \supset K_2 \supset \cdots$ be a descending sequence of right ideals of CG. Then $K_1 B \supset K_2 B \supset \cdots$ is a descending sequence of right ideals of BG. Hence, for some n, $K_n B = K_{n+1} B = \cdots$. It follows that also $K_n = K_{n+1} = \cdots$, in view of the observation that, for any right ideal K of CG,

$$KB \cap CG = K,$$

the proof of which will be left as an exercise.

We may thus assume, without loss in generality, that A is a field.

Case 1. A has characteristic 0. By the Corollary to Proposition 4, AG is semiprime. Being also right Artinian, it is completely reducible. Therefore G is finite, by Proposition 3.

Case 2. A has characteristic p. If AG is semiprime, we argue as above. Otherwise, by the Corollary to Proposition 5, $G = G_1$ contains a finite normal subgroup H_1. We also know that the order of H_1 is divisible by p, hence $H_1 \neq \{1\}$. Consider $G_2 = G/H_1$. If AG_2 is not semiprime, G_2 contains a finite normal subgroup H_2/H_1, and $H_2 \neq H_1$. We then consider $G_3 = G/H_2$, etc. The sequence of subgroups $H_1 \subset H_2 \subset \cdots$ must break off, so finally we obtain $G_n = G/H_{n-1}$ such that AG_n is semiprime. Then G_n is finite as in Case 1. Now

$$G_n \cong (G/H_{n-2})/(H_{n-1}/H_{n-2}),$$

where G_n and H_{n-1}/H_{n-2} are finite. Therefore $G_{n-1} = G/H_{n-2}$ is finite. Working backwards, we ultimately get $G = G_1$ finite, and the proof is complete.

Before returning to the investigation of semiprime group rings, we need one general ring theoretical result.

LEMMA 5. *Let M be a set of non-zero-divisors closed under finite products and contained in the center of R, and let Q be the complete ring of right quotients of R. Then*

$$RM^{-1} = \{q \in Q \mid \exists_{m \in M} qm \in R\}$$

is a subring of Q containing R, and all elements of M are units in RM^{-1}. Moreover

$$rad\ R = R \cap rad\ RM^{-1},$$

$$rad\ RM^{-1} = (rad\ R)M^{-1}.$$

(By the last expression we mean of course $\{q \in Q \mid \exists_{m \in M} qm \in rad\ R\}$. The reader who has not read Chapter 4, should construct RM^{-1} directly from "ratios" r/m.)

Proof. (See Section 4.3, for the definition of Q.) For any $m \in M$, the mapping $mr \to r$ is a homomorphism of the dense ideal $mR = Rm$ into R. (Use Section 4.3, Corollary to Proposition 4.) Therefore there exists $q \in Q$ such that $qm = 1$. (See Section 4.3, Corollary 2 to Proposition 5.) Now $mqm = m$, hence $mq - 1$ annihilates the dense ideal mR, and so also $mq = 1$. We may write $q = m^{-1}$. It follows immediately that every element of RM^{-1} has the form rm^{-1} with $r \in R$ and $m \in M$. As M is contained in the center of R, there is no difficulty about verifying that these elements form a subring of Q.

Finally, the proof of the two equations will be left as an exercise.

PROPOSITION 7 (Passman).

(a) *If $R = AG$ is semiprime then A is semiprime and the order of no finite normal subgroup of G is a zero-divisor in A.*

(b) *The converse holds when A is commutative.*

Proof. (a) Assume R semiprime. Then A is semiprime, since rad $A = A \cap$ rad R, by Lemma 4. Suppose $H = \{g_1, g_2, \ldots, g_n\}$ is a normal subgroup of G and $na = 0$. Put $K = \omega H$, and let K^1 be the left annihilator of the ideal K in R. Then

$$a(g_1 + g_2 + \cdots + g_n) = -a(1 - g_1) - \cdots - a(1 - g_n) \in K^1 \cap K,$$

by Lemma 2. But $(K^1 \cap K)^2 \subset K^1K = 0$, hence $K^1 \cap K = 0$, since R is semiprime. Thus $a = 0$, and so n is not a zero-divisor in A.

(b) Assume the two conditions and commutativity of A. Let M be the multiplicatively closed set generated by the orders of all finite normal subgroups of G, regarded as elements of A. Consider $RM^{-1} = (AM^{-1})G$. The orders of all finite normal subgroups of G are units in AM^{-1}. By Lemma 5, rad $AM^{-1} = (\text{rad } A)M^{-1} = 0$, hence AM^{-1} is also semiprime. Since, again by Lemma 5, rad $R = R \cap$ rad RM^{-1}, it will follow that R is semiprime if we show that RM^{-1} is semiprime.

Writing A for AM^{-1} and R for RM^{-1}, we may therefore assume that A is commutative semiprime and that the order of every normal subgroup of G is a unit in A, and we wish to prove that R is semiprime. Now A is a subdirect product of commutative integral domains B, hence $R = AG$ is a subdirect product of the corresponding group rings BG. Since a subdirect product of semiprime rings is semiprime, it suffices to prove that each BG is semiprime. Take any B. The order of any finite normal subgroup of G is a unit in B, since B is a homomorphic image of A.

Now let M be the set of nonzero elements of B and consider $(BG)M^{-1} = (BM^{-1})G$. BM^{-1} is a field whose characteristic is either 0, or else does not divide the order of any finite normal subgroup of G. It follows from the Corollaries to Propositions 4 and 5 that $(BM^{-1})G$ is semiprime, and again we argue, with the help of Lemma 5, that BG is semiprime. The proof is now complete.

EXERCISES

1. Show that AG is a ring, for any ring A and any group G. Verify that the result remains valid if G is taken to be any semigroup with 1, and that the polynomial ring $A[x]$ is then a special case of the construction.

2. Prove that $a \to a^*$ and $g \to g^+$ are monomorphisms, as stated in the text. Also verify the formulas $(rg)(h) = r(hg^{-1})$, etc.

3. Prove Lemma 1, and show that, even if H is not a normal subgroup of G, $A(G/H)$ may reasonably be interpreted as a left A-module. [*Hint:* To prove the last statement of the lemma observe that each element of H is

a word in the g_i and their inverses. Use induction on the length of the word and the identity $1 - hg_i^{\pm 1} = (1 - h)g_i^{\pm 1} + (1 - g_i^{\pm 1})$.]

4. Prove Lemma 2. [*Hint:* If $r(\omega H) = 0$, r must be constant on every left coset of H.]

5. If $R = AG$, G finite, show that $\operatorname{Hom}_A(R,A)$ is a right R-module isomorphic to R_R.

6 (Connell). If $R = AG$, A_A injective and G finite, show that R_R is injective.

7 (Connell). If $R = AG$ and R_R is injective, show that A_A is injective and that every finitely generated subgroup of G is finite.

8. Prove Lemma 4. (*Hint:* Let P be a prime ideal of AG. If B is in the center of A, $BG \cap P$ is a prime ideal of BG. If H is in the center of G, $AH \cap P$ is a prime ideal of AH.)

9. Show that the centralizer $C(g)$ of an element g of G has finite index if and only if g has only a finite number of conjugates in G. Show that the set G^* of all such elements g is a normal subgroup of G.

10. If C is the center of the simple ring B, and K is any right ideal of CG, show that $KB \cap CG = K$. (*Hint:* B_C is a vector space.)

11. Let M be as in Lemma 5. Prove that rad $RM^{-1} = (\operatorname{rad} R)M^{-1}$, by showing that rm^{-1} is strongly nilpotent in RM^{-1} if and only if r is strongly nilpotent in R. Deduce that $R \cap \operatorname{rad} RM^{-1} = \operatorname{rad} R$.

12. A group G is simply ordered if $(G, \leq)$ is a simply ordered set and, for all a, b, c, $d \in G$, $a \leq b$ & $c \leq d \Rightarrow ac \leq bd$. Show that AG is semiprimitive if A is a commutative integral domain and G is simply ordered. (*Hint:* First show that every unit in AG has the form ag, where a is a unit in A. If $r \in \operatorname{Rad} AG$, $1 + rg$ is a unit for all $g \in G$.)

13. If A is a commutative integral domain and G is a simply ordered group, show that AG is semiprimitive if and only if A is semiprime.

SEMIPRIME GROUP RINGS

IAN G. CONNELL

In this continuation of Appendix 2 we will remove the commutativity assumption in Proposition 7; that is, we will prove the following:

PROPOSITION 8. *$R = AG$ is semiprime if and only if A is semiprime and the order of no finite normal subgroup is a zero-divisor in A.*

We will also determine when R is a prime ring. However we will have to quote results not treated in the book, so the proof will not be entirely self-contained.

The "only if" part is contained in Proposition 7, so it remains to prove the "if" part.

Let G^+ denote the set of elements in G^* of finite order; with the help of Dietzmann's Lemma the following facts are easily verified:

(i) G^+ *is a normal subgroup of G, in fact the join* (*in the subgroup lattice*) *of all the finite normal subgroups of G.*

(ii) *Every finitely generated subgroup of G^+ is finite and is contained in a finite normal subgroup of G.*

We will use the following striking result of B. H. Neumann (1951):

(iii) G^*/G^+ *is Abelian torsion-free.*

The idea of the proof is to reduce the problem from AG to AG^*, then to AG^+, and finally to AH where H is finite. The first reduction has already been carried out (Proposition 5), so the next step is to deduce that AG^* is semiprime assuming that AG^+ is. A Zorn's Lemma argument shows that every torsion-free Abelian group can be simply ordered (see Birkhoff, 1948, p. 224); hence if g_i are coset representatives of G^+ in G^*, we can assume that they are simply ordered in such a way that

$$g_i < g_j, \quad g_k < g_l, \quad g_i g_k = h_1 g_m, \quad g_j g_l = h_2 g_n, \quad h_1, h_2 \in G^+ \Rightarrow g_m < g_n.$$

Now every element $r \in AG^*$ is uniquely representable in the form $r = \sum r_i g_i$, $r_i \in AG^+$. When $r \neq 0$ we define $tr = r_i$ where g_i is the smallest among the g_j with $r_j \neq 0$, and we put $t0 = 0$. If J is an ideal in AG^* then calculation shows that $tJ = \{tj \mid j \in J\}$ is an ideal in AG^+, and if $J^2 = 0$ then $(tJ)^2 = 0$. (It is convenient to assume that one of the g_i is 1.)

We have thus reduced the problem to proving that rad $AG^+ = 0$. If $r \in$ rad AG^+, let H be the normal subgroup of G generated by the support of r; H is finite, by remark (ii) above, and its order n is a non-zero-divisor in A by assumption. By Lemma 4, $r \in$ rad AH, so it remains to prove that rad $AH = 0$.

By Lemma 5 we may assume that n is a unit in A, and by the subdirect product argument we may assume that A is prime. Thus the center F of A is an integral domain, and again by Lemma 5 we may assume that F is a field. Since the characteristic of F does not divide n, by Maschke's Theorem we have

$$FH \cong I_1 \times I_2 \times \cdots \times I_k$$

where the I_i are simple rings. If I denotes one of them, its center K is a field. The canonical map $FH \to I$ embeds F in K, so K is an extension of F;

it is of finite degree, since FH has finite F-dimension. Now $L \otimes_F FH \cong LH$ is completely reducible for every extension field L of F, so FH is a separable algebra, hence K is a separable extension of F. (See Bourbaki, 1958, p. 92.) Since $AH \cong A \otimes_F FH \cong (A \otimes_F I_1) \times \cdots \times (A \otimes_F I_k)$, it remains to prove that $A \otimes_F I$ is semiprime.

LEMMA 6. *If K is a field, I a central simple K-algebra, and B any K-algebra, then*

$$rad\,(B \otimes_K I) \cong rad\,B \otimes_K I.$$

Proof. In Jacobson, 1964, p. 109, it is shown that $J \to J \otimes I$ gives an isomorphism between the ideal lattices of B and $B \otimes I$. A simple calculation shows that products are preserved, so that prime ideals correspond to prime ideals, and the result follows.

The map $\sum (a \otimes k) \otimes i \to \sum a \otimes ki$ gives a ring isomorphism

$$(A \otimes_F K) \otimes_K I \cong A \otimes_F I;$$

by Lemma 6 we wish to prove that $A \otimes_F K$ is semiprime, and finally this follows from:

LEMMA 7. *Let K be a finite separable extension of the field F and B an F-algebra. Then $B \otimes_F K$ is semiprime if and only if B is.*

Proof. (We do not attempt to prove a more general result as is done for the Jacobson radical in Bourbaki, 1958, p.84.) If $u_1, \ldots, u_m$ is a basis for K over F then every element in $B \otimes_F K$ is uniquely expressible in the form $\sum b_i \otimes u_i$, $b_i \in B$ and we may identify B with the subring of elements of the form $b \otimes 1$. If P is a prime ideal in $B \otimes_F K$ then $P' = P \cap B$ is a prime ideal in B; for, if $xBy \subset P'$, then

$$x(\sum b_i \otimes u_i)y = \sum (xb_i y \otimes 1)(1 \otimes u_i) \in P,$$

so x(say) $\in P$, hence $x \in P'$. Thus, if $B \otimes_F K$ is semiprime, so is B. It remains to prove the converse.

Let L be a finite normal separable extension of F containing K. We wish to show that $B \otimes_F L \cong (B \otimes_F K) \otimes_K L$ is semiprime; for then, by the half already proved, $B \otimes_F K$ will be semiprime. Let the elements of the Galois group of L over F be $\psi_1, \ldots, \psi_d$ and let $\{\psi_i u\}$ be a normal basis, so that the matrix $(\psi_i \psi_j u)$ admits an inverse, say (v_{ij}), $v_{ij} \in L$ (Bourbaki, *Algèbre*, Chap. 5, p. 158). Since $\sum b_i \otimes \psi_i u \to \sum b_i \otimes \psi_j \psi_i u$ is a ring automorphism and the radical is sent onto itself by any automorphism, if $x = \sum b_i \otimes \psi_i u \in rad\,(B \otimes_F L)$ then $x_j = \sum b_i \otimes \psi_j \psi_i u \in rad\,(B \otimes_F L)$ for each j. Thus $\sum_j v_{kj} x_j = b_k \otimes 1 \in rad\,(B \otimes_F L) \cap B \subset rad\,B = 0$. Hence $b_k = 0$ for each k, and $x = 0$ as required.

PROPOSITION 9. $R = AG$ *is prime if and only if A is prime and* $G^+ = 1$.

Proof. First let R be prime. If J is an ideal in A then JR is an ideal in R and $(JR)^1 \supset J^1$; hence A must be prime. If H is a finite normal subgroup of G then ωH is an ideal and $(\omega H)^1 \neq 0$ by Lemma 2, so $\omega H = 0$ and $H = 1$. Thus $G^+ = 1$.

Conversely, if $r \in R$ define $\psi r = \sum_{g \in G*} r(g)g \in AG^*$. If J is a nonzero ideal in R, clearly $\psi J = \{\psi j \mid j \in J\}$ is a nonzero ideal in AG^*. As Passman has pointed out, a simple modification of the proof of Proposition 5 yields the following: if J,K are ideals in R with $JK = 0$ then $\psi J \psi K = 0$. This allows us to assume $G^* = G$. Since $G^+ = G^{*+} = 1$, G is Abelian torsion-free and therefore simply ordered. Finally, using the mapping t defined earlier, if J is an ideal in R with $0 \neq x \in J^1$, then $0 \neq tx \in (tJ)^1$, so $tJ = 0$, whence $J = 0$ and the proof is complete.

Comments

The following comments, arranged by chapter numbers, consist of some casual historical information and other afterthoughts. However, I have not gone out of my way to trace the authorship of theorems which have already appeared in other books. References are to author and year of a publication, as listed in the bibliography below, on the presumption that any remaining ambiguity is easily resolved.

Section 1.1. The study of equationally defined classes of algebraic systems was pioneered by Birkhoff (1935, 1949). Some laws other than identities may be reformulated as such. For example, in group theory, the law

$$\forall_a \exists_b ab = 1$$

may be replaced by the identity

$$aa^{-1} = 1.$$

The reader may easily verify that any equationally defined class of algebras is closed under direct products. This is why the class of division rings is not equationally definable. (See also Section 1.3.)

Birkhoff showed that a class of sets with common operations is equationally definable if and only if it is closed under direct products, subsystems, and quotient systems.

Section 1.2. It is essential to the statement concerning the sup of a simply ordered family of subrings in Proposition 1 that the operations in a ring are n-ary, where n is finite.

In the last few years, even while this book was being written, it has become fashionable to define mono-, epi-, and isomorphisms for abstract categories by certain cancellation rules. The reader who is aware of this trend should bear in mind that the definitions given here for rings are equivalent to the modern definitions in the category of sets (after all, a

166

ring is a set "with" operations), but not in the category of rings. (According to most recent usage, the canonical embedding of the integers into the rationals is an epimorphism in the category of rings!) The new definitions in the category of modules are equivalent to ours, but this is a nontrivial fact.

Homomorphic relations were first introduced by Shoda (1949) under the name "meromorphisms" and have been rediscovered by several authors since. Systems with a ternary operation $f(x,y,z)$ such that $f(x,y,y) = x$ and $f(y,y,z) = z$ were discussed by Mal'cev (1954) and the author (1957).

Section 1.3. This rather pedestrian discussion of direct products and sums may be contrasted with the categorical treatment in Sections 4.1 and 4.2.

Section 1.4. The use of Lemma 2 in the proof of the Krull-Remak-Schmidt Theorem is believed to be new. Both this and the Jordan-Hölder-Schreier Theorem are usually proved in a more general setup, thus for groups with operators in the book by Zassenhaus. The most general statement of these theorems may probably be found in the papers by Goldie (1950, 1952), see also the author's paper (1957). For another proof of the Krull-Remak-Schmidt Theorem see Section 3.7.

Section 2.1. It is to be noted that both maximal and prime ideals are proper ideals in our terminology. For the history of the two radicals, the reader is referred to other books on ring theory, for example the very readable book by McCoy (1964).

At one time, subdirectly irreducible rings were considered to be the building blocks from which all rings are made. Today they have been replaced in importance by local rings. Similarly, subdirect products have been replaced by sheaves (see Appendix 1).

Section 2.2. Proposition 1 asserts that ideals of Boolean rings are dual filters. Many authors prefer to say that filters are dual ideals. However, dual filters exist in other ordered sets, while dual ideals do not exist in other rings. Incidentally, if we had interpreted ∨ rather than ∧ as multiplication, we should have been forced to say that filters are ideals.

Corollary 2 to Proposition 1 is of considerable importance in logic. When applied to the free Boolean algebra with countably many generators, it may be interpreted to say: *A formula in the propositional calculus is a theorem if and only if it is a tautology.*

Section 2.3. The complete ring of quotients of a ring (not only in the commutative case) was first studied by Utumi (1956), generalizing a construction by Johnson (1951). The presentation here leans on a paper by Findlay and the author (1958). For variety, a different treatment is followed in the general case (see Section 4.3).

Section 2.4.   While Proposition 1 is due essentially to Johnson, the simplifications that arise in the commutative case were first pointed out by Fine et al. (1965).   For the general case, see Section 4.5, Proposition 2.

A *complete Boolean algebra* is of course a Boolean algebra which is complete as a lattice (see Section 1.1).   The Dedekind-MacNeille completion is called thus in Birkhoff's "Lattice Theory."

The fact that the complete ring of quotients of a Boolean ring is its Dedekind-MacNeille completion (Corollary to Proposition 6) was first established by Brainerd and the author (1959) using a more straightforward method.

Fine et al. (1965) considered the ring $R = C(X)$ of all real-valued continuous functions defined on a compact Hausdorff space X.   They showed that its complete ring of quotients is the ring $Q(X)$ of all real-valued continuous functions defined on dense open subsets of X, modulo the obvious equivalence relation.   (Identify two functions if they agree on the intersection of their domains.)

Banaschewski (1965) generalized this result to arbitrary commutative semiprime rings.   He also obtained the complete ring of quotients of a Boolean ring as a special case.

Section 2.5.   The topology on the space of maximal ideals is also called the "hull-kernel" topology by functional analysts.

The inf of an infinite family of regular open sets is not their intersection, but the interior of their intersection.

Section 3.1.   An example of a right primitive ring which is not left primitive is given by Bergman (1964).

Our proof of Jacobson's Density Theorem (Proposition 3) is adapted from one by Artin and Tate (see Artin, 1950).

The reader is urged to distinguish carefully between "dense subrings" and "dense ideals."   While the former usage of "dense" is topological, the latter is not.

Section 3.2.   The concept of "strong nilpotency" is a variation of Jacobson's treatment using "m-sequences."

Further exercises on the two radicals will be found at the end of Section 3.5.   For deeper results on the Jacobson radical the reader may wish to consult Chapter I of Jacobson's book (1964); see also, Amitsur (1956).

Section 3.3.   Here is the precise definition of "bimodule:" A *bimodule* ${}_R M_S$ is a left module ${}_R M$ which is at the same time a right module M_S such that

$$(rm)s = r(ms)$$

for all $r \in R$, $m \in M$, and $s \in S$.   The socle is due to Dieudonné (1950).

Section 3.4. The treatment of completely reducible rings here is more elementary and less modern than that in Jacobson's "Structure of Rings," where much is deduced from the Density Theorem (Section 3.1, Proposition 3). I have avoided "semisimple" altogether, because of conflicting usages of this term.

Section 3.5. The proof of Levitzki's Theorem (Proposition 5) was originally much longer. Utumi's proof given here is based on an earlier one by Herstein. Proposition 3 appears to be due to C. Hopkins.

Section 3.6. Jacobson, in Chapter III of his book "Structure of Rings," introduced a special class of rings "suitable for building idempotents." Lemma 1 allows us to replace this by the apparently larger class of rings in which idempotents modulo the radical can be lifted. It is now clear that one can do with the semiperfect rings of Bass what was done with Artinian rings in the old days (and with certain "semiprimary" rings in Jacobson's book).

Section 3.7. Actually Azumaya (1950) proved a more general theorem in which the number of summands was not restricted to be finite.

Section 4.1. The concepts if not the names "projective" and "injective" go back to Reinhold Baer, but their important position in modern algebra is due to the influence of homological algebra, in particular to the pioneering book by Cartan and Eilenberg. A weaker form of Proposition 7 (see Exercise 3) is attributed by these authors to Kaplansky. They also have the crux of Proposition 8 (see Exercise 6). One is tempted to extend the names "hereditary" and "semihereditary" to modules.

Section 4.2. Different but analogous character groups may be defined using the reals in place of the rationals. The character group of a discrete Abelian group may then be endowed in a natural way with a compact topology. However, for our purely algebraic purposes the rationals will do.

The fact that every module is isomorphic to a submodule of an injective module was discovered by Baer (1940). The present proof, via Proposition 4, is also found in Northcott's book (1960). The existence of a minimal injective extension seems to have been discovered independently by Eckmann and Schopf (1953) and Shoda (1952). The latter establishes an analogy with the algebraic closure of a field.

Section 4.3. The complete ring of quotients has already been commented upon in the commutative case (Section 2.3). The present treatment is due to the author (1963). A whole collection of generalized rings of quotients was introduced by Gabriel (1962) (see also the exercises in Bourbaki, Fasc. 27, pp. 157–166). These include not only subrings of our complete ring of quotients, but also rings which are not faithful extensions of R.

Section 4.4. Concerning Proposition 2, see also, Lesieur and Croisot (1963). Exercise 5 brings out the analogy between modules and fields:

$$\frac{\text{Rational completion}}{\text{Injective hull}} = \frac{\text{Maximal pure inseparable extension}}{\text{Algebraic closure}}$$

Rational completions were treated by Findlay and the author (1958) and Wong and Johnson (1959).

Section 4.5. Johnson originally constructed regular rings of quotients directly, without using our definition of Q.

Section 4.6. See also Goldie (1958, 1960), Lesieur and Croisot (1959). The proof of Proposition 3 given here arose from a study of the proof by Johnson and Wong (1961). Faith, in his lecture notes, gave a similar proof for the semiprime case.

Small is said to have proved the following interesting theorem: *A right Noetherian ring R possesses a classical right Artinian ring of right quotients if and only if all non-zero-divisors of R/rad R can be "lifted" to non-zero-divisors of R.*

Section 4.7. Proofs of this result appear in the paper by Faith and Utumi (1965), also in a recent paper by Johnson (1965) and in an appendix to the newly revised book by Jacobson.

Section 5.1. The tensor product was first introduced by Whitney (1938). It has been widely popularized by Bourbaki.

Section 5.2. The notation in this chapter comes from an old collaboration with Findlay. A general definition of "functor" presupposes the concept of "category," which has not been introduced here. For categories, functors, and natural transformations the reader may wish to consult the recent exposition by MacLane (1965).

Section 5.3. Assertion (3') of Proposition 2 and the corollary have only been pointed out recently (1964).

Section 5.4. The concept of "flatness" was mentioned by Cartan and Eilenberg. Later Bourbaki devoted a whole chapter to it, where many more results are to be found. In an important article, Bass (1960) characterized those rings for which every flat left module is projective. They turn out to be exactly those rings for which every nonempty set of principal right ideals has a minimal element. He called these rings "perfect," hence the "semiperfect" rings which play a role here. See also the papers by Faith (1959) and Chase (1960).

Section 5.5. The two-square theorem and the method of chasing squares was first published by the author (1964), but both Eckmann and Hilton had been using similar techniques. The recent book by Jans offers a particularly gentle introduction to further results in homological algebra.

My original proof of Proposition 1 was different. It was based on the following, due to Goursat (1889), stated here for modules instead of groups.

LEMMA. *Let G be a submodule of A × B. Then*

$$\frac{\{a \in A \mid \exists_{b \in B}(a,b) \in G\}}{\{a \in A \mid (a,0) \in G\}} \cong \frac{\{b \in B \mid \exists_{a \in A}(a,b) \in G\}}{\{b \in B \mid (0,b) \in G\}} .$$

In the proof of Proposition 1 a suitable submodule of $B \times E$ was used.

Conversely, it is not difficult to deduce the lemma from Proposition 1. Thus writing it in abbreviated form

$$\frac{C}{D} \cong \frac{C'}{D'} ,$$

it follows readily from a consideration of the diagram

$$
\begin{array}{ccc}
D' & \longrightarrow & C' \\
\downarrow & & \downarrow \\
\end{array}
$$
$$
\begin{array}{ccccc}
D & \longrightarrow & G & \longrightarrow & C' \\
\downarrow & & \downarrow & & \downarrow \\
C & \longrightarrow & C & \longrightarrow & 0
\end{array}
$$

with obvious homomorphisms.

Appendix 1. For a classical discussion of the *P*-component of an ideal see Northcott (1953).

Appendix 2. References are to Connell (1963), Passman (1962), Auslander (1957), and MacLaughlin (1958). Dietzmann's Lemma was taken from Kurosh, Vol. II, p. 154.

To find out when the group ring is semiprimitive is more difficult than when it is semiprime. Results on this problem were obtained by Villamayor (1959), Amitsur (1956), and Connell (1963).

Appendix 3. These results were generously contributed by Ian G. Connell. They allow one to construct many interesting prime and semiprime rings. They assume some knowledge of material unfortunately not developed in this book. In addition to two quoted theorems concerning torsion-free Abelian groups there is presupposed the concept of an algebra (a ring "extending" a commutative ring, in the sense of Exercises 5.1), separable extensions of fields and algebras, central simple algebras, and the tensor product of two algebras (see Section 5.1, Exercise 1).

Bibliography

The following bibliography is not complete. All books I can think of are mentioned, but many worthy articles are not, in particular many of those that have already been listed in Jacobson's "Structure of rings." Preference is given to articles which were actually consulted, or in which some of the topics treated here are further developed. If the journal or page numbers of an article are not listed, this means that I have only seen it in manuscript.

ALBERT, A. ADRIAN. *Modern Higher Algebra*. Chicago: University of Chicago Press, 1947.

———. *Linear Algebras*. National Academy of Sciences—National Research Council Publication 502. Washington, D.C., 1957.

AMITSUR, S. A. "The Radical of a Polynomial Ring," *Can. J. Math.*, 8 (1956), pp. 355–361.

———. "On the Semi-simplicity of the Group Algebra," *Michigan Math. J.*, 6 (1959), pp. 251–253.

ANDERSON, F. W. "Lattice-ordered Rings of Quotients," *Can. J. Math.*, 17 (1965), pp. 434–448.

ARTIN, EMIL. "The Influence of J. H. M. Wedderburn on the Development of Modern Algebra," *Bull. Am. Math. Soc.*, 56 (1950), pp. 65–72.

———. *Rings with Minimum Condition*. Ann Arbor: University of Michigan Press, 1940.

AUSLANDER, M. "On Regular Group Rings," *Proc. Am. Math. Soc.*, 8 (1957) pp. 658–664.

AZUMAYA, GORÔ. "Corrections and Supplementations to My Paper Concerning Krull-Remak-Schmidt's Theorem," *Nagoya Math. J.*, 1 (1950), pp. 117–124.

BAER, REINHOLD. "Abelian Groups Which Are Direct Summands of Every Containing Group," *Proc. Am. Math. Soc.*, 46 (1940), pp. 800–806.

BANASCHEWSKI, BERNHARD. "On Projective and Injective Modules," *Arch. Math.*, 15 (1964), pp. 271–275.

———. "Quotient Extensions of Modules," *Math, Nachr.*, 28 (1965), pp. 245–255.

———. "Maximal Rings of Quotients of Semi-simple Commutative Rings," *Arch. Math.*, *16* (1965), pp. 414–420.

———. "On Coverings of Modules," *Math. Nachr.* (1965).

BASS, HYMAN. "Finitistic Homological Dimension and a Homological General-ization of Semi-primary Rings," *Trans. Am. Math. Soc.*, *95* (1960), pp. 466–488.

———. "Injective Dimension in Noetherian Rings," *Trans. Am. Math. Soc.*, *102* (1962), pp. 18–29.

———. "Torsion Free and Projective Modules," *Trans. Am. Math. Soc.*, *102* (1962), pp. 319–327.

BERGMAN, G. M. "A Ring Primitive on the Right but Not on the Left," *Proc. Am. Math. Soc.*, *15* (1964), pp. 473–475.

BIRKHOFF, GARRETT. "On the Structure of Abstract Algebras," *Proc. Cambridge Phil. Soc.*, *31* (1935), pp. 433–454.

———. "Subdirect Unions in Universal Algebra," *Bull. Am. Math. Soc.*, *50* (1944), pp. 764–768.

———. "Universal Algebra," *Proc. First Can. Math. Congr.* (1945), pp. 310–326.

———. *Lattice Theory.* Am. Math. Soc. Colloquium Publications 25. Rev. ed. New York: American Mathematics Society, 1948. (A multigraphed 1963 version of this is available from the Department of Mathematics, Harvard University.)

BOURBAKI, NICOLAS. *Algèbre.* Chapter 8 (Fasc. 23). Paris : Hermann & Cie, 1958.

———. *Algèbre Commutative.* Chapters 1 and 2 (Fasc. 27). Paris: Hermann & Cie, 1961.

———. *Algèbre Commutative.* Chapters 3 and 4 (Fasc. 28). Paris: Hermann & Cie, 1961.

BRAINERD, BARRON, and JOACHIM LAMBEK. "On the Ring of Quotients of a Boolean Ring," *Can. Math. Bull.*, *2* (1959), pp. 25–29.

BRAUER, RICHARD. *Non-commutative Rings.* Multigraphed lecture notes. Cambridge: Harvard University Press.

BROWN, BAILEY, and NEAL H. MCCOY. "Radicals and Subdirect Sums," *Am. J. Math.*, *69* (1947), pp. 46–58.

———. "The Radical of a Ring," *Duke Math. J.*, *15* (1948), pp. 495–499.

———. "The Maximal Regular Ideal of a Ring," *Proc. Am. Math. Soc.*, *1* (1950), pp. 165–171.

CARTAN, HENRI, and SAMUEL EILENBERG. *Homological Algebra.* Princeton, N.J.: Princeton University Press, 1956.

CHASE, STEPHEN U. "Direct Product of Modules," *Trans. Am. Math. Soc.*, *97* (1960), pp. 457–473.

CHRISTENSEN, JOANNE. "On Maximal Rings of Right Quotients," *Can. Math. Bull.*, *5* (1962), pp. 147–149.

COHN, P. M. "On the Embedding of Rings in Skew Fields," *Proc. London Math. Soc.*, *11* (1961), pp. 512–530.

———. *Universal Algebra.* New York: Harper & Row, 1965.

CONNELL, IAN G. "On the Group Ring," *Can. J. Math.*, *15* (1963), pp. 650–685.

———. "A Number Theory Problem Concerning Finite Groups and Rings," *Can. Math. Bull.*, *7* (1964), pp. 23–34.

CURTISS, C. W., and I. REINER. *Representation Theory of Finite Groups and Associative Algebras*. New York: Interscience Publishers, Inc., 1962.

DEURING, MAX. *Algebren*. New York: Chelsea and Springer, 1948.

DICKSON, LEONARD EUGENE. *Algebras and Their Arithmetics*. New York: G. E. Stechert and Company, 1938.

DIEUDONNÉ, JEAN. "Les Produits Tensoriels," *Ann. Éc. Norm.*, *64* (1947), pp. 101–117.

———. "Les Idéaux Minimaux dans les Anneaux Associatifs," *Proc. Int. Cong. Mathematicians*, *2* (1950), pp. 44–48.

ECKMANN, BENO, and A. SCHOPF. "Über injektive Moduln," *Arch. Math.*, *4* (1953), pp. 75–78.

FAITH, CARL. "Rings with Minimum Condition on Principal Ideals I; II," *Arch. Math.*, *10* (1959), pp. 327–330; *12* (1961), pp. 179–181.

———. "Orders in Simple Artinian Rings," *Trans. Am. Math. Soc.*, *114* (1965), pp. 61–64.

———. *Lectures on Injective Modules and Quotient Rings*. Multigraphed lecture notes. New Brunswick, N.J.: Rutgers University Press, 1964.

FAITH, CARL, and YUZO UTUMI. "On a New Proof of Litoff's Theorem," *Acta Math.*, *14* (1963), pp. 369–371.

———. "Baer Modules," *Arch. Math.*, *15* (1964), pp. 266–270.

———. "Quasi-injective Modules and Their Endomorphism Rings," *Arch. Math.*, *15* (1964), pp. 166–174.

———. "On Noetherian Prime Rings," *Trans. Am. Math. Soc.*, *114* (1965), pp. 53–60.

———. "Intrinsic Extensions of Rings," *Pacific J. Math.*, *14* (1964), pp. 505–512.

FELLER, EDMUND H. "Properties of Primary Noncommutative Rings," *Trans. Am. Math. Soc.*, *89* (1958), pp. 79–91.

———. "Noetherian Modules and Noetherian Injective Rings," *Tôhoku Math. J.*, *17* (1965), pp. 130–138.

FELLER, E. H., and E. W. SWOKOWSKI. "Reflective N-prime Rings with the Ascending Chain Condition," *Trans. Am. Math. Soc.*, *99* (1961), pp. 264–271.

———. "On Ring Extensions for Completely Primary Noncommutative Rings," *Trans. Am. Math. Soc.*, *105* (1962), pp. 251–263.

———. "The Ring of Endomorphisms of a Torsion-free Module," *J. London Math. Soc.*, *39* (1964), pp. 41–42.

FINDLAY, GEORGE D. "Reflexive Homomorphic Relations," *Can. Math. Bull.*, *3* (1960), pp. 131–132.

———. "Multiplicative Ideal Theory and Rings of Quotients."

FINDLAY, GEORGE D., and JOACHIM LAMBEK. "A Generalized Ring of Quotients I; II," *Can. Math. Bull.*, *1* (1958), pp. 77–85; pp. 155–167.

FINE, NATHAN J., LEONARD GILLMAN, and JOACHIM LAMBEK. *Rings of Quotients of Rings of Functions*. Montreal: McGill University Press, 1965. (See also *Notices of Am. Math. Soc.*, *7* (1960), pp. 980; and *8* (1961), pp. 60–61.)

FLEISCHER, ISIDORE. "A Note on Subdirect Products," *Acta. Math.*, *6* (1955), pp. 463–465.

FUJIWARA, TSUYOSHI. "On the Existence of Algebraically Closed Algebraic Extensions," *Osaka Math. J.*, *8* (1956), pp. 23–33.

GABRIEL, PIERRE. "Des Catégories Abéliennes," *Bull. Soc. Math. France*, *90* (1962), pp. 323–448.

GENTILE, ENZO R. "On Rings with One-sided Field of Quotients," *Proc. Am. Math. Soc.*, *11* (1960), pp. 380–384.

――――. "Singular Submodule and Injective Hull," *Indag. Math.*, *24* (1962), pp. 426–433.

GOLDIE, ALFRED W. "The Jordan-Hölder Theorem for General Abstract Algebras," *Proc. London Math. Soc.*, *52* (1960), pp. 107–131.

――――. "On Direct Decompositions," *Proc. Cambridge Phil. Soc.*, *48* (1952), pp. 1–34.

――――. "Decomposition of Semi-simple Rings," *J. London Math. Soc.*, *31* (1956), pp. 40–48.

――――. "The Structure of Prime Rings under Ascending Chain Conditions," *Proc. London Math. Soc.*, *8* (1958), pp. 589–608.

――――. "Semi-prime Rings with Maximum Condition," *Proc. London Math. Soc.*, *10* (1960), pp. 201–220.

――――. "Non-commutative Principal Ideal Rings," *Arch. Math.*, *13* (1962), pp. 214–221.

――――. *Rings with Maximum Condition.* Multigraphed lecture notes. New Haven: Yale University Press, 1961.

GOURSAT, É. "Sur les Substitutions Orthogonales . . . ," *Ann. Sci. Éc. Norm. Sup.* (3), *6* (1889), pp. 9–102.

GOVOROV, V. E. "Rings over Which Flat Modules are Free," *Dokl. Akad. Nauk. SSSR*, *144* (1962), pp. 965–967.

GROTHENDIECK, ALEXANDER, and JEAN DIEUDONNÉ. *Éléments de Géométrie Algébrique*, I. (Inst. des Hautes Études Scient., Publications Mathématiques, 4.) Paris: Presses Universitaires de France, 1960.

HALMOS, PAUL R. *Boolean Algebras.* Multigraphed lecture notes. Chicago. University of Chicago Press, 1959.

――――, *Lectures on Boolean Algebras.* Princeton, N.J.: D. Van Nostrand Company, Inc., 1963.

HERSTEIN, ISRAEL N. *Theory of Rings.* Multigraphed lecture notes. Chicago. University of Chicago Press, 1961.

――――. "A Theorem of Levitzki," *Proc. Am. Math. Soc.*, *13* (1962), pp. 213–214.

HILTON, P. J., and W. LEDERMANN. "On the Jordan-Hölder Theorem in Homological Monoids," *Proc. London Math. Soc.*, *10* (1960), pp. 321–334.

HILTON, P. J., and S. WYLIE. *Homology Theory.* London: Cambridge University Press, 1960.

JACOBSON, NATHAN. *Theory of Rings.* American Mathematical Society Surveys, Vol. 2. New York; American Mathematical Society, 1943.

――――. *Lectures in Abstract Algebra.* I; *Basic Concepts.* Princeton, N.J.: D. Van Nostrand Company, Inc., 1951.

――――. *Lectures in Abstract Algebra.* II; *Linear Algebra.* Princeton, N.J.: D. Van Nostrand Company, Inc., 1953.

――――. *Structure of Rings.* American Mathematical Society Colloquium, Vol. 36. Rev. ed. Providence, R.I.: 1964.

JAFFARD, PAUL. *Les Systèmes d'Idéaux.* Paris: Dunod, 1960.

JANS, JAMES P. *Rings and Homology.* New York: Holt, Rinehart and Winston, Inc., 1964.

JOHNSON, RICHARD E. "Prime Rings," *Duke Math. J.*, *18* (1951), pp. 799–809.

———. "The Extended Centralizer of a Ring over a Module," *Proc. Am. Math. Soc.*, *2* (1951), pp. 891–895.

———. "Representations of Prime Rings," *Trans. Am. Math. Soc.*, *74* (1953), pp. 351–357.

———. "Semi-prime Rings," *Trans. Am. Math. Soc.*, *76* (1954), pp. 375–388.

———. "Structure Theory of Faithful Rings: I, II," *Trans. Am. Math. Soc.*, *84* (1957), pp. 508–522; 523–544.

———. "Structure Theory of Faithful Rings. III: Irreducible Rings," *Proc. Am. Math. Soc.*, *11* (1960), pp. 710–717.

———. "Quotient Rings of Rings with Zero Singular Ideal," *Pacific J. Math.*, *11* (1961), pp. 1385–1392.

———. "Principal Right Ideal Rings," *Can. J. Math.*, *15* (1963), pp. 297–301.

———. "Distinguished Rings of Linear Transformations," *Trans. Am. Math. Soc.*, *111* (1964), pp. 400–412.

———. "Prime Matrix Rings," *Proc. Am. Math. Soc.*, *16* (1965), pp. 1099–1105.

JOHNSON, RICHARD E., and EDWARD T. WONG. "Quasi-injective Modules and Irreducible Rings," *J. London Math. Soc.*, *36* (1961), pp. 260–268.

KAPLANSKY, IRVING. "Modules over Dedekind Rings and Valuation Rings," *Trans. Am. Math. Soc.*, *72* (1952), pp. 327–340.

———. *Infinite Abelian Groups.* Ann Arbor: University of Michigan Press, 1954.

———. *Rings of Operators.* Multigraphed lecture notes. Chicago: University of Chicago Press, 1959.

———. "Projective Modules," *Ann. Math.*, *68* (1958), pp. 372–377.

KASCH, FRIEDRICH. "Projektive Frobenius-Erweiterungen," *Sitzungsberichte der Heidelberger Akademie der Wissenschaften, Mathematisch-naturwissen-schaftliche Klasse* (1960–1961), 89–109.

KOH, KWANGIL. "A Note on a Self-injective Ring," *Can. Math. Bull.*, *8* (1965), pp. 29–32.

———. "A Note on a Certain Class of Prime Rings," *Am. Math. Monthly*, *72* (1965), pp. 46–48.

KRULL, WOLFGANG. *Idealtheorie.* New York: Chelsea and Springer, 1948.

KUROSH, A. G. *The Theory of Groups.* New York: Chelsea Publishing Company, 1956.

LAMBEK, JOACHIM. "Goursat's Theorem and the Zassenhaus Lemma," *Can. J. Math.*, *10* (1957), pp. 45–56.

———. "On the Structure of Semi-prime Rings and their Rings of Quotients." *Can. J. Math.*, *13* (1961), pp. 392–417.

———. "On the Calculus of Syntactic Types," *Proc. Symp. in Appl. Math.*, *12* (1961), pp. 166–178.

———. "On Utumi's Ring of Quotients," *Can. J. Math.* *15* (1963), pp. 363–370.

———. "A Module Is Flat If and Only If Its Character Module Is Injective," *Can. Math. Bull.*, *7* (1964), pp. 237–343.

———. "Goursat's Theorem and Homological Algebra," *Can. Math. Bull.*, *7* (1964), pp. 597–608.

———. "On the Ring of Quotients of a Noetherian Ring," *Can. Math. Bull.*, *8* (1965), pp. 279–289.

LAWVERE, F. WILLIAM. "Functorial Semantics of Algebraic Theories," *Proc. Natl. Acad. Sci.*, *50* (1963), pp. 869–872.

LESIEUR, L., and R. CROISOT. "Sur les Anneaux Premiers Noethériens á Gauche," *Ann. Sci. Éc. Norm. Sup.*, *76* (1959), pp. 161–183.

———. *Algèbre Noethérienne Non-commutative* ("Mémorial des sciences mathématiques," Fasc. 44.) Paris: Gauthier-Villars, 1963.

———. "Coeur d'un Module," *J. Math.*, *42* (1963), pp. 367–407.

LEVY, LAWRENCE. "Torsion-free and Divisible Modules over Non-integral Domains," *Can. J. Math.*, *15* (1963), pp. 132–151.

———. "Unique Subdirect Sums of Prime Rings," *Trans. Am. Math. Soc.*, *106* (1963), pp. 64–76.

MACLANE, SAUNDERS. "An Algebra of Additive Relations," *Proc. Natl. Acad. Sci.*, U.S. *47* (1961), pp. 1043–1051.

———. *Homology*. Berlin: Springer-Verlag OHG; New York: Academic Press, 1963.

———. "Categorical Algebra," *Bull. Am. Math. Soc.*, *71* (1965), pp. 40–106.

MAL'CEV, A. I. "Über die Einbettung von assoziativen Systemen in Gruppen, II," *Mat. Sb.* 8 (50) (1940), pp. 251–264.

———. "On the General Theory of Algebraic Systems," *Mat. Sb. N. S.*, *35* (1954), pp. 3–20.

MARANDA, JEAN-M. "Injective Structures," *Trans. Am. Math. Soc.*, *110* (1964), pp. 98–135.

MARES, ERICA A. "Semi-perfect Modules," *Math. Z.*, *82* (1963), pp. 347–360.

MATLIS, EBEN. "Injective Modules over Noetherian Rings," *Pacific J. Math.*, 8 (1958), pp. 511–528.

McCOY, NEAL H. "Subdirectly Irreducible Commutative Rings," *Duke Math. J.*, *12* (1945), pp. 381–387.

———. *Rings and Ideals*. ("Carus Math. Monographs," 8.) Menascha, Wis.: Mathematical Association of America, 1948.

———. "Prime Ideals in General Rings," *Am. J. Math.*, *71* (1949), pp. 823–833.

———. "The Prime Radical of a Polynomial Ring," *Publ. Math.* (*Debrecen*), *4* (1956), pp. 161–162.

———. "A Note on Finite Unions of Ideals and Subgroups," *Proc. Am. Math. Soc.*, *8* (1957), pp. 633–637.

———. "Certain Classes of Ideals in Polynomial Rings," *Can. J. Math.*, *9* (1957) pp. 352–362.

———. *The Theory of Rings*. New York: The Macmillan Company, 1964.

McLAUGHLIN, J. E. "A Note on Regular Group Rings," *Mich. Math. J.*, *9* (1958), pp. 127–128.

MORITA, KIITI, YUTAKA KAWADA, and HIROYUKI TACHIKAWA. "On Injective Modules," *Math. Z.*, *68* (1957), pp. 217–226.

MURDOCH, DAVID C. "Subrings of the Maximal Ring of Quotients Associated with Closure Operations," *Can. J. Math.*, *15* (1963), pp. 723–743.

NAGATA, MASAYUSHI. *Local Rings*. New York: Interscience Publishers, Inc., 1962.

NEUMANN, B. H. "Groups with Finite Classes of Conjugate Elements," *Proc. London Math. Soc.*, *1* (1951), pp. 178–187.

NORTHCOTT, D. G. *Ideal Theory*. Cambridge Tracts in Mathematics, 42. London: Cambridge University Press, 1953.

———. *An Introduction to Homological Algebra*. London: Cambridge University Press, 1960.

OSOFSKY, BARBARA. "Rings All of Whose Finitely Generated Modules are Injective," *Pacific J .Math.*, *14* (1964), pp. 645–650
———. "On Ring Properties of Injective Hulls," *Can. Math. Bull.*, *7* (1964), pp. 405–413.
PASSMAN, D. S. "Nil Ideals in Group Rings," *Mich. Math. J.*, *9* (1962), pp. 375–384.
PONTRJAGIN, LEON. *Topological Groups.* Princeton, N.J.: Princeton University Press, 1958.
POSNER, EDWARD, C. "Prime Rings Satisfying a Polynomial Identity," *Proc. Am. Math. Soc.*, *11* (1960), pp. 180–183.
RIBENBOIM, PAULO. *Modules and Rings.* Multigraphed lecture notes, London, Ont.: Queen's University, 1965.
ROSENBERG, ALEX, and DANIEL ZELINSKY. "Finiteness of the Injective Hull," *Math. Z.*, *70* (1959), pp. 372–380.
———. "Annihilators," *Port. Math.*, *20* (1961), pp. 53–65.
SANDERSON, DONOVAN F. "A Generalization of Divisibility and Injectivity in Modules," *Can. Math. Bull.*, *8* (1965), pp. 505–513.
SHODA, KENJIRO. "Allgemeine Algebra," *Osaka Math. J.*, *1* (1949), pp. 182–225.
———. "Zur Theorie der algebraischen Erweiterungen," *Osaka Math. J.*, *4* (1952), pp. 133–144.
———. "Berichtigung zu den Arbeiten über die Erweiterungen algebraischer Systeme," *Osaka Math. J.*, *9* (1957), pp. 239–240.
SIKORSKY, R. *"Boolean Algebras.* Berlin: Springer-Verlag OHG, 1960.
SZÁSZ, F. "Über Ringe mit Minimalbedingung für Hauptrechtsideale, III," *Acta Math.*, *14* (1963), pp. 447–461.
SZÁSZ, GÁBOR. *Introduction to Lattice Theory.* New York: Academic Press, 1963.
TALENTYRE, T. D. "Quotient Rings of Rings with Maximum Condition on Right Ideals," *J. London Math. Soc.*, *38* (1963), pp. 439–450.
TAMARI, DOV. "On the Embedding of Birkhoff-Witt Rings in Quotient Fields," *Proc. Am. Math. Soc.*, *4* (1953), pp. 197–202.
TEWARI, KRISHNA. "Complexes over a Complete Algebra of Quotients," *Can. J. Math.*, *17* (1966).
THIERRIN, GABRIEL. "On Duo Rings," *Can. Math. Bull.*, *3* (1960), pp. 167–172.
———. "Anneaux Métaprimitifs," *Can, J. Math.*, *17* (1965), pp. 199–205.
TOMINAGA, HISAO. "Some Remarks on Radical Ideals," *Math. J. Okayama Univ.*, *3* (1954), pp. 139–142.
———. "A Note on Matrix Rings," *Math. J. Okayama Univ.*, *4* (1955), pp. 189–191.
UTUMI, YUZO. "On Quotient Rings," *Osaka Math. J.*, *8* (1956), pp. 1–18.
———. "On a Theorem on Modular Lattices," *Proc. Japan Acad.*, *35* (1959), pp. 16–21.
———. "A Remark on Quasi-Frobenius Rings," *Proc. Japan Acad.*, *36* (1960), pp. 15–17.
———. "On Continuous Regular Rings and Semi-simple Self-injective Rings," *Can. J. Math.*, *12* (1960), pp. 597–605.
———. "On Continuous Regular Rings," *Can. Math. Bull.*, *4* (1961), pp. 63–69.
———. "On Rings of Which Any One-sided Quotient Rings Are Two-sided," *Proc. Am. Math. Soc.*, *14* (1963), pp. 141–147.

————. "A Note on Rings of Which Any One-sided Quotient Rings Are Two-sided," *Proc. Japan. Acad.*, *39* (1963), pp. 287–288.

————. "A Theorem of Levitzki," *Am. Math. Monthly*, *70* (1963), p. 286.

————. "On Prime I-Rings with Uniform One-sided Ideals," *Am. J. Math.*, *85* (1963), pp. 583–596.

VAN DER WAERDEN, BARTEL L. *Algebra*, I. Berlin: Springer, 1960. II. Berlin: Springer, 1959.

VILLAMAYOR, O. E. "On the Semi-simplicity of Group Algebras," *Proc. Am. Math. Soc.*, *9* (1958), pp. 621–627; *10* (1959), pp. 27–31.

VON NEUMANN, J. "On Regular Rings," *Proc. Nat. Acad. Sci.*, *22* (1936), pp. 707–713.

WALKER, CAROL L., and ELBERT A. WALKER. "Quotient Categories and Rings of Quotients," *Trans Am. Math. Soc.*

WHITNEY, HASSLER. "Tensor Products of Abelian Groups," *Duke Math. J.*, *4* (1938), pp. 495–528.

WONG, EDWARD T., and RICHARD E. JOHNSON. "Self-injective Rings," *Can. Math. Bull.*, *2* (1959), pp. 167–174.

WYLER, OSWALD. *Categories of Structures*. Technical report 32. Albuquerque, N. M.: University of New Mexico, 1963.

ZARISKI, OSCAR, and PIERRE SAMUEL. *Commutative Algebra*, I. Princeton: D. Van Nostrand Company, Inc., 1958.

ZASSENHAUS, HANS, I. *The Theory of Groups*. New York: Chelsea Publishing Company, 1958.

Index

List

$a \wedge b = \inf\{a, b\}$, 2

$a \vee b = \sup\{a, b\}$, 3

$\psi \circ \phi$, composition, 8

$\phi * \psi$, composition, 9

$A \mathrel{.^{\cdot}} B$, over, 12

$B \mathrel{^{\cdot}.} A$, under, 12

$\sum^*$, direct sum, 18

$B(R)$, Boolean algebra of central idempotents, 25

K^*, annihilator, 35, 42, 111

$Q = Q(R)$, complete ring of (right) quotients, 38, 94

$Q = Q_{c1}(R)$, classical ring of (right) quotients, 39, 109

$B^*(R)$, Boolean algebra of annihilator ideals, 43

$X^{\vee}$, set of upper bounds, 44

$X^{\wedge}$, set of lower bounds, 44

$D(S)$, Dedekind-MacNeille completion, 44, 45

$\Gamma A = \{P \in \Pi \mid A \not\subseteq P\}$, 47

$\Delta V = \bigcap_{P \in V} P$, 48

$R[x]$, polynomial ring, 59, 70

$L(A)$, lattice of submodules, 60

M_R^*, character module, 89

$I_R = I(R_R)$, 94

$H = H(R) = \mathrm{Hom}_R(I, I)$, 94

$J(M_R)$, singular submodule, 106

A^r, right annihilator of A, 107

$B \oslash_S A$, over, 120

$B \otimes_T C$, under, 120

$\beta \oslash \alpha, \beta \otimes \gamma, \gamma \otimes \alpha$, 121

Im 1, Ker 2, 137

A_P, P-component, 145

$A^P = \{q \in Q \mid q^{-1}A \not\subseteq P\}$, 147

AG, group ring, 154

ωH, 155

A^l, left annihilator of A, 155

$C(g), C(r^*)$, centralizer, 158

G^*, 158

G^+, 164

tr, 164